WORLD-CLASS MANUFACTURING

WORLD-CLASS MANUFACTURING

Jim Todd

McGRAW-HILL BOOK COMPANY

London · New York · St Louis · San Francisco · Auckland
Bogotá · Caracas · Lisbon · Madrid · Mexico · Milan
Montreal · New Delhi · Panama · Paris · San Juan
São Paulo · Singapore · Sydney · Tokyo · Toronto

Published by
McGRAW-HILL Book Company Europe
Shoppenhangers Road · Maidenhead · Berkshire · SL6 2QL · England
Tel 01628 23432; Fax 01628 770224

British Library Cataloguing in Publication Data

Todd, Jim
  World-class Manufacturing
  I. Title
  658.5

  ISBN 0-07-707623-0

Library of Congress Cataloging-in-Publication Data

Todd, Jim,
  World-class manufacturing / Jim Todd.
    p. cm.
  Includes bibliographical references and index.
  ISBN 0-07-707623-0 :
  1. Industrial management. 2. Production management.
  3. Manufacturing processes. 4. Competition, International.
  I. Title.
  HD31.T632   1994
  670'.68—dc20   94-17157
                                                              CIP

1234 CUP 98765

Typeset by Paston Press Ltd, Loddon, Norfolk
and printed and bound in Great Britain at the University Press, Cambridge

CONTENTS

PREFACE

Anyone who is involved in the management of a manufacturing company is likely to have an interest in the subject of world-class manufacturing, but the level of detail appropriate to particular individuals will depend on their personal responsibilities and background experience. In order to meet these varying needs the book is structured in three parts:

- Part One provides a management overview of the world-class manufacturing concepts and techniques; the differences (and similarities) between the various approaches are explained in a way that is easy for everyone to understand, whatever their discipline and without the need for a detailed knowledge of manufacturing processes.
- Part Two explains the various world-class concepts and philosophies in more detail and describes the key techniques that may be appropriate, so that those readers who are more directly involved can consider in more depth what their company needs to do, what priorities to set, and which of the new management techniques might help them achieve their objectives.
- Part Three is aimed at those readers who are likely to be directly concerned with implementing the new approach and who therefore require more detailed information and guidance. Each chapter in Part Two is linked to a corresponding chapter in Part Three where the concepts are explained in more detail and advice on methods and procedures is provided, making it a useful source of reference during the important initial stages of a world-class programme.

When you have read this book, I hope you will be sufficiently convinced that a step change improvement in your own company's competitive edge can be achieved by following the world-class approach, and that you will want to start your own campaign. Don't be surprised if you meet resistance at first: people don't like change and you will hear all sorts of excuses to try to put you off. Foremost of the excuses will be statements like: 'We're already doing that'; or 'We've already got teams working on improving customer service'; or 'We've looked at just-in-time, but found it wouldn't work in our sort of business'. Don't believe any of them; get the facts for yourself – you will find suggestions in Chapter 9 which should enable you to identify the scope for improvement in how *your* company is currently run. And remember, your main competitor may already have started!

ACKNOWLEDGEMENTS

The case studies in this book are all real-life examples. I am grateful to the management of those companies who have allowed their names to be used, and to those others who, while requesting that the identity of their company be disguised, have still taken the trouble to check the accuracy of the reports.

Copyright for Figs. 3.12, 11.22 and 11.23 remains with US Department of Defense.

ONE

MANAGEMENT OVERVIEW

Part One provides a management overview of the world-class manufacturing concepts and techniques; the differences (and similarities) between the alternative approaches are explained in a way that is easy for everyone to understand, whatever their discipline and without them needing to have a detailed knowledge of their manufacturing processes. This understanding of the basics by every member of the top management team is essential if they are all to play a constructive part in agreeing which techniques are relevant to their company's particular needs, and then participate fully in the process of drawing up a company-wide action plan.

PART
ONE

MANAGEMENT OVERVIEW

THE WORLD-CLASS CHALLENGE

This chapter provides a management overview of the world-class manufacturing concepts and techniques. The differences (and similarities) between the alternative approaches are explained and a brief summary of the topics covered by the book is provided to give readers an insight into what is likely to be involved for their company to achieve and maintain world-class status. The chapter concludes with a summary of typical benefits that can be gained, based on actual results reported by a number of companies in the USA and Europe, followed by a case study describing the experiences and achievements of a medium-size UK manufacturing company.

1.1 THE MEANING OF 'WORLD-CLASS'

Put simply, 'world-class' means being the best in your field in the world. 'Best' can be in terms of:

- Product design and performance
- Quality and reliability
- Least manufacturing cost (so that you can undercut your competitors on price *or* spend more than they can afford on research and development, or on advertising)
- The ability to keep introducing innovative designs more quickly than your competitors
- Shorter lead times and more reliable delivery performance
- 'Customer service' performance that makes your customers bend over backwards to buy from you rather than from your competitors

The list is not intended to be exhaustive – you may well be able to add others. It would be nice if you could be better than your competitors in all these aspects, but it's unlikely. Chapter 2 includes some suggestions on how to determine the priorities for improvement, reflecting in particular what is likely to be of most significance to *your* potential customers.

Whatever techniques you use to assess and improve your competitive edge, the ultimate objective is to ensure that your sales force never needs to be afraid of any of your major competitors, so that they can always say with confidence 'If they can sell there, so can I'. But beware of complacency. Even when you *can* hold your own against the best in the world, the pace of change is becoming so great that without constant efforts to keep on top, you could all too quickly find yourself losing out to a more dynamic competitor.

If you really want your company to be world-class in the future, you will almost certainly have to find ways of doing things better than you have ever done them before – and not just in manufacturing, but in every aspect of the company's business. Why this is so, irrespective of your company's past and present success, is explained in the next section.

1.2 COMPETING IN WORLD MARKETS

Well-managed manufacturing companies have always recognized the need for continuous improvement. So, why all this fuss today, with government officials, politicians of all complexions, union leaders, the media, numerous 'expert' academics and management consultants, all urging manufacturing industry to get its act together and *do* something to make the industry more competitive? Isn't that precisely what we've all been doing for many years?

Ever since the days of Henry Ford (and probably long before that), managements of manufacturing companies have recognized the need to keep plugging away at finding better ways to do things. There is nothing new about striving to improve product design in order to attract more sales, or working out more effective ways of using manufacturing resources in order to reduce costs, or providing a better service to customers so that they are encouraged to give you more business.

Cars provide an excellent example that everyone is familiar with. Early motor cars were individually built and expensive – only the rich could afford them. Henry Ford realized that if he could find a way of cutting the cost of manufacture significantly, he could reduce the selling price of his cars to the point where many more people would be able to afford to buy them. As we all know, the mass-produced Model T was the result. When Ford opened their first UK plant in Manchester in 1911, they were able to sell the Model T for £135, at a time when comparable British cars cost over £300. Not surprisingly, the number of cars on the road increased rapidly, with Ford by far the market leader.

The motor industry has continued to lead the way – most of the new ideas for improving manufacturing performance described in this book have originated through car manufacturers throughout the world trying to find ways of making cars both better and cheaper. As a result, most families in the developed world now have a car, and some have more than one. Many other industries have adopted similar techniques, so that today the average home will be equipped with mass-produced goods, such as a washing machine, a television or a video recorder, all of which we take for granted today, but which would have been beyond the reach of the average family as little as 30 years ago.

If you think about it, we all want this drive for continuous improvement in manufacturing to succeed, because it's what gives us and our children the chance of a better standard of living. But it has its drawbacks:

- We need to improve *our* manufacturing efficiency at least as fast as all our competitors just to survive.
- We really need to improve a lot faster than our competitors if we want to keep the job security and prospects for promotion that come from success.

The industrial revolution started in the Western world, and until relatively recently the standards of manufacturing efficiency, against which we all had to compete, were set by companies in the USA and Europe. Manufacturers tended to compete mainly with firms similar to themselves, all of them trading in similar markets and having similar costs of production. In many cases they were protected from overseas competition in their home markets by import restrictions and tariff barriers.

Although some of the artificial obstacles to the growth of international trade still exist, most have now been demolished (for example as a result of the worldwide GATT negotiations), and in the process we have become increasingly exposed to competition – and not just at home, but in many of our traditional export markets too. Our customers have woken up to the fact that they can demand more and more improvements on an ever shorter time-scale, and if we don't satisfy their demands someone else probably will.

In short, in the last few years the pace of change has been dramatically speeded up. If we can respond positively, then we can turn this changing situation to our advantage by becoming a world-class manufacturer ourselves, opening up all sorts of new opportunities overseas in newly developed countries; if we fail to respond, we may well see our traditional markets and customers steadily decline – and not just overseas but in our home markets too.

This means that the level of continuous improvement we have achieved in past years is no longer sufficient, as Figs. 1.1 and 1.2 show:

- Figure 1.1 shows how things used to be, before the 'Japanese miracle' started. Manufacturing companies in the USA and Europe led the world in industrial efficiency, with a steady improvement in productivity being achieved over the years. In those days, Japanese productivity levels lagged behind, and their products generally had a poor reputation for quality. That started to change in the 1950s when a number of Japanese companies, led by Toyota, set out to bring their performance up to the standards set by the Western world. Partly by visiting successful manufacturers in the West, and partly by following the teachings of production experts such as Shigeo Shingo in Japan and quality 'gurus' Juran and Deming from the USA, they developed new ways of improving manufacturing performance that enabled them to make a step change in both quality *and* productivity.
- Figure 1.2 illustrates how this step change enabled them to overtake their competitors in the West: Toyota, once just an 'also-ran' in the world automotive industry, became

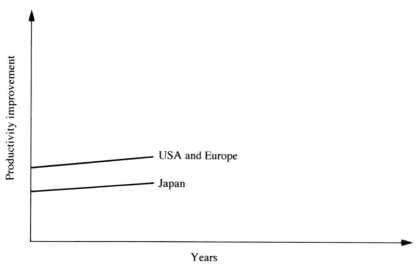

Figure 1.1 Productivity improvement: pre-1950s.

widely recognized as the most efficient volume car manufacturer in the world. And as if that wasn't enough, once they had caught up through their 'step change' improvements, they continued to draw ahead of the rest of the world thanks to the faster rate of their ongoing 'continuous improvement' activities. The changes initiated by Toyota have spread to other Japanese manufacturers, particularly in the automotive and consumer electronics fields, and in recent years they have also been introduced in other centres of manufacturing in the Far East, such as Korea and Singapore.

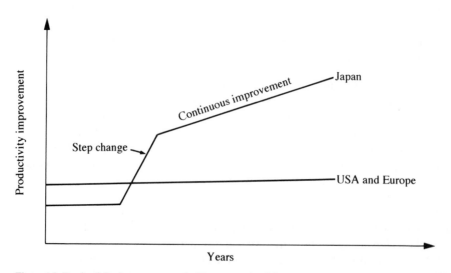

Figure 1.2 Productivity improvement: the 'Japanese miracle'.

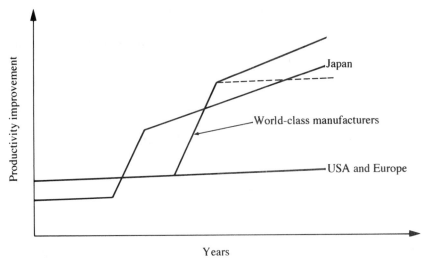

Figure 1.3 Productivity improvement: the future.

The lesson is clear. If we want to survive in world markets, we have to do two things:

- We have to make our own step change, to recover the ground we've lost.
- We need to speed up our rate of continuous improvement to make sure that we don't fall behind again.

There's nothing special about what Japanese industry has done that can't be done equally well in other countries, as has already been demonstrated in numerous Japanese 'transplants' in USA and Europe.

Figure 1.3 illustrates what I believe will happen when we apply similar techniques to those adopted by the Japanese, but going further and adding the extra ingenuity and innovation that I am convinced Western manufacturers can bring to the improvement process once we shake off our past complacency and open up our minds to new ideas.

However, we have to recognize that it is not enough for us just to concentrate on achieving our own step change: the dotted line in Fig. 1.3 shows how we will inevitably slip behind again if we don't also take action to ensure that our continuous improvement activities are greatly enhanced *and maintained at this enhanced level over the long term* – it will be a never-ending task. You could say that achieving a step change improvement in performance will set your company on the path to becoming world-class, but only a well-organized continuous improvement programme, *involving the whole workforce*, will enable you to remain world-class in the longer term.

This book on world-class manufacturing is therefore concerned not just with the step change type of improvements, but also with the subsequent continuous improvement activities that are essential if you want your company to stay on top.

1.3 WORLD-CLASS IMPROVEMENT TECHNIQUES

There is normally more than one route you could take to get from A to B, and the route to becoming a world-class company is no exception. Indeed, you may well need to follow more than one path.

Many experts concentrate on just one route, plugging it as if it were the *only* way to become a world-class company. I believe that each has its part to play, the choice *you* need to make depending on your particular circumstances.

The principal techniques (many prefer to call them philosophies) are:

- Total quality management (TQM)
- Just-in-time (JIT)
- Lean production
- Teamwork (sometimes called total employee involvement)
- Continuous improvement

There is considerable overlap between these different approaches, with all placing particular emphasis on:

- *People*: tapping into the skills and experience of the whole workforce
- *Waste*, which can be loosely translated as *any activity which does not add value*

The concept of using the skills and experience of your whole workforce to attack waste in all its forms is fundamental to becoming a world-class manufacturer. Some examples of what is meant by 'waste' are:

- Poor quality, and the associated inspection activities that are required to identify errors, together with the costs of correction or scrap
- Inventory, which has to be held as a protection against errors being made (for example, in forecasting)
- Time spent in changing set-ups between batches
- The loss of customer goodwill, through failing to provide the level of customer service required

These and other forms of waste are explored in more detail in subsequent chapters and in the brief summary of each technique below.

1.3.1 Total Quality Management

The total quality concept is based on *preventing* errors, in contrast to the traditional approach of accepting that some errors will occur and then identifying and correcting them. Total quality management (TQM) should not be confused with quality *systems* such as BS 5750/ISO 9000, which are limited to providing standards and guidelines for '... the organisational structure, responsibilities, procedures, processes and resources for implementing quality management'. Obtaining accreditation to one or more of these quality standards may well form part of a TQM implementation, but you must understand that it is only a small part of it.

TQM can be thought of as a 'quality creation' approach, in which every member of the workforce, from Chief Executive to shop floor worker, is encouraged to accept personal responsibility for 'getting it right, first time, every time'. They are taught that everyone in the company is both a customer and supplier: we all receive materials, information and instructions which enable us to do our jobs – the person we receive these from is our 'supplier'; the person we pass our output to is our 'customer'. We all depend on our suppliers giving us the correct materials and information to enable us to do *our* job right, and our customers all depend on us in turn giving *them* the right material and information so that they can do *their* job right. You could think of it as a chain, in which each of us makes up one link: if just one link fails, the whole chain can fail. That is the essential message of total quality management.

The theory is fine – if we can get it to work well, we will eliminate all that wasted effort that goes into putting things right that should never have gone wrong in the first place. In most organizations, as much as 50 per cent of people's time (particularly that of managers) can be spent on overcoming problems which have arisen because someone along the line has failed to do something 'right first time': it is probably the most costly of all the various categories of waste, quite apart from the effect it can have on your customer service reputation. The problems come when we try to turn the theory into practice, which is why so many companies that have tried to adopt the TQM philosophy have found that it failed to live up to their expectations. These problems arise, I believe, because it's difficult to convince people to give up long-accustomed ways of working and to adopt a new approach just on the basis of what many will see as management's latest ideology. The British Government found this when it tried to apply the TQM approach to how the public sector satisfies its 'customers' – the general public; some readers will be aware of the cynical reactions with which the Citizen's Charter efforts were greeted.

The other world-class techniques, in contrast, all involve management setting 'hard' goals that employees can readily relate to, such as 'cut lead time from eight weeks to three weeks', or 'reduce warranty claims by 70 per cent before the end of the year'. Most people can see how achieving specific improvements such as these will lead to increased sales and so help protect their jobs for the future; it is not so easy for them to understand how applying the TQM message of 'getting it right first time, every time' will have such a direct effect on their personal job security.

The problem is particularly difficult in large multinational corporations because of the sheer number of people and locations involved in TQM's top-down consultation and education process. I know of one such corporation which spent two years on this 'cascading' process before it eventually reached the level of the actual operators at each site – the people who actually dealt with the customers! Throughout this time top management had been publishing progress reports and raising expectations, while the people at the sharp end saw nothing actually changing. Not surprisingly, when the time eventually came for them to be directly involved, the force of the message had been lost.

In spite of these difficulties, TQM *can* succeed, and has done so in many companies in a wide range of industries. It is particularly appropriate in companies where the manufacturing operations are of only minor significance compared with, say, the sales and distribution side. However, unlike the other key techniques, for which a do-it-yourself approach is well worth considering, I believe that very few companies will succeed in implementing the TQM philosophy properly without expert help. There are a number of consulting organizations around that can provide the support required; but make sure you choose one that has a wide range of training material to draw on *which is appropriate to your sort of business*, and make sure that the consultants who will actually be assigned to your project have the right experience. Ideally, you should ask them to arrange for you to visit one or two of their past clients (if possible without the consultant being present), so that you can hear at first hand how well they did, and how successful they were in overcoming the inevitable resistance to change.

To sum up, the TQM philosophy follows a typical 'world-class' approach, in that it requires the involvement of the whole workforce in attacking waste. The key difference from the other techniques or philosophies is that while TQM encourages *any* actions that improve efficiency, it places particular emphasis on attacking 'quality' wastes, i.e. the primary objective is to avoid errors by 'getting it right first time'.

1.3.2 Just-In-Time

If your priority is to cut stock levels and reduce lead times, you'll probably want to consider what is generally called 'just-in-time' (JIT).

First, we need to dispel a few myths. JIT is *not* just concerned with turning the screws on your suppliers, or getting deliveries of materials at the last moment, or persuading suppliers to hold stocks for you. In fact, in the initial stages it might not even involve your suppliers at all. JIT, like charity, begins at home, in your own factory.

JIT, like the other world-class approaches, aims to involve the whole workforce in attacking 'waste'. Where it differs is that JIT places particular emphasis on 'wastes' that affect stock levels and lead times. The JIT process involves the progressive reduction and elimination of relevant wastes by exposing fundamental problems and then *putting them right once and for all,* so that they don't keep recurring, in contrast to the traditional solution of holding plenty of stocks to provide cover just in case things go wrong. The aim is to make production processes as simple as possible, with short throughput times, usually involving the introduction of cell manufacture and fast changeover techniques to maximize flexibility. In many cases this removes the need for complex MRP11 and scheduling systems.

The sort of inventory problems experienced by most manufacturers can no longer be tolerated in a JIT environment: you are committed to shorter lead times, which means less time is available to overcome problems, and you have less stock to draw on when things go wrong. This is all part of the process of 'exposing the problems', referred to above. You need to identify and correct the problems in your control systems which are the root cause of incorrect stock data. You also have to improve the performance of your suppliers through techniques such as *partnership sourcing* (sometimes referred to as '*forging strategic alliances*'), the objective being to ensure that deliveries are made to you on time, in the quantities you require, and *with zero defects.*

You will probably have to take action to improve labour flexibility through additional training, so that you can switch resources around at short notice and get closer to the JIT ideal of '*make today what we need to ship tomorrow*'.

You may well find that there is a limit to what you can do in the shorter term because of constraints imposed by the design of your products, or the machinery and processes used to manufacture them. However, this doesn't mean that the JIT approach isn't appropriate for you; it just means that it will take rather longer for you to achieve your full potential, because you will have to allow time for introducing new designs which are more suitable for a JIT environment. You may also have to delay some actions until you can develop new technical solutions to the manufacturing process or get to the point where you are ready to invest in new manufacturing equipment. But don't despair – there's sure to be plenty that you can do in the meantime!

To sum up, the JIT philosophy follows a typical 'world-class' approach, in that it requires the involvement of the whole workforce in attacking waste. The key difference from the other techniques or philosophies is that while JIT encourages *any* actions that improve efficiency, it places particular emphasis on attacking those 'wastes' which affect your ability to provide a fast, reliable and flexible response to your customers' requirements, with minimum dependence on inventory to achieve this.

1.3.3 Lean Production

I started the previous section by explaining that 'JIT is *not* just concerned with turning the screws on your suppliers, or getting deliveries of materials at the last moment, or persuading suppliers to hold stocks for you'. In the description of total quality management I explained that 'TQM should not be confused with quality *systems* such as BS 5750/ISO 9000', and in Chapter 4 I explain that the 'management' part of the TQM term is misleading, since the concept involves the whole workforce and not just management. This is a real problem: most people in manufacturing are familiar with the JIT and TQM labels, but there are many misconceptions of what they really involve – so much so that any company embarking on a JIT or TQM programme has to start by explaining what it *doesn't* mean! As you will see later, this is one of the reasons why I prefer to use the term 'world-class'.

The Massachusetts Institute of Technology introduced an alternative term, '*lean production*', which goes some way towards overcoming this problem. Their approach emphasizes the importance of teamwork, flexibility of both equipment and people, and a commitment to total quality, all aimed at providing a rapid and efficient response to meeting customers' needs, while at the same time continually striving to minimize the resources needed to achieve this objective: less people, less equipment, less space, and less time and effort to develop new products.

In order to achieve the desired emphasis on teamwork, lean production typically requires the introduction of a simplified organizational structure, such as that described in the Barr & Stroud case study in Sec. 13.6. This will nearly always involve the introduction of cell manufacturing techniques (described in Sec. 11.9), partly to provide a better opportunity for developing a team-based organizational structure, and partly to speed up the flow of materials as a means of reducing stocks and getting closer to the ideal of manufacturing only to customers orders within an acceptable time-scale, thus eliminating the need to hold stocks. The concept of 'providing a rapid and efficient response to meeting customers needs' should include the design and development of new products, whether specific to the needs of an individual customer, or more generally to your own range of products; lean production will therefore usually require the introduction of the '*simultaneous engineering*' approach, described in Sec. 3.9 and in the Cincinnati Milacron case study in Sec. 11.7.

'Lean production' follows a typical 'world-class' approach, in that it requires the involvement of the whole workforce in attacking waste. However, whether or not it was intended by its originators at MIT, in practice most applications of the lean production approach have concentrated on the engineering and production aspects of the business, so that it only covers part of the full world-class approach (albeit a very important part).

Because it overlaps so much with JIT, lean production is not considered separately in Parts Two and Three of this book.

1.3.4 Teamwork and Continuous Improvement

As you will now realize, TQM and JIT have a great deal in common. In both cases the aim is to get the whole workforce involved in attacking waste. They differ mainly in terms of the type of performance improvement they are aiming at, and consequently in the types of waste that are given the most attention. Initial training in TQM techniques tends to be more formalized, but this is mainly because of the need to change the way in which people think and operate, initially almost as an act of faith. Formal training, while useful, is less essential in the case of JIT because most employees will readily accept the 'hard' benefits that management sets as its JIT improvement goals.

Because of this similarity some managers argue 'Why bother with calling it TQM or JIT? Why not just get a number of improvement teams working, and set each team specific improvement goals?'. This has the advantage of not committing yourself to a company-wide programme of major change, and so tends to be most appropriate when you want to confine what you are doing, initially at least, to just part of your organization. For example, you may have several divisions, each of which operates in different types of market with very different competitive conditions. Or you may have a specific short-term problem, perhaps associated with the introduction of a new range of products.

I'm less happy with the situation where a company decides to concentrate on some sort of 'teamwork' concept, such as *quality circles* or *productivity improvement groups*, *without* doing so as a clearly defined and planned part of a world-class, TQM or JIT programme. All too often a 'bottom-up' attempt to get the shop floor involved has been tried without there being sufficient ongoing support from management. In my experience, 'bottom-up' will only work if it is accompanied by and closely linked to 'top-down': the efforts of the teams need to be guided to ensure that they concentrate on worthwhile improvements and managers need to demonstrate that they too are doing their bit.

The Japanese word Kaizen is sometimes used to describe a particular application of the teamwork approach. Each part of the factory is encouraged to set up a Kaizen team, their objective being to attack any type of waste that they can identify in their own working area. Anyone who works in that area can join the group, but attendance is normally voluntary. The Kaizen approach therefore qualifies as a world-class technique because everyone in the factory is encouraged to participate, the aim is to attack waste, and it is intended to be a long-term continuous improvement activity strongly supported by management. In practice, however, it is normally used as part of a wider world-class programme, particularly in Japanese-owned factories. I know of one company where the term Kaizen is used as the focus for their world-class type improvements, but I would personally prefer to avoid using a Japanese word, as it can alienate too many people – hence my preference for a term such as world-class manufacturing. In the company I referred to, Nissan and Toyota are important customers, so for them it probably is appropriate.

I referred earlier to the difficulty of persuading people to give up long accustomed ways of working and adopt a new approach. Resistance to change, particularly among middle management, is a powerful force in many companies. Shop floor and office workers can be a very fruitful source of ideas for improving performance, but they will quickly become demotivated and cynical of management's true commitment to the world-class philosophy if their initial ideas are not treated seriously. Attempts to develop a new world-class culture in your company are unlikely to succeed unless you do something positive to overcome this problem. Chapters 5 and 13 describe some of the techniques that have proved successful in other companies, such as 'empowering people' (i.e. allowing people to make more decisions in their own areas without having to refer to 'higher authority' for approval), or even by restructuring to reduce the number of management levels and to concentrate decision-making as far as possible within self-contained business units.

1.3.5 The Origin of World-Class Manufacturing

Since the new thinking about manufacturing management which lies behind the world-class drive originated in Japan, it is worth looking to see which of the above techniques has found most favour with Japanese manufacturers. The interesting point is that *none* of them do. The Japanese prefer to think of their improvement campaign in terms of what it achieves, rather than in terms of the particular technique or techniques that they use – this must, surely, be the right way to look at it.

For example, Nissan, who tend to emphasize the TQM aspects, refer to their methods as 'The Nissan Approach'. Toyota, who invented what in the West we call 'just-in-time', never use that term themselves – they call their approach 'The Toyota System', and so it is for all the Japanese companies that I have come across. Toyota actually started their campaign with what we would call JIT, placing particular emphasis on reducing manufacturing cycle time and reducing (or eliminating) stock. After about five years they had got so far ahead of their nearest competitor (Toyota's stockturn was 60 against their nearest rival's 10) that they switched the emphasis to improving quality. Later, when rivals started to catch them up on stockturn, they switched the emphasis back to JIT type activities until their stockturn was up to 100 times per year, at which point they switched the emphasis again, this time to improving product design.

This is why I prefer to use the term 'world-class', which emphasizes what you are trying to achieve, rather than the name of one or more of the techniques you might want to use initially, but which could well become less important at a later stage. To me, the 'right' techniques for a world-class project are *any* techniques that help you to achieve your objectives. This means that, although the emphasis is likely to be placed on the key techniques listed above, you may also need to make use of other techniques, for example:

- MRP11 (or even CIM)
- Total productive maintenance (TPM)
- Automation and flexible manufacturing systems (FMS)
- Quality accreditations (BS 5750 etc.)
- Simulation
- Design for manufacture

However, the key techniques or philosophies listed earlier are likely to be the driving force, setting the parameters, while the techniques included in this second list are more likely to be used as 'enabling' tools to overcome specific problems identified as road-blocks on the path to becoming a world-class manufacturer.

1.4 REVIEWING BUSINESS STRATEGY

In deciding which approach is likely to be most appropriate in your own case, you need to begin by considering 'where are we now, and where do we want to be in the future?'. Establishing what changes you need to make, why you need to make them and what rewards should follow will help you decide what emphasis you need to place in your world-class programme. For example, is the priority to reduce lead times and improve delivery performance, or is it primarily to enhance your image as a 'quality' company?

Your starting point should therefore be a review of your business strategy, typically encompassing:

- A 'mission statement', clarifying management's vision of the business you are in and how you wish to be perceived in the market-place
- An analysis of strengths, weaknesses, opportunities and threats to ensure that you fully understand your current market position and competitiveness
- A statement of quantified aims and objectives for the next few years (comparison of these with present performance will enable specific improvement objectives to be identified and quantified)
- Detailed financial and operating plans for the next year, usually supported by outline plans for, say, the following two years

When you are analysing your current market position and competitiveness it is very important that you get it right, because this is the foundation on which you will be building all your future plans. You should therefore consider seriously whether you should undertake a competitive benchmarking study, or commission other types of independent market research, rather than relying solely on the views of your own sales and marketing staff.

Chapter 2 provides guidance on the process of developing your world class strategy and Chapter 10 includes sample worksheets and further detail on how to carry out a review of strategy.

You may well be tempted to say 'We already do all that'. Even if you do, and even if you feel that your review is as thorough as suggested in Chapter 2, are you sure that everyone in your management team knows the outcome, understands it and, above all, agrees with it? I know from experience with many companies that even when the Board members have all been involved in the review process, individual directors are liable to put their own interpretations on what has been 'agreed', and this can all too easily lead to different parts of the company having different priorities.

There's a simple way of testing whether you are all fighting the same battles (or even taking part in the same war!). Get your managers together and ask them to write down for you on a piece of paper (without reference to each other, and without looking in their files) their understanding of:

- Your company's mission
- Management's current priorities for action, i.e. what has to be changed or improved to make it possible for the company's current business plan to be achieved

You'll be surprised at the variety of responses you get – even from your most senior colleagues. The lesson we can learn from this is that it's not sufficient for the Managing Director and a few senior management colleagues to go through the review process and agree what the company's future strategy should be: the results must also be clearly understood by all those who are involved in 'making it happen'. There are, of course, limits as to how far you can relax constraints of confidentiality, but, if you want your company to achieve world-class performance, at the very least you need to make sure that the whole workforce understands the second of the two points above, *management's current priorities for action.*

1.5 WORLD-CLASS INFORMATION SYSTEMS

1.5.1 Will New Systems Be Needed?

You may be worrying about what the impact on your existing computer systems will be if you decide to 'go world-class'. The two questions most commonly asked by managements at this stage are:

- *Situation A*
  'We've committed a lot of money and people's time to developing our current computer systems: are we going to have to throw much of this away (and possibly lose management credibility in the process)?'
- *Situation B*
  'I recognize that a world-class company ought to have world-class information systems, but ours are hopeless at the moment. Should we go ahead first with the plans for a new MRP11 system we've been considering and leave the world-class initiatives until later?'

In both situations the answer is likely to be 'No'.

In Situation A, although some changes to existing systems may well be required, much of what you will need will already be there: all you have to do is to decide *what* information you need, and then work out how to 'unlock' it from the system's database. If you're lucky you may find that your system already provides query- or report-generating facilities to enable you to do this without too much difficulty.

In Situation B it's best to delay investing in new computer systems for the time being. Once you've started to implement world-class techniques the nature of the operations you want to control will change, and so will your views about what systems you need. For years, when things have gone wrong in manufacturing, we've considered the power of the computer as a key weapon in our efforts to bring order out of chaos. We are used to designing systems which expect complexities and try to cope with them. The world-class way, in contrast, is to simplify processes and to place particular emphasis on removing the root causes of problems so that chaos is avoided. The introduction of cell manufacturing techniques effectively transforms jobbing/batchwork environments into simple flow lines, which significantly reduces the problem of keeping track of material as it moves through the factory; and shorter lead times mean less work-in-process, which again reduces the problem of keeping track of material. Furthermore, implementing world-class techniques should start delivering noticeable benefits within the first six months: a new computer system would still be in the development stage at that point and even in the longer term is most unlikely to deliver comparable benefits.

So, ideally, before investing in new computer systems you should wait until the situation has more or less stabilized (i.e. until you've completed most of your step change projects and are well into the continuous improvement phase). Unfortunately, it's rarely as straightforward as that. Few manufacturing organizations can operate successfully today without reasonably efficient systems to control their production processes and resources, and you may not be able to wait any longer before doing something about them. If this really *is* the case, you may have to go ahead with developing new systems, but do make sure that you do so in parallel with and as part of a wider world-class improvement programme, so that your new system as far as possible reflects how you are likely to be operating in the future.

1.5.2 What Makes Information Systems World-Class?

Systems should not be thought of in their own right as the means of achieving world-class performance, but rather as an enabling tool. There is really only one test or key indicator that matters: do your current systems *help* or *hinder* you in your efforts to improve performance and achieve world-class standards?

Chapters 6 and 14 provide further information and guidance about what information systems you are likely to need to support your world-class operations, and Sec. 9.6 includes a brief check-list to help you assess how your present systems measure up to world-class standards.

1.6 THE REWARDS

At this stage you may well be worried about the magnitude of the task facing you. Don't be. Provided you don't get carried away and try to do too many things at once, and provided you select the most appropriate improvement tasks to start with and tackle them using the right techniques (discussed later in the book), then you should soon start to get very encouraging results.

In recent years I have helped quite a few companies to get started on the world-class path: in every case, the rewards achieved within the first six months exceeded expectations and provided a degree of improvement in competitive edge that would have taken several years to achieve in the days before they embarked on their world-class projects. And there are many examples, reported at conferences and in the technical press, of similar results achieved by a wide range of manufacturing companies in the UK and elsewhere. Here is a brief summary to help convince you that it's worth taking the plunge, followed by a more detailed case study describing the experiences of a medium-size manufacturing company in the UK.

1.6.1 North America

A telecommunications equipment manufacturer

- Manufacturing lead time reduced from 7–10 weeks to less than 1 week
- Product assembly area reduced from 2000 ft^2 to 400 ft^2

- 'First off' acceptance rate increased to 99 per cent from an average previously of around 70 per cent

An automotive parts manufacturer

- Floor space savings of 37 per cent
- Work-in-progress inventory reduced by 99 per cent
- Labour productivity increased by 54 per cent
- Scrap reduced by 74 per cent

An automotive electrical components manufacturer

- Total 'cost of quality' reduced by 70 per cent
- Scrap reduced by 79 per cent
- Inspection costs reduced by 85 per cent

A manufacturer of oilfield equipment

- Lead time reduced from 25 days to 2 days
- Inventory turnover increased from 5 to 30 times a year
- Late deliveries cut from 40 per cent to 2 per cent
- Rework reduced from 6 per cent to 1 per cent
- Total manhours per unit cut from 330 to 200

1.6.2 The UK

A machine tool manufacturer

- Achieves lead time of 2 months, against industry average of 6 months
- Inventory reduced to less than 2 months, industry average 4 months

Construction equipment manufacturer

- Stock turnover up from 3.2 to 15.3 times a year
- Labour productivity up 125 per cent

Commercial vehicle parts manufacturer

- Inventory down by 20 per cent, with a further 15 per cent reduction expected
- In-house manufacturing lead time reduced to 1.5 weeks from a previous lead time of more than 6 weeks
- Labour productivity increased by at least 20 per cent
- Factory space requirements reduced by 25 per cent

Commercial diesel engines manufacturer

- Reduction of set-up times on machine tools ranging from 68 per cent to 100 per cent, in most cases at negligible cost

Computer manufacturer

- Manufacturing cycle time reduced by 80 per cent
- Inventory value reduced by 66 per cent

Portable tool manufacturer

- Lead time reduced from 5 weeks to 2 weeks
- Inventory turnover up from 8 to 29 times a year
- 'Cost of quality' halved
- Scrap reduced by a factor of four

Domestic appliance manufacturer

- Warranty failure levels reduced progressively over five years by a total of 75 per cent

1.6.3 Intangible Benefits

In virtually all the above cases, managements also reported significant side benefits as a result of the cultural change that their world-class projects had brought about. These intangible benefits are likely to prove the most important of all their achievements when one considers the long-term prospects for their companies. Typical examples of these are summarized below.

- *Teamwork* Greatly improved cooperation between individuals and between departments, as a result of their working together over many months as members of improvement teams which crossed functional and departmental boundaries
- *Morale* As a direct result of their greater involvement, and the increased emphasis on teamwork, companies reported lower staff turnover rates, greater job satisfaction and a marked reduction in industrial relations problems
- *Attitudes* A greater awareness throughout the workforce of the need for continuous improvement, and a commitment by all employees, regardless of rank, to improving customer service, quality and productivity

These sorts of result were not achieved overnight: it could take as long as five years to complete the tasks, depending on the complexity of your operations, but you can expect to start reaping significant benefits on a much shorter time-scale, typically within six months. Further guidance on the sort of time-scale you should plan for is included in Sec. 7.2.

I hope that these brief illustrations of the sort of rewards you too could achieve will be sufficient to encourage you to start your own world-class project. If you are still hesitant, remember that as time goes by, more and more companies around the world, *including in your own home country* will achieve results like those quoted above – perhaps some of your competitors have already taken the first steps! Your long-term survival may well depend on whether your organization is truly world-class, or just the leading light in a smaller and rather vulnerable empire.

1.7 CASE STUDY: VOKES LIMITED

1.7.1 Background

Vokes Limited has been a specialist in filtration technology for over 60 years and is an acknowledged leader in the manufacture of air and liquid filters. From its headquarters and principal manufacturing site at Henley Park, near Guildford in the south of England, Vokes (which is part of the BTR Group) supplies filtration products to original equipment manufacturers and end users throughout the world. The manufacturing facilities are broadly based and reflect the diverse nature of the company's business, which ranges from the manufacture of disposable filter cartridges to the fabrication of filter vessels. The Henley Park site, which is the subject of this case study, has an annual turnover of around £18,000,000. At the time when the world-class project started there were approximately 370 employees.

Early in 1990 Vokes started on a programme of change which their Managing Director, Mike McCabe, called 'Steps to a World-Class Goal'. Their experiences over the next two years can best be described by letting two of those closely involved, Mike McCabe (whose 'vision' it was and who made it all happen) and Martin Boyman (who was a member of one of the action teams), tell it in their own words.

I am grateful to Mr McCabe and Mr Boyman for allowing me to include this extract from a presentation they made in 1992 to Managing Directors of other BTR Group companies. For reasons of commercial confidentiality, the actual values of Vokes's Return on Sales and Return on Net Assets ratios originally quoted have been replaced by comparative figures.

Mike McCabe: Before starting on our 'world-class' journey Vokes was a typical British manufacturing company, with traditional working practices and incentive schemes, a functional organization structure, suffering from long lead times, high inventory levels and excessive travel distance between manufacturing processes. On the employee front there was minimal training and communication, and only a limited number of employees were actively involved in change.

But our financial results were good. Our Return on Sales and Return on Net Assets ratios compared fairly well with those for the BTR Group as a whole, which you can see from the Group's Annual Accounts for the year 1989 were 17.6 per cent and 45.3 per cent respectively, so that there was no real motivation to drastically change the way we were doing things. So what was it exactly that helped us to recognize that special need for change?

Well, firstly, we needed to meet the Group's demands for ever better performance. We also had to be able to survive increasing world competition. And, faced with the alternative, we had to grow: but organic growth was something Vokes had not been successful at in recent years.

So, we had to change. After all, if you always do what you've always done, you'll always get what you always got! And we were convinced that what we'd always got wouldn't be good enough in the future as world competitive pressures kept on increasing.

We were not sure what we had to do, but we did recognize that:

- We had to do better at meeting customer requirements because if we didn't, we had no future.
- We also had to fully utilize our most valuable asset: the skills and knowledge of our employees were to be our competitive edge against increasing competition.

With this in mind, in 1990 we took these 'initial steps':

- We changed the organization structure from a functional one to a focused divisional/business structure; a major upheaval, but essential if we were to focus on meeting customer requirements.
- We achieved certification to the British Quality Assurance Standard BS 5750 Part 1, which emphasized to our customers and employees our commitment to product quality.

- We set up volunteer improvement teams to harness the skills and knowledge of our workforce: the response from the workforce was good but, alas, progress was slow.
- Above all, we started to learn what 'world-class manufacturing' was all about.

We soon recognized that the results from the initial steps taken weren't sufficient to bring about the culture change necessary to become a world-class manufacturer. We needed to do more and in 1991 we proceeded to what we refer to as 'the assured steps'.

We appointed a consultant, but as we wanted to retain the ownership of the programme we restricted the consultant's role to:

- Carrying out an initial investigation to identify the key tasks that needed to be undertaken
- Providing initial training to employees to equip them to undertake the key tasks effectively
- Providing support to the improvement teams for a period of nine months on a part-time basis.

The cost of this consultancy support was £20,000.

We also undertook additional Executive Management training in world-class manufacturing. We attended various seminars and read books and articles so that senior management could understand what we were trying to do and also that we needed their commitment as well as involvement.

We reviewed our 'vision' (what we wanted to be). We wanted to be 'world-class' and this meant we wanted to be the best in our field in the world. We wanted our sales force never to be frightened off by any of our competitors.

Lastly, we started to create an Environment For Change. We formed a Quality Steering Committee; we issued a total quality manual titled 'Becoming World-Class by Meeting Customer Requirements' as a management guide; and we increased employee training.

Having taken these Assured Steps our consultant advised us to go for a 'stepped' improvement in performance. It was argued that if we adopted this approach in key areas we could prove to employees that substantial improvements could be achieved, and that success would sell itself and thus help with the culture change.

We selected the following strategic project areas from our four operating divisions:

- Air filter bags
- Fuel and lubrication filter cartridges
- 'Streamline' insulating oil treatment plants
- Flexible metallic bellows

We then identified the key improvements which would give the greatest potential rewards and agreed project objectives which were common to all projects. These were to reduce:

- Lead time by 70 per cent
- Travel distance by 70 per cent
- Inventories by 50 per cent
- Floor space by 30 per cent

These were certainly major challenges and secretly we all had doubts whether these levels of improvement were possible.

We then had to establish teams of our employees to work on the four projects. One of the members of those first strategic project teams was Martin Boyman, our Warehouse and Despatch Supervisor; he will describe how he and his fellow team members reacted to being involved in such an undertaking and how they responded to these challenges.

Martin Boyman: There were eleven people in our team: our Production Manager, someone from Sales, a management accountant, an inspector, two from Planning, a shop floor operative, two supervisors (one of whom was responsible for the area we were going to look at), myself from Warehousing and Despatch, and the Facilitator (he was from Purchasing, which meant that he didn't feel he owned the project or the problems).

The terms of reference for our project had been set by management, and our goal had been clearly defined by what appeared to be some pretty demanding objectives.

Training had been arranged. We all attended either a one-day or a three-day training course designed to help us with our approach to the project and provide basic skills we would need such as brainstorming and analysis techniques. We were constantly made aware of the importance of identifying and eliminating 'waste'.

We were told about some techniques that had helped other companies become world-class: Kanbans, smaller batch quantities, the Pareto Principle, and the importance of involvement and contribution by all which would be needed to maintain a united team and keep it on track.

So now, in theory, we were ready to start. During the three-day course we had used the brainstorming method to generate a lot of ideas for improvements and had short-listed those which we felt would give us the best chance of achieving our project objectives. We decided to meet fortnightly to discuss what needed to be done, and then delegate actions to various team members with clear deadlines to make sure that the work was actually done. Progress would be minuted at each meeting so that we would have a record of our achievements. Everyone thought that was a great idea until they were given something to do: 'everybody' thought 'somebody' was better placed to do it, but 'nobody' could decide who that 'somebody' was!

Eventually we did start moving along the line of approach we'd been told about. Suddenly we were analysing and illustrating everything: 'How did we do it?'; 'How did we perform?'; 'How much did we have?'; 'What problems could we identify?'. We had more information about what we were doing than we'd ever had before so it was quite easy to decide where we needed to improve. Orders for our particular product had been taking 10 days to despatch and our vision was three days, so the project became the 'three-day cycle': receive it day one; make it day two; despatch it day three. We'd been able to monitor our performance, so it seemed no problem to continue monitoring in order to measure our success. The major problem came when we had to decide *how* to improve.

Once again we ran into the same problems as before: time, people resistance, opinions, and differing views on what was important. Nobody, for example, had any time to spare, everybody was always busy, meetings dived off at tangents, but basically we weren't looking at the 'core' of the problem. Higher ranking members of the team wanted to dominate the ideas but delegate the actual work to others. Team members with specific ability areas were quite happy within those areas but wouldn't participate elsewhere. Supervision and shop floor members were very reluctant to change, especially as they were the ones who would have to make the team's ideas work. They just said 'It won't work' or 'That's no use'. People's ideas were so entrenched that discussions on occasion became very heated. At times we couldn't decide what to do first: one member's priority was another member's irrelevance.

The project moved forward in phases: it was slow to start, then, when we were analysing our situation, we seemed to be on a high with information pouring in, but we hadn't actually made any changes and therefore there were no improvements to encourage us. Then we had another lull, but first one idea came, then another, and then steadily we moved forward again. Team members were involved at different levels: one always turned up but just listened; two others (who were always late) were verbally very active but made very little practical contribution. But, in spite of everything, five or six of the team eventually took a grip of the situation and, by using their individual flair and innovation, actually moved the project forward, which encouraged the others to join in. Some of the ideas stemmed from things we thought management had been doing wrong for years; this was our chance to put things right. The salesman on our team helped us do the formal presentations and he really sold our ideas to top management. We followed the usual company procedure for requesting project approval, submitting the appropriate 'justification' forms, and management gave us the backing we were looking for by approving our investment proposals.

The backbones of all that we did were some simple straightforward ideas that worked well and were easy to operate. Now that the ball was rolling and we had gained our momentum, we just kept going, and within nine months of starting we have already met most of our objectives. This is what we have actually achieved:

- Lead time reduced by 80 per cent
- Travel distance reduced by 95 per cent
- Inventory value reduced by 42 per cent
- Floor space reduced by 30 per cent

And the team hasn't finished by any means. They are now working on continually improving performance against the objectives and are also beginning to tackle other products. To start with, individuals in the team did not believe that the improvements set would be achievable. We went along with management, you might say, for the sake of an easy life, but, acting as a team, we proved that anything is possible.

Mike McCabe: Martin has talked about the experiences of just one of the project teams: the others tell similar stories. All have achieved major improvements which are currently being implemented across the company.

The 'Streamline' team brought all of their manufacturing processes, which were located all around the site, into one cell and are now well set to achieve their improvement targets.

The 'Fuel and Lube' team recognized that individual piecework schemes were actually hindering change and productivity improvements and are currently pursuing a team bonus scheme based on new quality indicators.

Martin's team, as he has explained, majored in lead time reduction. An important aspect in achieving this was setting up Partnership Sourcing arrangements with key suppliers to make sure that we didn't run out of materials; drawing on this experience, we are now spreading the Partnership Sourcing concepts to other business areas.

The 'Bellows' team had to find ways of coping with extreme variations in demand. They identified the need to train employees in other skills both to improve flexibility and to increase productivity and reduce throughput times. The extensive training programmes they developed covered technical and administrative functions as well as shop floor skills.

The benefits: First, the benefits that relate to employees.

Working as a team member identifies hidden talent and provides a platform for developing leadership and presentation skills. It also helps management to identify training requirements and to develop the 'team building' concept which is carried through to everyday working. Finally, as a result of the 'stepped change' projects, we now have a number of converted believers and this is important because they are now spreading the word which will result in the 'culture change' necessary to achieve our world-class goal.

Some of the financial benefits from the stepped change projects will not show up in the accounts until next year, but already there is a noticeable improvement:

- There has been a steady reduction in inventory values over the last eight months, from £3 242 000 to £2 417 000 (i.e. a 25 per cent reduction).
- Our Return on Sales ratio improved by 1.2 per cent in the first year, mainly as a result of our initial steps; but in the following year, when the stepped change projects were under way, it improved by a further 3.2 per cent in spite of a slight reduction in sales revenue.
- Our Return on Net Assets ratio improved by 5.0 per cent in the first year, and by a further 12.1 per cent in the second year.

Having achieved this stepped improvement, how are we going to maintain this rapid rate of change? Well, our success to date has convinced us that it *is* possible; indeed, it is *essential* if we are to 'keep a step ahead' of our competitors over the longer term.

The future: We plan to keep a step ahead by rapid continuous improvement. Our strategy for the next three years will be:

- Above all, to continue to focus on the customer and eventually be capable not just of *meeting* their expectations, but of *exceeding* them
- To encourage all employees to participate in improvement teams; for example, in the next year we will be running 15 strategic projects and numerous departmental and personal projects
- To improve communication, with a capital 'C', at all levels
- To improve employee development by increased training, particularly of first line supervision, who are the key to success

Finally, we will undertake regular customer and employee attitude surveys, which will help us to monitor objectively the health of the organization.

When Vokes started on the world-class journey there were many sceptics thinking that it was just another 'flavour of the month' project which would soon be forgotten. Now, having seen the changes within the company, there are many employees concerned that they will get left behind and wanting to know more about achieving 'a world-class goal', so that they too can get involved.

If *you* haven't yet started on a total quality management or world-class programme I would recommend that you do so now, before you also get left behind, by your competitors.

Voke's initial experience, described at the beginning of the above case study, illustrates a common problem in companies that have tried in the past to introduce some of the world-class concepts. You will remember that the Managing Director, Mike McCabe commented:

We soon recognized that the results from the 'initial steps' taken weren't sufficient to bring about the 'culture change' necessary to become a 'world-class manufacturer'.

This book should help those who haven't started yet to get it 'right first time'. The key to success, as I will explain in Chapter 2, is to start by identifying a few key 'step change' improvements that you are confident will have a significant impact on your customers' views of how effectively you meet their needs. You'll find that these customer-oriented step change improvements will catch the imagination of your workforce, because employees at all levels will realize how achieving them will affect their company's future success and so have a direct effect on their own job security and future prospects. And, if the improvement targets are sufficiently challenging, everyone will realize that they can only be achieved by a radical re-think of the current operating procedures. In the case study, Vokes set targets of:

- 70 per cent reduction in lead times
- 70 per cent reduction in travel distance
- 50 per cent in inventory
- 30 per cent in space

As team member Martin Boyman said:

To start with, individuals in the team did not believe that the improvements set would be achievable. We went along with management, you might say for the sake of an easy life but, acting as a team, we proved that anything is possible.

Less demanding targets would never have forced the fundamental re-think that enabled the team to achieve so much, and it was these tremendous achievements that, in turn, encouraged other employees across the company to want to get involved. This 'grass roots' interest is what stimulates the culture change essential to a company that wants to be 'world-class'.

1.8 CONCLUSION

To become a world-class manufacturer means striving to be the best in your field in the world, so that your sales force are never frightened off by any of their competitors. The check-lists in Chapter 9 will help you to assess how your company currently measures up against world-class standards and, at the same time, will indicate where action is most needed.

You'll probably need to start with a number of strategic improvement projects, not just for the sake of the stepped change improvement in performance, but also because everyone will want to get involved once they see the initial teams getting some very impressive results – everyone wants to join a winning team. Continuous improvement groups (like quality circles) will follow naturally, providing the company-wide enthusiasm and commitment that are necessary to make sure you stay on top.

You don't *have* to use the term world-class manufacturing. But the sort of changes you'll be making will be seen by many of your people as revolutionary and every revolution needs a banner that people can rally to. Whether you choose names such as 'world-class', or 'just-in-time', or 'lean production', or 'total quality', or some other term of your own invention will depend on your particular circumstances: I hope this book will help you decide what's most appropriate for you. But whatever title you use, the fundamental approach remains the same. 'World-class', or whatever other term you decide on, is about *attacking waste*: the waste of people's time spent on tasks that do not add value; the waste that comes from not getting it right first time, every time; the waste of holding inventory in order to overcome inadequacies in the way in which you operate; the waste of customer goodwill in failing to meet agreed quality standards or breaking delivery promises; and above all, it is about attacking the waste of not making the best use of the skills and experience of all your employees.

People are the key to success. You need to listen to them, invite their ideas, and then *use* their ideas. This will mean empowering people: delegating responsibility for finding better ways of doing things to those who are most closely involved with the problems and who will have to make the new ideas work, and then *giving them the authority to implement their ideas*. Those companies that have tried and failed invariably didn't pay sufficient attention to the need to involve the whole workforce in this way. They failed to recognize that management *doesn't* always know best, and that changes imposed by management will rarely bring about the culture change that is essential for achieving the world-class goal.

You should start to see noticeable improvements within a few months of starting your world-class initiatives. But the real benefits will come in the longer term as you start using your people more effectively than ever before, when barriers between departments break down as a result of the cooperation initiated through team projects, and when people find that managers listen to their ideas and actively encourage them to implement the improvements they've thought up. The attitude changes that follow, right across the company, will provide the driving force for sustained continuous improvement in every part of your business, unlike anything you've experienced before.

This is the most important message to remember: people are the key to achieving and then maintaining your world-class goal. If you forget this you may well gain some initial benefits, but in the longer term you will fail to maintain your lead in increasingly competitive world markets.

Finally, a word about the way in which Parts Two and Three of the book are structured. Most 'experts' would say that *planning your strategy, involving people*, and *developing effective systems* are integral parts of both the just-in-time and total quality approaches. I agree with them. However, in this book these topics are dealt with in separate chapters for three reasons: first, because I believe they are sufficiently important to merit a separate chapter on each; second, to avoid the need to repeat much of the material in the chapters on just-in-time and total quality, respectively; and third, for the convenience of those who may wish to pay particular attention to strategy, people or systems in the initial stages of implementation, and who may therefore wish to read these specific chapters again.

PART
TWO

CONCEPTS

Part Two is intended to help readers decide what their company needs to do to become world-class, what priorities to set, and which of the new management techniques might help them achieve their objectives.

Each chapter in Part Two has a corresponding chapter in Part Three, which provides further details to help the reader during the initial implementation stages.

TWO

DEVELOPING A WORLD-CLASS STRATEGY

This chapter first explains why you should review your company's business strategy before starting on the process of improving manufacturing performance through the introduction of just-in-time, total quality or other world-class concepts. It then goes on to describe the procedures for determining your current market position and assessing your competitive strengths and weaknesses, to provide a firm basis for deciding what actions need to be planned in order to protect the company's future and enable it to develop as a world-class manufacturer. Further details on these procedures can be found in Chapter 10, together with sample worksheets and two illustrative case studies.

2.1 INTRODUCTION

It may seem obvious to you that before starting on any major improvement programme you should first decide what products or services you want to sell, and to whom you want to sell them. And yet, over the years, I must have seen hundreds of sophisticated manufacturing installations, many of them costing a great deal of money, which had turned into white elephants soon after going into production. True, the new equipment had enabled unit production costs to be cut significantly, *but only on the basis of past demand levels.* In so many instances the new facilities had taken so long to develop that, by the time they came on line, circumstances in the market-place had changed, or competitors had developed alternative products; as a result the levels of output now required to meet demand were too low to carry the greatly increased overheads resulting from the capital investment.

So what went wrong? In most cases it was simply that management hadn't planned its strategy properly. It hadn't looked hard enough at likely changes in the market-place and as a result, the Manufacturing department, through lack of communication isolated from the outside world in which its products were being sold, had just been left to get on with the task of improving its efficiency in whatever way seemed best *from the manufacturing point of view.*

No company that wants to be world-class can afford to make that sort of mistake. So, before looking at how we might make our manufacturing more efficient, let's look at what we need to do to make sure we know *what* it is we want to be more efficient at making.

This is, simply, putting the customer first, which is a fundamental principle of being world-class. We need to start by looking at the *demand* side; only when we have decided what customers are likely to want in the future and what factors are likely to influence their purchasing decisions, can we move on to looking at how well the *supply* side (our own *and* our competitors') satisfies these wants at present. That should make it clear where we need to improve in order to come out on top.

A word of warning: most companies of any size these days have some sort of business plan, and many will claim that they review their future strategy annually, when preparing budgets for the next financial year. Unfortunately, in my experience, although the resulting budgets are widely circulated, it's unusual for the underlying strategy for the future development of the company to be communicated effectively beyond the Boardroom. Even among the Board members, individual directors are liable to put their own interpretations on what has been 'agreed', and this can all too easily lead to different parts of the company having different priorities. Before deciding on your world-class action plan, therefore, you need to find out what each of the directors *thinks* the strategy is, and identify any differences in emphasis so that these can be resolved by the Chief Executive; otherwise you can end up with them all fighting different battles – not a good start for a company that wants to be world-class!

Some people might say that it's the Chief Executive's job to decide the future development of the company: it's not a job for a committee. I would agree that it's the Chief Executive's job to *decide* on the strategy, but in a world-class company the Chief Executive needs to involve all of the top management team in the detailed consideration of alternative strategies so that they both *understand* and have been *involved* in the logical process which has led to that decision.

The remaining parts of this section give a brief summary of what you might need to consider when developing *your* world-class strategy. A more detailed explanation, with sample worksheets, can be found in Chapter 10.

2.2 UNDERSTANDING YOUR MARKET POSITION

The process of developing your world-class strategy involves deciding:

- *Where you are now*, i.e. what products and services do you sell? Who are your customers? How are their needs likely to change over the next few years? Who are your competitors? How well do you perform compared to your competitors? What are your strengths, on which you can build for the future? What are your weaknesses, which might hold you back? What other factors might intervene to help or hinder your progress, such as the world economic situation, political changes at home or abroad, and so on? This 'where are we now?' review is usually called a SWOT – **S**trengths, **W**eaknesses, **O**pportunities, **T**hreats – analysis.

- *Where you want to be*, i.e. what do you see as your company's mission? What products or services do you want to be selling and to whom, both in the short term (the next one to two years), and in the longer term? How do you want your company to be perceived by your potential customers relative to your competitors (i.e. what will differentiate your company and your products from the rest?)?
- *What you have to do* to enable you to get from where you are now to where you want to be.

Companies often make the mistake of answering these questions in terms that are too general, overlooking the fact that different answers often apply depending on who the customer is and which markets are being considered. For example, a European-based industrial garment manufacturer might expect to sell the whole range of its products in the home market, including for example ordinary boiler suits at quite low margins; but when exporting to a country such as China, which has a heavily protected local garment industry, it might only aim to sell specialized garments (such as protection suits for use in radioactive environments) – and for these it might expect to achieve a high profit margin.

These sort of differences need to be recognized when analysing your existing products and markets, *but only if they are a significant part of your business*. The best way of doing this is to draw up a spreadsheet, with all the main product groups listed down the left-hand side, and all the market types across the top. Then ask your 'experts' (usually Marketing and Accounts departments) to make an estimate of the percentage contribution of annual sales to total company turnover for each combination of product and market type and enter it in the grid, ignoring any combination that is less than, say, 5 per cent of turnover. With the completed spreadsheet in front of them, by applying the Pareto Principle the Board can usually select without difficulty the combinations which are worth analysing in more detail.

This approach also helps to get home to people an important point that is often overlooked: *your basis for competing in different markets may need to be different, even if the product is the same*. This means that for each of the product/market combinations selected for detailed analysis, you need to decide which of the three classic ways of competing apply (or, perhaps, which would you *like* to apply if you achieve your improvement objectives):

- *Cost leadership*: you manufacture at a lower cost than your competitors; this enables you to undercut them on price, *or* you can keep your prices in line with those of your competitors and use the extra profit margin to fund additional development, advertising etc. to increase your market dominance still further.
- *Differentiation*: customers buy from you because they believe your products or services to be unique, or at least better than those of your competitors in one or more aspects that are important to them.
- *Niche*: you carve out a particular favoured position in a restricted area of the market, applying *either* a cost leadership *or* a differentiation strategy within this limited market niche.

In the case of cost leadership one or more of the following are likely to apply:

- Market share is high
- You have access to more competitive raw material prices than your competitors
- Your products have been better designed for ease of manufacture
- You manufacture a wide range of products with a high degree of synergy
- You have up-to-date, highly efficient equipment ('state of the art')
- You have a highly motivated workforce who cooperate fully with a 'continuous improvement' policy

Sustaining a differentiation strategy is likely to involve having a widely recognized and respected brand name, or products perceived as having technological or design advantages compared with your competitors' products, or providing a level of customer service that is second to none. This implies that you have an above average product design and development team, that your marketing and advertising is successful in getting your message across to potential customers, and that your staff are very customer conscious: *fall down on any of these and you may well find your differentiation policy unsustainable as customers start deserting you in favour of lower priced competitors.* The warning sign to look out for is increased pressure on prices: if you are following a differentiation policy and find that you are losing more and more orders on price, then your customers are, effectively, telling you that they no longer see you as a 'superior' supplier. The correct response in most cases, surely, is not to slide into a price-cutting mode, but to do something to restore your image as a superior supplier.

A niche strategy tends to be followed by smaller companies, which don't have the resources to attack the full potential markets for their products. The niche may be selected by type of customer (e.g. a software house that develops computer systems specifically for, say, solicitors and so becomes expert in understanding their requirements), or a specific geographical area may be selected (taking advantage, for example, of the preference many people have for dealing with their local supplier). Strictly speaking, a niche strategy can be either cost- or differentiation-based, within a constrained product/market area. In practice, however, it tends to be differentiation biased, in that customers buy from you because they *think* you are the best in your field. If you're *not* in fact the best, but are just where you are through some historical associations, you may well be very vulnerable to a new competitor arriving on the scene who really *is* the best. For these reasons, if you decide that much of your business falls into the niche category, my advice to you is to make sure that you can live up to the differentiation criteria outlined above, or you could be in for a nasty surprise!

I came across an interesting example recently of how it pays to consider which of these three ways of competing is appropriate. The company concerned manufactured various 'standard' products for the electrical contracting industry, competing within the UK on a cost leader basis. Since their products were made to the appropriate British Standard specifications, there was little to choose between their products and those of their competitors and this was reflected in the comparatively low margins achieved. However, when they came to do the product/market analysis, they realized that their catalogue included all the less popular sizes that their competitors no longer offered, having rationalized them out of their catalogue. They decided to re-classify these as differentiation products, and pay particular attention to ensuring that they were always available from stock, advertising them as specialities. They could now increase their prices for these items to give a level of profit which changed them from nuisance products to useful contributors.

Once you've decided what products and services you are currently selling, and who your customers are for each, you need to assess how these are likely to change. Such changes could be a result of you deciding to take some action to change the current products/markets mix, or they could be the result of external changes, such as changing customer requirements or competitor activities. Your Sales and Marketing team may be well enough informed on what external changes are likely to occur for you to rely on their assessment, but it's usually safer to invest in some market research, particularly in those areas which are particularly important to you.

Traditional market research will usually help to establish how the overall market for your products and services is likely to change, but it's not so good at establishing what the key factors are which cause a potential customer to buy from a competitor rather than from you. Recognizing the increasing emphasis that is being placed these days on total quality and customer care, some market research consultancies are now offering a form of research that concentrates on what the *customers* think are the sort of improvements most likely to influence their purchasing decisions.

An example of this approach is the 'Problem Ranking Process' (PRP). As a first step, a PRP consultant talks with company staff and with a representative sample of customers, and from these discussions produces a list of a hundred or so 'problem statements', covering all the sorts of complaints or shortcomings that have been mentioned: the concept is that, while it's difficult to get customers to tell you what improvements would be important to them (they'll usually just say 'price'!), you get a very much better response if you ask them questions such as 'What goes wrong?' and 'What irritates you?'. This list of problem statements is then sent to a large sample of customers, asking them to rank the importance of each on a 3, 2, 1, 0 scale. The points allocated by each respondent to each problem statement are added up, and the problems are then listed in descending order of importance in the PRP Report. Typically, because of interaction and overlap, the most important 20 to 30 problem statements will have between 5 and 10 different causes: if you can take action to resolve these causes you should be well placed to increase your market share (or, perhaps, increase your prices without losing customers).

Competitive benchmarking is another tool that can be used. This technique was pioneered by the Xerox Corporation a few years ago, when their traditional supremacy in the photocopier market was challenged very successfully by Japanese manufacturers. Xerox first analysed what factors potential customers might take into account when assessing competing products: for example, price, delivery, quality of reproduction, speed of reproduction, ease of use, reliability and availability of spares. They then did their own assessment of how the products of Xerox and each of the major competitors rated against each of these factors. From this analysis they drew up a theoretical 'benchmark' product which consisted of the best rating for each of the competitive factors: they made this the target for improving their own products. Their success can best be judged by how well they have recovered their market position from what at one time had looked to be very dismal future prospects. A case study in Chapter 10 describes how another company, Cincinnati Milacron, used the competitive benchmarking process as the basis for developing a completely new range of world-class products, and the Bibliography includes details of further reading on the subject of competitive benchmarking.

In recent years the competitive benchmarking technique has spread far beyond its original application as a market research tool and become increasingly popular as the focal point of many companies' world-class initiatives. The benchmarking technique is used initially to identify those performance ratios that are most appropriate and meaningful to the company in its particular market situation. These ratios are then used firstly to establish and quantify the specific performance improvements the company must achieve if it is to compete on a world-class basis, secondly to provide the basis for monitoring progress towards achieving those goals. Some users of the technique prefer the alternative name of '*comparative benchmarking*', particularly when it is used in this ongoing monitoring mode.

Whatever the original reason for undertaking a competitive benchmarking study, do remember that the world, and one's competitors, don't stand still. The relative importance of the various competitive factors will inevitably change over the years, either as a result of changes in your customers' views of what matters most, or as a result of competitor's activities (probably both). Therefore, like most world-class improvement activities, competitive benchmarking needs to be viewed as a continuous process. This means you need to regularly update the benchmarks you originally established and then reconsider whether the comparative ratios or other measures used to monitor your own performance against these benchmarks are still operative.

Finally, no review of 'where are we now' can be considered complete without an assessment being made of where each product is in its life cycle. Looking at existing products is all very well, but they won't last for ever. You also need to decide when to launch their successors if you want to protect the future of your company. If you're not familiar with the 'product life cycle' concept, refer to Fig. 2.1. This shows how the rate of sales for virtually all products goes through an initial 'market entry' stage, followed by a period of rapid growth, which typically starts to fall off when competitors increase in number and/or the initial market demand is satisfied. The product life cycle then moves into a period of 'maturity', in which competition will probably affect margins. Finally, the product moves into a period of 'decay', during which market capacity may well exceed demand and pressure on prices increases accordingly (although opportunities for higher margins sometimes come back as some manufacturers withdraw from the market).

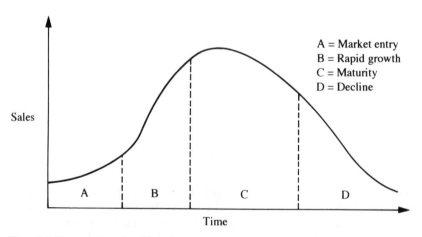

Figure 2.1 The typical product life cycle.

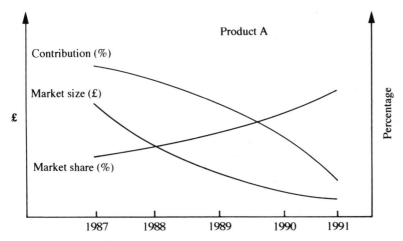

Figure 2.2 Product life cycles: monitoring market trends.

Figure 2.2 shows how monitoring information on factors such as percentage contribution, the size of the market for all suppliers, and your share of that total market can help you identify progress through the product's life cycle. The diagram illustrates how monitoring just your own sales could be misleading: in this instance the total market is actually declining – your own sales level may not have changed, because you've increased your market share (possibly through price discounting, as indicated by the reduction in product contribution). Because of your increasing market share you might eventually be able to improve your margins again, when your competitors finally give up, but clearly there's no long-term future for you unless you have some new products coming on stream to replace Product A.

Figure 2.3 shows what can happen if you don't monitor the life cycles of key products. This company may well have been quite profitable in the past, but now its two

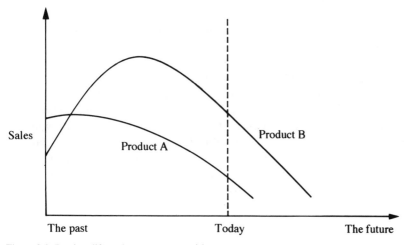

Figure 2.3 Product life cycles: a company with a past.

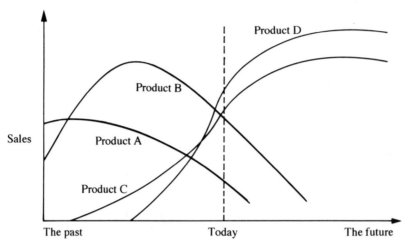

Figure 2.4 Product life cycles: a company with a past *and* a future.

main products are in terminal decline: by the time it realized what was happening it was too late for new products to be introduced in time to maintain past performance. The company illustrated in Fig. 2.4, in contrast, realized when sales of existing products had peaked, and in order both to replace them *and* to enable overall profit margins to be maintained, they've planned the introduction of two new products, C and D, in good time. As a result, they have a future to look forward to.

2.3 ASSESSING YOUR MANUFACTURING OPERATIONS

Consultants make a very good living out of helping companies to assess their manufacturing operations. At the end of their audit they will usually come up with a long list of opportunities for improvement, and if you follow their advice you will undoubtedly make your manufacturing operations very much more efficient. You might also end up with an expensive white elephant (see the opening paragraph of this chapter)! As I hope you now realize, what matters most is to improve your performance in ways which your *customers* think are important, and which will influence their future purchasing decisions.

So, my advice is *don't* start with a comprehensive review of all aspects of your manufacturing operations: concentrate instead on the factors which, if you've followed the advice in Sec. 2.2, you will by now have identified as critical to improving your competitive edge, and see how well you currently measure up on these. That will give you more than enough to do for the foreseeable future – and you *know* that any improvements you can make in these areas will have a high probability of increasing customer satisfaction and hence of earning a quick reward through increased sales.

Typical of the sort of performance improvements your customers might want most are:

- Shorter lead times
- More reliable delivery performance

- Better design (e.g. appearance, packaging, features)
- Better quality (e.g. fewer defects on delivery, lifetime reliability)
- Better after-sales support and service
- Lower operating costs
- Lower initial price

Having identified which of these are *perceived by your potential customers* as the ones which they most want improved, you can look at you own performance: first to assess how well or badly you are doing at the moment and second to assess how your performance compares with that of your competitors. Your objectives should be partly to identify your current strengths, on which you can build; but most of all you should be trying to identify your current *weaknesses* compared with your competitors, since it is on these that you will most need to concentrate if you want potential customers to buy more from you in the future.

For example, your review may reveal that your efforts to introduce JIT concepts into your production processes are being severely hampered because these processes are still organized along conventional lines. If your customers put a high rating on short lead times and flexibility in respect to batch size (i.e. they want you to provide a 'just-in-time' service), then your lack of cell manufacturing facilities will be a serious weakness because these are usually an essential element of JIT-oriented manufacturing. However, if your customers are more concerned with product cost, then any weaknesses you may have in your product design, or in your manufacturing or process engineering support, will be of higher priority.

When you have completed this review, you should be able to identify with confidence how you need to improve and develop your manufacturing resources to enable your company to achieve its strategic objectives. In drawing up your plans you will need to cover all aspects of manufacturing, such as:

- Product design
- Equipment and processes
- People (in particular, training requirements)
- Increasing flexibility, reducing rigidity
- Make vs. buy
- Systems and procedures for planning, control and monitoring
- Suppliers (one of your key resources)
- Quality performance (in all the above areas)

The IFS publication *Competitive Manufacturing* (see Bibliography) gives some useful advice on how to assess performance in these areas.

When reviewing your manufacturing processes you should also take the opportunity to consider what are your core competencies, and make a list of any superfluous activities that you should try and remove. Although the question of what products should be included in your product range is primarily a marketing responsibility, there must be a manufacturing input to this and it's therefore important at this stage to identify what you are good at doing, and what you are *not* good at, with the products currently manufactured. A world-class company should try and concentrate its manufacturing activities on core products and processes: if you are *not* good at any of these at present, you will need to do something about it, by improving your equipment or skills until you achieve the necessary competency. Non-core processes should either be sub-contracted or, where feasible, designed out of the product, and non-core products should be removed from your product range unless there are sound commercial reasons for retaining them (for example, because their inclusion encourages customers to buy more of your core products).

There is one other aspect which I personally think is most important, but which is all too often overlooked: your people's *attitudes*, particularly their attitudes to custo-mers and to quality. If you are only just starting out on your world-class journey you will nearly always need to change people's attitudes in these two respects. It may well be worth getting external consultants to carry out an *attitude survey* across your workforce, to make sure you understand how significant a problem this is likely to be, and to provide a benchmark for assessing at a later date how successful you have been in changing attitudes. I suggest you use external consultants, since it is notoriously difficult to get a truthful response from your workforce if the attitude survey is undertaken by your own staff.

2.4 DEVELOPING YOUR NEW STRATEGY

Let's just recap on how far we've got. The demand side was considered in Sec. 2.2 and the supply side in Sec. 2.3, so that you should now know what business you are currently in, what threats and opportunities there are which might affect you in the years to come, and also what *your* strengths and weaknesses are compared with those of your com-petitors. You have therefore completed the 'where are we now' part of the process for developing your world-class strategy, referred to above.

To save you turning back, I'll repeat the next steps in the process:

- *Where you want to be*, i.e. what do you see as your company's mission? What products or services do you want to be selling and to whom, both in the short term (the next one to two years), and in the longer term? How do you want your company to be per-ceived by your potential customers relative to your competitors?
- *What you have to do* to enable you to get from where you are now to where you want to be.

You should now have sufficient information to enable you to answer these two questions, and so complete the preparation of your strategy. One of the key purposes of a mission statement is to enable top management to communicate its vision of the company's future to the whole workforce, so that this can become the focal point of its world-class improvement initiatives: this way the workforce should all end up fighting in the same battle and on the same side! To do this effectively you need to keep the message simple and concise so that all can understand and relate to it, whatever their job. If your mission statement is at all ambiguous or woolly, not only will you have difficulty in using it as the focal point of your world-class initiatives, it's also unlikely that it will generate the enthusiasm and support for these that you are hoping for.

On the other hand, it's also important to include sufficient detail on the level of improvements you are looking for to shock everyone into realizing that what they are being asked to deliver is in a different league from anything they have ever done before. You then have to make them believe you are serious, by explaining the competitive pressures that have given rise to the new challenging targets, and convincing them that the company's prosperity (perhaps even survival) in the longer term depends on them delivering the step change in performance called for in your mission statement.

To some extent these two requirements of keeping it simple, and yet spelling out the improvements looked for in some detail, are in conflict. The way to resolve this is to produce two documents:

1. A brief mission statement, summarizing your vision for the future of your company as simply as possible. For example: 'We aim to be the fastest growing and most innovative widget manufacturer in Europe within three years; thereafter we intend to concentrate on achieving further growth primarily through Eastern European markets'. This document satisfies the 'where do you want to be?' part of the strategy review process.
2. A one-page statement of short-term improvement objectives, setting out the priorities that need to be tackled in the first year in order to get you moving positively towards achieving your vision. For example, you might set objectives of reducing late deliveries to less than, say, 2 per cent, and at the same time cutting lead time for standard products in half, and for 'specials' by two-thirds. This document satisfies the 'what do we have to do to get there?' part of the strategy review process, at least in the short term.

The first document, setting out your vision of the company's future, will in most cases remain unchanged for several years, demonstrating top management's consistency of purpose. When you change the short-term objectives in the second document every twelve months or so, everyone can see that all you are doing is to alter the emphasis in the light of the then current circumstances.

When preparing the second, 'what do we have to do?' document, you will need to consider whether your present range of products is sufficient, or whether you need to introduce new products in order to achieve your mission. For example, Archilighting GmbH (not their real name), who are the subject of a case study in Chapter 11, decided that they needed to develop a new range of products if they were to achieve their declared mission of becoming 'The fastest growing manufacturer of high-quality architectural lighting products in the world'; and a case study in Chapter 10 describes how Intertronic plc realized that they needed to introduce a new type of business to replace their core product, which was nearing the end of its life cycle.

You may also have to think about whether you can achieve your objectives solely through internal developments, or whether acquisitions (or disposals) will also need to be considered. With all the preparatory work you've done you shouldn't find these final steps difficult (though some of the decisions you have to make may well be!), but if you do require further guidance you should find the *Competitive Manufacturing* workbook helpful.

The recession of the early 1990s has highlighted the importance of another aspect of strategic planning which is all too often neglected by many organizations: I call it 'planning for downturn'. In the immediate aftermath of the recession I expect that most Boards will be very cautious in their plans for expansion, but I wonder how long this will last. A world-class company has to make sure that, even when times are hard, its financial position is not over-stretched, and it can still continue to make reasonable profits. Look at the BTR Group, for example, where in 1990 they were still able to achieve profits of £966 million on a sales turnover of £6,742 million (compared with profits of £1,057 million in 1989 and £811 million in 1988): true, they were hit by the very difficult trading conditions in 1990, but their planning was good enough to keep the impact under control and enable them to go on to make a major acquisition in 1991; there was barely a hiccup in their long-term strategic development.

'Planning for downturn' means identifying actions you need to take to reduce the effects of a downturn in the economic cycle. For example:

- Reducing your dependence on one sector of the market by expanding into a number of different geographical areas (e.g. Pacific Rim, the Americas etc.), or into different types of market-place (e.g. public as well as private sector, or into industrial sectors where the down part of the economic cycle tends to differ in time from your traditional markets).
- Planning more flexibility into your capacity, so that your fixed costs are lower (i.e. you have a lower break-even point). For example, in the Japanese automotive industry as much as a third of the workforce at maximum capacity is typically made up of 'temporary workers' on short-term contracts, enabling them to flex their workforce to match seasonal demand patterns as well as to adjust easily to downturns in the economic cycle.
- Making sure you have new products under way in case you need to stimulate additional demand.
- Anticipating the downturn early enough to invest in additional sales and marketing effort, so that the resultant increase in your market share enables you to maintain 'normal' sales levels.

If you include this 'planning for downturn' in your strategy, when a downturn turns into a recession you won't have to put all your efforts into survival; instead, you can take advantage of the reduced pressure on manufacturing capacity in order to refurbish equipment, retrain and cross-train staff, and implement major change projects without the disruption that these inevitably cause adversely affecting your service to customers. For a well-run world-class company, a recession can provide the best opportunity for increasing market share at the expense of less efficient competitors.

2.5 MAKING YOUR NEW STRATEGY WORLD-CLASS

So far, as many readers will realize, I've kept pretty close to the classic strategy review procedure, but I've stressed that the whole of the top management team should be involved, and that the emphasis throughout the review should be on what is important to *customers*, i.e. what will make them want to buy more from you, rather than from your competitors. We now need to take this a step further, to make sure that the strategy really will help your company to be world-class.

I explained in Chapter 1 that to become a world-class manufacturer meant striving to be the best in your field in the world, so that your sales force are never frightened off by any of their competitors; and that to get there you have to do two things, as shown diagrammatically in Fig. 1.3:

- You have to make your own 'step change', to recover any ground you've lost and get a lead on your competitors.
- You need to speed up your rate of continuous improvement to make sure that you don't fall behind again.

The step change will be achieved through what I call 'key strategic projects'. The next section will help you decide which projects to tackle first and how to set appropriate 'step change' targets; and it also explains why I think you should wait until you start to get results from these key strategic projects before launching any company-wide continuous improvement initiatives.

However, deciding what improvements to target is only the starting point in making your new strategy world-class. You also have to include in your action plans some positive steps to get the whole workforce to understand that what you are planning to do is going to be different from anything you've ever done before. You have to make sure that they understand what world-class is all about, which means that you need to include some sort of 'awareness' programme in your action plans, as well as specific training for those who are going to be involved in the key strategic projects, to ensure that they have the 'tools' to do the job. Details of what you might need to include in these awareness and training programmes are discussed in Chapter 13.

Finally, you need to decide what you're going to call your new initiatives. You don't *have* to use the term 'world-class manufacturing', but the sort of changes you'll be making will (rightly) be seen by many of your people as revolutionary, and every revolution needs a banner that people can rally to. This banner must, above all, appeal to *employees*, but you also need to think of your customers. If all your main customers use the term *just-in-time*, and are putting pressure on you to join the JIT bandwagon, then it might make good commercial sense for you to use the same term in your own company. Similarly, if your main customers prefer total quality, then that may well be your first choice; if you are in the pharmaceutical or aerospace industries, for example, anything with 'quality' in it will be readily accepted as relevant throughout your organization (although it may not get the 'revolution' part of the message across sufficiently). Nevertheless, I still prefer 'world-class' unless there are very strong reasons for using some other term, for the reasons explained in Chapter 1. Whichever term you decide on for your own banner, remember that the message you have to get across, to managers as well as the rest of your employees, is that at the heart of your new strategy is a determination to make better use of the skills and experience of your whole workforce than you have ever done before.

2.6 DECIDING ACTION PRIORITIES

The preceding sections have summarized what you need to do to develop your world-class strategy. All that remains is to decide where to start. You'll probably have identified so many areas for improvement that you couldn't possibly tackle them all at once without your existing levels of performance being adversely affected, and you certainly won't want that to happen. Fortunately, the process I've described in the preceding sections should make it easy for you to identify the areas where the quickest returns lie. You know what step change improvements are considered by your potential customers to be the most important, so naturally the top two or three of these are the ones you will want to tackle first as key strategic projects, because success in these should be quickly rewarded by additional orders. Getting the whole workforce involved in the second stage, of continuous improvement, should be left until you start to get some visible results from these key strategic projects, as I will explain shortly.

The secret is to set yourself targets for the key strategic projects which are sufficiently challenging for everyone to realize that they can only be achieved through radical change, but at the same time to break them down into specific improvement tasks which people can understand, identify with, and accept as being achievable (once they've got over the first shock of hearing what you want them to do!). For example, a target to 'cut waste by 30 per cent' is far too overwhelming. Compare this with:

> Cut lead time for Type 3 widgets so that by the end of this year consistently 98 per cent of orders are despatched within four weeks, compared with the present achievement of 90 per cent within eight weeks.

Such a target is much more likely to be accepted by all concerned and so gain their commitment. Furthermore, the required performance level is clearly stated, so that progress towards achieving the targets can be quantified and demonstrated for all to see.

At the start of your world-class journey you should aim to set targets that are:

- Generally perceived by your *staff* as being important (so that they, and their bosses, will realize that it's worth putting the necessary time and effort into the improvement task)
- Generally perceived by your *customers* as being important, thus stimulating increased sales (improving manufacturing efficiency usually means that you need fewer people for the same level of output: *unless your people see that you're taking positive action to increase sales, they may well hold back on ideas for improvement because of worries about their future job security*)
- Ones in which quick and visible progress can be achieved towards the goals set (once you start getting results, everyone will want to join the winning team)
- Ones which involve a good cross-section of people, from different disciplines, different departments, and different levels of seniority; you should aim to get as many people as feasible involved from the start, and do it in a way that will help to break down traditional barriers
- Ones that will improve cash flow, for example through a reduction of stock and work-in-progress or a reduction in defective work and materials; the money released can then be used to pay for any expenditure that may be needed for other improvement tasks.

When you start to get results, be ready to make the best use of them to change attitudes, both internally with your own staff and externally with potential customers. If you are doing things better, and you are confident that you are going to be able to go on doing them better, shout it from the rooftops! Introducing the next stage of your world-class strategy, getting the whole workforce to participate in the process of continuous improvement, will then follow naturally – probably in response to the people themselves wanting and even demanding the chance to get involved.

2.7 UPDATING YOUR STRATEGY

The strategy review process described in this chapter should provide a firm basis for deciding what actions need to be planned in order to protect your company's future and enable it to develop as a world-class manufacturer. You will, of course, need to review progress at regular intervals, the usual procedure being to include this in the agenda for your monthly executive meeting.

However, we live in an increasingly dynamic world; being flexible in responding to customers' wishes is one of the features of a world-class manufacturer, and this flexibility doesn't just apply to day-to-day operations, but at the strategic level too. The whole of your strategic plan will have been developed on the basis of what customers most want from you, and how well you satisfy those wants compared to your competitors. If either of these changes significantly you should be prepared to review your strategy without waiting for when your next review has been scheduled, possibly twelve months later.

You should, therefore, plan for this eventuality. In addition to the normal progress review meetings, you should plan meetings at, say, three-monthly intervals for the specific purpose of going through the set of worksheets produced in the strategy review, looking for entries that are no longer valid and deciding whether any additional aspects should be added (to save time at the meetings, participants should be asked to go through the worksheets individually beforehand). The objective is to ensure that your planned strategy is *either* amended in order to take into account any new situations that have arisen, *or* it is left as it was because you are satisfied that it is still the best strategy to follow. In practice you'll probably find that there's no need for you to change your overall strategy: all that will need to be altered is the relative priority of different improvement projects. Unless your business is particularly volatile, this 'continuous improvement' of your planned strategy could actually save management time in the long run, making it unnecessary for you to carry out a complete review every year: once every two to three years could well be enough.

Most manufacturing companies recognize the need for continuous improvement. A world-class manufacturer needs to go further, and make sure that all its efforts are continually directed at improving performance *in the ways which its potential customers think important*.

THREE

JUST-IN-TIME

The chapter starts with an easy to understand description of the just-in-time (JIT) philosophy and explains the key objectives of providing a fast, reliable and flexible response to customers' requirements, with minimum dependence on inventory to provide this. The remainder of the chapter describes a range of techniques that can be used to achieve the just-in-time objectives. Further details on these techniques, together with guidelines for implementation, can be found in Chapter 11.

Improving quality, developing better information and control systems, and making more effective use of people are all essential to the successful introduction of the JIT approach. In addition to the material included in this chapter, they are dealt with in greater depth in Chapters 4–6 and their corresponding chapters in Part Three (Chapters 12–14).

3.1 THE JIT CONCEPTS

'First Generation' Just-In-Time

What we in the Western world refer to as 'just-in-time' has its origins in the pioneering work of Toyota in the 1950s. There have been various interpretations of the Toyota System in subsequent years but, until quite recently, too much attention was paid to specific techniques Toyota had used and most 'experts' missed the overall philosophy, of which the techniques were just part. As a result, there are almost as many 'explanations' of JIT as there are experts! Not surprisingly, quite a few of the early attempts to implement what people thought was just-in-time failed to live up to expectations. Nowadays, an increasing number of people are coming to understand the wider world-class philosophy and realize how JIT fits into this.

The Japanese production engineering consultant Shigeo Shingo was closely involved with the developments at Toyota for many years. He defines JIT as 'producing what is necessary when it is necessary in the amount necessary'.

I prefer to modify this slightly to:

> Let us make today what we have to ship tomorrow.

It's an oversimplification, but I've found that it gets the message across at all levels, and it puts the emphasis where it should be, in your own factory.

When the JIT approach was first introduced in the Western world, many people thought that it was all about getting your suppliers to deliver much more frequently, and in much smaller batch sizes, than in the past (this aspect of Toyota's methods was very visible to visitors, which is presumably why so many came away with the impression that it was the heart and soul of this revolutionary just-in-time approach). In many cases this so-called JIT goal was achieved simply by persuading a supplier to hold stocks for you to call off on demand, which really missed the point: we now realize that it doesn't matter *where* inventory is held, in your factory or at your supplier's premises: it's still a 'waste' which the end user ultimately has to pay for. The aim of the JIT philosophy, as we understand it today, is to eliminate wastes, such as inventory, so that *no one* has to pay for them. That's why the new world-class approach to JIT places so much emphasis on working together with suppliers so that together you can find ways of enabling them to satisfy your requirements for frequent small batch deliveries *without* the need for additional inventory.

The introduction of cell manufacturing concepts, and the application of new techniques for reducing batch changeover times dramatically, will enable you to achieve similar improvements in flexibility in your own factory, again without the need for additional inventory (in fact your work-in-progress inventory should be significantly reduced as a result).

To sum up, over the last five to ten years many companies claim to have introduced JIT in their factories. In most cases all they have done is to improve suppliers' delivery performance at the expense of increased inventory in the total supply chain. While this does bring some important benefits, there's a lot more than this involved in true world-class JIT. These early attempts at what I call 'first generation just-in-time' all interpreted JIT as simply another system or set of techniques and missed the underlying philosophy which is essential to achieving truly world-class performance.

3.1.2 World-Class Just-In-Time

The aim of world-class JIT is to provide a fast, reliable and flexible response to customers' requirements at least cost and with minimum dependence on inventory.

To achieve this requires the progressive elimination of waste, particularly those wastes which affect how much stock and work-in-progress you have, how quickly you can deliver what a customer wants, and how flexible you can be in responding to customers' changing demands. The term 'waste' was defined in Chapter 1 as *any activity that does not add value*. A more detailed explanation follows in Sec. 3.2.

The key elements of the JIT philosophy are:

- Exposing fundamental problems and then putting them right once and for all, so that they don't keep recurring (in contrast to the traditional solution of holding extra stocks 'just-in-case' things go wrong)
- Striving for simplicity, because simple processes are less likely to cause problems and are easier to put right when they do go wrong
- Reducing manufacturing throughput times, effectively replacing traditional batch production by as close as you can get to continuous processing through the use of cell manufacturing and set-up reduction techniques. Most companies will find these two techniques vital to the successful introduction of JIT. An explanation of cell manufacturing is provided in Sec. 11.9, while set-up time reduction techniques are described in Secs. 3.4 and 11.3
- Improving supplier performance to stop material problems interfering with your ability to satisfy your customers' requirements
- Improving quality, because short lead times and lower stocks mean that you no longer have the protection against things going wrong that you've been used to in the past
- Improving labour flexibility through cross-training, so that you can switch people between tasks to cope with the everyday ups and downs in customers' demands

The remainder of this chapter explains what you might need to do in order to put this philosophy into practice in your own company. But first we need to look in more detail at the subject of waste.

3.2 ATTACKING WASTE

At the heart of JIT is the continuing drive to achieve more efficient use of resources through the reduction or elimination of waste. The term 'waste' is used here in its widest sense to mean, in effect:

any activity or operation that does not add value

The Toyota Motor Company, who were the pioneers in what we call the JIT approach, identified so many examples of waste that they decided to divide them into seven categories:

- *Waste from over-production*, e.g. making a batch of 100 when they only had orders for 50, so that the balance had to go into stock; or making a batch of 52, instead of 50, in case there were rejects. Both tie up production facilities longer than necessary, and excess production may eventually have to be scrapped if it can't be sold.
- *Waste of waiting time*, e.g. allowing queues to build up between operations, resulting in longer lead times and higher work-in-progress.
- *Transportation waste*, e.g. the time and effort spent in moving products around the factory as a result of poor layout.
- *Processing waste*: this is what most people in our factories think of when the term 'waste' is used, e.g. offcuts of raw material.

- *Inventory waste*: inventory does not add value; not only does it cost money to run a store, interest has to be paid on the money tied up in stock and, in many cases, production of customers orders will have been delayed as a result of production resources being tied up in producing items for stock.
- *Waste of motion*, e.g. as a result of inefficient layout of tools and materials around the workplace.
- *Waste from production defects*, i.e. as a result of not getting it right first time.

In looking for ways to improve productivity in clients' factories, I have defined a further five categories of waste, most of which will be found in a typical manufacturing company in the Western world:

- *Inspection*: the process of inspection does not add value, which is one reason why, increasingly, Western manufacturers are following the Japanese example and making operators responsible for the quality of their own work, so reducing the need for separate inspection operations.
- *Administration*: no comment!
- '*Relabelling*', e.g. taking a finished product and altering it in some way to suit a particular customer's requirements (the term originates from the particular case of taking the outer wrapping off a product held in stock and substituting a wrapping with the printing in a different language; however, it has much wider application – I've seen it happen in aircraft manufacture, when major electronic equipment has been stripped out of a nearly completed 'stock' aircraft and replaced with equipment from another manufacturer to meet a customer's specification).
- *Waste of elapsed time*: if a manufacturer can increase sales by offering a shorter lead time than the competitors, then it follows that any avoidable delays between the time when a customer's order is received and the time when the goods are delivered must be a waste.
- *Waste of customers' goodwill*: in an increasingly competitive world, most companies recognize the need to improve customer service. Very often, it would be more effective (and cheaper) for them to find ways of reducing customer annoyance.

Once you have understood this concept of waste, the task of improving productivity is relatively straightforward. All you have to do is:

1. Look at what's happening at present (for example, using process flow analysis techniques).
2. Take each activity in the process flow in turn and decide if it adds value; if it doesn't, then it's a waste.
3. Decide how you can reduce, or eliminate, all the activities that you have listed as waste.

Be warned that this will take a long time: Toyota started over 30 years ago and they're still at it! So you'll need to decide where to start: Chapter 11 gives further guidance on how to identify examples of waste in your own company, and how to decide which to tackle first.

3.3 REDUCING LEAD TIMES

Reducing lead times is one of the most important ways to improve competitive edge. If a company can offer significantly shorter and more reliable delivery times than its competitors it will often be able to increase market share and, at the same time, may even be able to charge more for its products and services. Reducing lead times by as much as 50 per cent can often be surprisingly easy, and in many cases won't cost a lot. The key, as in so many things in life, is to understand what is happening, what takes the time and what causes things to go wrong. Once you understand this the solution is often blindingly obvious.

The first step, therefore, is to look in detail at what happens between when an order is received and when the finished goods are despatched to the customer. If you prepare a detailed process flow diagram, and put typical times required on each step, you should be able to identify which are the stages which account for the bulk of the lead time. Since the Pareto Principle nearly always applies to lead times, there should only be a few areas in which you need to take action to achieve a dramatic reduction in lead time. A typical example of this is shown in Fig. 3.1. In this case, if you are trying to reduce lead time by, say, 50 per cent, you will clearly need to do something about the time taken for Technical Specification and Design since this accounts for 40 per cent of the current lead time. Component Manufacture and procurement of Special Materials together take up a further 25 per cent, but as they take place in parallel both will need to be reduced for there to be any impact on overall lead time. These three areas *must* be reduced if you are to achieve your objective of cutting lead time in half, since all the other steps in the process flow diagram together only account for about a third of current lead time.

When you look in detail at what happens at present you may well find that delays (such as shortage of materials, tooling problems and changing priorities) frequently interrupt production, resulting in work being completed later than planned; as a consequence you are unable to keep to the delivery dates promised to customers. In this case you will need to get your production staff to keep records of *why* each delay occurred; analysing these will give you further guidance on where to start. Chapter 11 includes an example (in Fig. 11.10) of the sort of log sheet you could use for this.

You should also check the theoretical lead time, derived from your process flow diagram, against the actual lead time performance achieved during a representative period. Figures 3.2, 3.3 and 3.4 show three different ways of illustrating the results of your lead time analysis (Chapter 11 includes guidance on how to analyse the data and produce the diagrams, and explains the advantages of each type of presentation).

In the example illustrated, lead times from receipt of order to despatch are typically 8 to 10 weeks, but 36 per cent take longer than this; an individual order can take anything between 5 and 17 weeks. It is highly likely that even if a lead time of 8 to 10 weeks is acceptable in the market-place, the delivery performance achieved is so poor that customers may well be encouraged to go elsewhere in future.

You can see from this that as far as the customer is concerned there are effectively two ways in which you can improve lead time. You can reduce the *average* lead time (in the example above, from 8 to 10 weeks to, say, 4 weeks). Or you can improve *delivery performance* so that your customers know that whatever delivery date you promise, they can be confident that you will keep to it. Of course, the ideal would be to do both, but it makes sense to concentrate on just one of them at first. Some experts recommend that

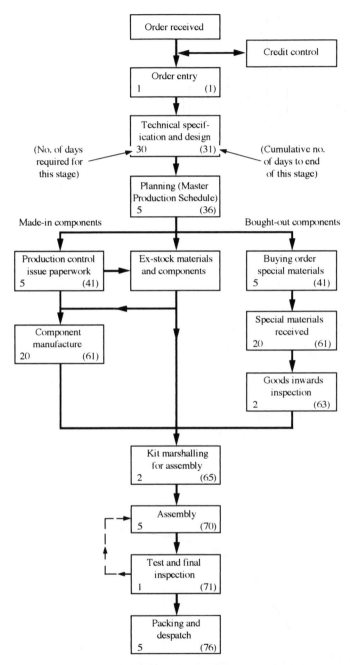

Figure 3.1 Process flow diagram: satisfying a customer's order.

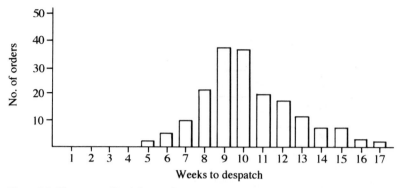

Figure 3.2 Histogram of lead time performance.

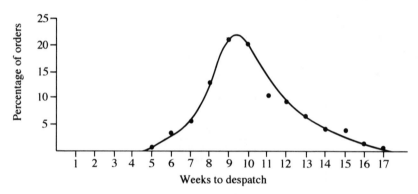

Figure 3.3 Lead time performance: frequency distribution diagram.

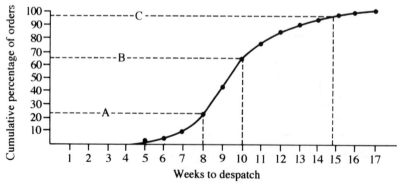

Figure 3.4 Lead time performance: cumulative frequency distribution diagram.

you should start by attacking *average* lead time, arguing that delivery performance will improve automatically as a result. I personally prefer to tackle the *delivery performance* problem first, for the following reasons:

- Attacking the late delivery problem first usually gets quick results that are highly visible.
- Most customers rate really being able to rely on your delivery promises as even more important than how long your lead time is.
- Poor delivery performance is usually symptomatic of being out of control; production schedules are often little better than wish lists, what is actually produced being determined primarily by what materials are available. It's better to get things under control before starting on the process of reducing average lead times.
- Internal conflicts between the Sales and Production departments are inevitably counter-productive: broken delivery promises are often the root cause of these conflicts.
- Improving delivery performance can significantly reduce the troubleshooting demands on managers (and the continual alterations and interruptions to production that result) as a result of complaints from customers whose expected deliveries are overdue.
- Finding out *why* promised delivery dates are being missed is usually a very good way of learning about what happens at present, what goes wrong and why it goes wrong. This typically provides useful pointers as to what will have the greatest effect when you subsequently move on to the task of reducing *average* lead times.

The exception to my 'delivery performance first' rule is where you know that it takes you, say, eight weeks to satisfy customers' requirements, but for commercial reasons you actually quote four to six weeks. In this case there's little point in trying to find out why some orders take longer than others to complete; it will almost certainly be because some customers are considered to be more important than others (or shout louder!). You *must* do something first of all to bring your real lead time into line with what you are promising to customers.

Whichever you decide to attack first, the key areas in which you may need to take action are shown below. All will help to reduce both lead time and inventory, but do remember that some will also be necessary in order to compensate for the additional risk of interruptions to production that you would otherwise be exposed to as a result of removing your traditional protection of high stocks and long lead times:

- *Order processing*: order intake, specification and planning procedures are often as significant a cause of delay as the manufacturing processes themselves, particularly where special materials have to be ordered from outside suppliers (see Fig. 3.1).
- *Reducing the size of production batches*: all too often production equipment is tied up on long production runs, because it is 'uneconomic' to produce just the quantity required by the customer – so a larger batch is made and the surplus is put into stock in the hope that it can eventually be used on another order. Meanwhile, the longer production run ties up the equipment and reduces flexibility in responding to true customer requirements. The solution is to attack the time it takes to set up the machine for a new batch (see Sec. 3.4).

- *Resolving inventory problems*: inaccurate stock records and incorrect bills of materials are frequent causes of delay to both assembly and piece part manufacture. In many cases these shortages are accompanied by complaints from management that stocks are too high (see Sec. 3.5).
- *Improving labour flexibility*: with the introduction of JIT, as batch sizes are reduced and layout improved to incorporate cell manufacturing concepts, it becomes increasingly necessary to be able to move people around from one machine or process to another. Shorter lead times mean that less time is available to smooth fluctuations in demand and this must be compensated for by increased labour flexibility (see Sec. 3.6).
- *Kanbans*: supply problems with frequently used materials can often be overcome by replacing traditional ordering procedures by a simple process in which the materials are automatically replaced as they are used (see Sec. 3.7).
- *Improving supplier performance*: another frequent cause of delay is late delivery of materials and components from outside suppliers. With shorter lead times and stock levels reduced in the drive to reduce waste, you become increasingly dependent on the performance of your suppliers. This means that you need to work much more closely with them and you need to make sure that *you* don't contribute to supplier problems through late or inadequate instructions about your requirements (see Sec. 3.8).
- *Improving design*: whether a part is made in-house or purchased from an outside supplier, there is a lot that Design staff can do to contribute to lead time reduction (see Sec. 3.9).
- *Maintenance*: in conventional manufacturing there are usually only two or three machines in a factory which are true bottlenecks (i.e. if the machine breaks down, the output of the factory is likely to be directly affected); occasional breakdowns in other machines can usually be tolerated. Just-in-time usually leads to an increase in the number of bottleneck machines and the shorter lead times you have introduced mean that you will have less time to put things right. If this is likely to be the case with *your* production processes you will need to take extra precautions to improve machine reliability (see Sec. 3.10).
- *Layout*: every time material has to be moved from one part of the factory to another, a delay occurs and frequently there is a need to hold a buffer stock of work-in-progress to cover any delays in movement. Ideally, in a JIT environment, manufacturing will be carried out in 'cells', where all the operations needed for the manufacture of a part are carried out on a sequence of adjacent machines, often with operators moving with the parts from one machine to the next (more details on cell manufacture can be found in Sec. 11.9). Even where this is not feasible, if you want to cut lead time significantly you will probably need to change the layout of the factory in order to reduce or eliminate movements between operations.
- *Organization*: the review of layout may well need to include where you locate supporting services, such as order processing, specification and planning, production control and purchasing. Many companies that have introduced JIT have replaced their traditional centralized support services with dedicated 'Business Units' in which everyone who contributes to processing and satisfying the customer's order works in one self-contained unit 'close to the action', so minimizing barriers to communication. If the 'empowering people' concept is also introduced the restructuring may well extend to slimming down the management structure; organizational implications are considered in Sec. 5.8 and the 'empowering people' concept in Sec. 13.1.

Attacking all the action areas listed above could well take several years to complete. Remember that the best way of deciding where to start is to look at the process flow diagram, referred to earlier, which will show you which activities are responsible for the bulk of the current lead time. Further guidance on this and the other topics listed above can be found in Chapter 11.

There's inevitably a degree of risk involved in introducing the sort of changes outlined above. Implementing just-in-time rarely goes as smoothly as you would like, however thoroughly you prepare for it. But there's a lot you can do to reduce risks to a minimum: make sure you read Sec. 3.11 on reducing the risks of change *before* starting on your implementation programme.

3.4 REDUCING SET-UP TIMES

3.4.1 The Need

Quick set-up (or changeover) times are fundamental to the successful implementation of JIT because they enable smaller batches to be made economically. The terms 'set-up' and 'changeover' have the same meaning in this context – which is used generally depends on the type of manufacturing environment. For convenience, I shall use 'set-up' in this section.

In most manufacturing operations changes to set-ups take up a significant proportion of production time. If this occurs in 'bottleneck' processes, then the lost production time results in a loss of throughput. If you can reduce this set-up time then you can not only reduce lead time, you can also increase the total output of the factory. Even if the process is not a bottleneck activity, reducing set-up time reduces a waste, since setting up for a new production batch does not add value.

There are other benefits to be gained by reducing set-up times:

- Shorter set-up times cost less, and therefore you can, if you wish, afford to change the set-up more often, i.e. you can make smaller batches. Making smaller batches doesn't tie up production machinery for so long, which increases flexibility and reduces lead times.
- if you can reduce set-up times sufficiently, you may even be able to make to order, instead of having to make to forecast. Not only will this reduce inventory cost, it will also avoid the situation where machines are tied up in producing parts or material against stock orders, so that you can't produce what customers actually want. .
- Production defects are often not identified until a subsequent inspection operation. If batch sizes can be reduced, the batches which have to be scrapped, or require rectification work, are smaller.
- If you know that you can replace faulty output quickly in small batches, there is less temptation to over-produce on the original batch, just-in-case.
- With greatly reduced set-up times, work-in-progress will be much less and you may well find you can avoid the need for complex computer-based control systems.

Traditionally, production managers prefer to manufacture in 'economic batch quantities', an approach which has been practised throughout the industrialized world for over 70 years. If we are going to challenge this policy, we need to understand *why* the economic batch quantity theory is now considered by so many people to be seriously flawed.

3.4.2 Challenging the Economic Batch Size Theory

In case you're not an expert on it, let's first of all recap on the economic batch size theory.

The total time required to process a batch consists of three elements: prepare, run and clear up (Fig. 3.5).

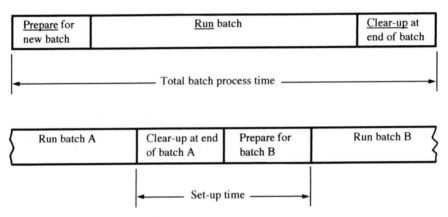

Figure 3.5 The elements of batch process time.

The prepare and clear up elements together make up the set-up time. The traditional policy is to make batches sufficiently large for the unit set-up time to be insignificant (*unit* set-up time is the total set-up time for the batch divided by the number of units in the batch). This usually means making more than you need to meet your immediate requirements, but the cost of holding the additional parts in stock until they are needed is compensated for by the lower unit set-up cost. As you can see from Fig. 3.6, inventory cost increases steadily as the batch size increases; unit set-up cost, however, drops rapidly at first but diminishing returns eventually set in. The economic batch quantity formula enables you to get the best trade-off between these two costs (don't bother to do the calculations: the 'least total cost' point derived from the formula is actually where the two lines on the diagram intersect).

The Economic Batch Size policy says, in effect:

Increase batch size to the point where set-up cost is balanced by inventory holding cost.

There are three fundamental flaws in this policy:

- Inventory does not add value: with the JIT philosophy the objective is to *reduce* waste – the economic batch policy adds additional waste (inventory) to counterbalance the waste involved in set-up time!
- Unless the process uses a bottleneck resource, *it doesn't always matter if set-up times are greater than run times.* In practice very few production resources are bottlenecks.

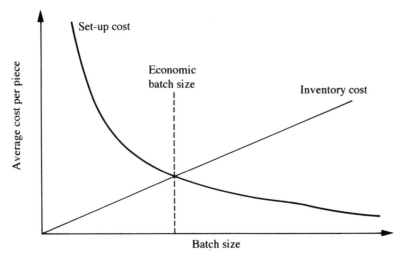

Figure 3.6 The economic batch size diagram.

- Making larger batches ties up a production resource, reducing flexibility and therefore increasing lead times.

Clearly the best solution, if you can manage it, is to reduce set-up times so much that there's no longer any need to make a larger quantity than you need at the time. The SMED technique will help you do this.

3.4.3 The SMED Technique

The SMED technique is by far the best method for achieving really significant reductions in set-up times. It is also surprisingly easy to understand, so that it can be learnt and successfully applied by machine setters and operators themselves after only a few hours instruction.

The concept was originally developed by a Japanese management consultant, Shigeo Shingo, in 1969, although he had already been using the all important first stage of SMED as far back as 1950. It's a sobering thought that it wasn't until the 1980s that his methods started to be applied in the Western world, and even today only a minority of manufacturers have realized the tremendous benefits that can be gained through SMED. Reducing set-up time to the point where it becomes economic to manufacture in small batches is a key step in changing to a truly just-in-time approach.

There are three stages to the SMED technique. The first stage, which he developed in 1950, enabled Shingo to reduce the average time for changing set-up on large steel presses from four hours to less than ninety minutes. The second and third stages, introduced in 1969, led to these same set-up changes being reduced to less than ten minutes. Because Shingo developed his ideas mainly on steel presses and plastic moulding and extrusion machinery, he called the technique 'Single Minute Exchange of Dies' ('single minute' meaning less than double figures, i.e. less than ten minutes). However, the same technique can be applied to virtually any type of manufacturing process where changes of set-up occur. I personally try to avoid using the term SMED on the shop floor because people react badly to reference to 'dies' if they don't use them; they may also be apprehensive about their ability to understand a technique that has such a strange name. The technique is actually so simple to understand (as you will see in a moment) that it seems a pity to put them off.

If you are interested in reading more about Shingo's work, I suggest you get hold of the English translation of his book *A Revolution in Manufacturing: The SMED System* (see Bibliography). The book includes a large number of line drawings, illustrating ideas for quick change tooling which are equally appropriate in other types of manufacturing situations.

Now for the explanation.

A set-up will normally consist of a number of separate tasks, some of which can only be carried out when the machine or process is stopped and some of which *could* be carried out when the machine or process is running. Shingo called these 'internal' and 'external', and I'll use his terminology in describing the process here. However, when you're applying the technique in your own factory you should consider choosing terms which are more meaningful in your particular environment. Some possibilities are:

- In Process (IP) and Not In Process (NIP)
- Run Time Activities (RTA) and Stop Time Activities (STA)
- Critical Change-Time (CCT) and Non-Critical Change-Time (NCT)

Examples of internal activities are:

- Removing work from the machine
- Removing tools/dies etc.
- Cleaning down the work surfaces
- Fixing new tools in place
- Fixing the new workpiece in place
- Trial run and adjusting the machine

Examples of external activities are:

- Getting instructions for the next job
- Getting material for the next job from stores
- Getting tools for the next job from tool stores
- Returning tools from the last job to tool stores
- Arranging for lifting equipment to be available when required
- Arranging for a setter to be available when required

The three stages of the SMED procedure are as follows:

Stage 1 Identify internal and external activities; arrange for external activities to be carried out *while the machine is working on another batch*, instead of during the set-up time.

Stage 2 Convert as many internal activities as possible into external activities, so that they too can be done while the machine is working on another batch.

Stage 3 Continuously strive to improve or eliminate each element of the remaining internal and external activities.

When you first try it out you'll be amazed at how successful you can be in cutting set-up times, just by looking in detail at what happens during the changeover process and then carrying out Stage 1 of the SMED procedure. Typically you can expect to cut set-up times by between 30 and 50 per cent within a matter of weeks *and at very little cost*. You probably won't achieve much reduction in the actual manhours spent on the changeover process, since much of the work will still need to be done as before, albeit at a time when the machine is running on another job. However, there will usually be *some* reduction in overall set-up time as a result of eliminating the obviously wasteful activities you're sure to find during your analysis.

Stage 2 will probably take a number of months to complete, and may well involve some expenditure on new tooling or equipment. Typical of actions taken, in order to convert internal activities to external, are the installation of mould pre-heating equipment or the purchase of quick change tooling, as illustrated in the set-up reduction examples included in Sec. 11.3.

The third stage will enable you to cut set-up time, even for quite complex equipment, to a matter of minutes, the ultimate objective being 'OTED' (One Touch Exchange of Dies). However, it could well take two or three years to complete (perhaps even longer), and it's likely to involve considerable expenditure. Because of this, it will only be worthwhile in those instances where the benefits of reducing set-up time, and hence total lead time, are particularly great.

This does not mean that you can forget about it. There is a compromise which you may well be able to adopt, thus enabling you to get the full benefits of even this third stage of the Shingo approach: next time you are ordering new production equipment, or next time your designers are working on a new or re-designed product, consider what internal activities will be required during the batch changeover process, and see if you can use the opportunity of this new equipment or new design to introduce the type of changes that would otherwise be too expensive to consider. If you do it at this stage, there may well be little extra cost involved.

Finally, don't think that reducing set-up time is something that only your production people need to know about. Your buyers should also understand how applying the SMED technique can enable much smaller batches to be produced economically. As part of your JIT initiatives they will be asking suppliers to deliver in smaller quantities: a knowledge of the SMED technique will enable them to resist requests for a price increase 'to.cover the extra cost' of either making smaller batches or holding stock to meet these new requirements. Larger companies, particularly in the motor industry, often go even further and offer the services of their own production experts to help a supplier introduce the SMED concepts.

Further guidance on how to apply the SMED process can be found in Sec. 11.3.

3.5 RESOLVING INVENTORY PROBLEMS

Earlier in this chapter I explained that 'the aim of world-class JIT is to provide a fast, reliable and flexible response to customers' requirements at least cost and *with minimum dependence on inventory*'. The various JIT techniques described in this chapter should enable you to operate effectively with much lower levels of inventory, but first you have to get rid of the problems that are almost certain to exist at present, whether you are aware of them or not. I am referring here to problems caused by inaccurate stock records and planning data, not shortages caused, for example, by late orders or deliveries, which are dealt with in Chapter 8.

In the vast majority of cases, these inventory problems are a direct result of something going wrong with the company's control procedures. This means that it's not enough just to reduce stocks, it's also necessary to find out *why* the stock levels are too high (or, for some items, too low), and then take appropriate action to stop things continuing to go wrong in the future. If you don't do this, the same problems will probably go on happening, and that could be disastrous once you've removed the protection of high stocks and long lead times that you've been used to in the past. A procedure for improving the accuracy of your computer systems, through identifying and correcting the main problem causes, is described in Sec. 14.7.

However, before starting on the process of identifying problem causes, you need to get a good understanding of what inventory you have, analysing this in a number of different ways. This will help you decide where to concentrate your efforts, in the first instance, for maximum effect; it will also provide a sound basis, subsequently, for reviewing stockholding policy. Guidance on how to prepare this analysis of inventory is included in Sec. 11.4.

3.5.1 Reviewing Inventory Control Parameters

Once you've identified the main sources of inventory problems, and taken action to avoid them occurring in the future, you can turn your attention to reviewing inventory control parameters – the 'rules' which determine what stock you should hold of each type of material, where it should be held, when you should place a replenishment order, and what quantity you should order. When you are doing this there are three basic world-class principles you should remember:

- *Challenge existing order frequencies*: if your existing practice is to schedule monthly, why not weekly? If it's already weekly, why not daily (with a provisional 'next day' back-up list)? If the answer is 'it can't be done', ask what needs to be changed to make it possible.
- *Challenge existing batch sizes*: they were probably set long ago when conditions (and demand patterns) were very different from now. Consider changing standard batch quantity figures on your computer system to just '1' for all items, leaving it for the planners and buyers to determine a suitable quantity depending on actual net requirements outstanding. If you're told that a smaller batch 'wouldn't be economic', see if something can be done to reduce set-up time (see Sec. 3.4).
- *Challenge the level of finished stocks demanded by Sales and Marketing*: they will normally reflect your past unreliable delivery performance; the action you have taken to reduce inventory problems should make it possible to reduce these stocks and still provide a higher level of customer service than in the past. If you hold stocks at depots, consider introducing a 'stock-capping' policy (this and other suggestions for improving stock control at depots are described below).

3.5.2 Improving Inventory Performance at Distribution Centres

Many manufacturing companies depend on a network of regional stockholding points from which customers can purchase products or spares. Whether these are company-owned depots or independent agents or distributors, sales will often be lost to competitors if customers can't get what they want when they want it. Depending on the nature of the product, 'when they want it' might mean there and then, when customers first visit the trade counter, or it might mean when they return to collect their list of materials two or three days later.

It's an expensive business to hold enough stocks at every distribution centre to meet the majority of customers' requirements, but if you keep too tight a reign on inventory you'll lose sales and, if you do that too often, some of your customers might desert you for good. It makes little difference who actually has to carry the stockholding cost, you or your distributor, because the cost of that stockholding will have to be reflected in the price paid by the customer. If you want to provide a world-class service you have to find ways of satisfying customers' needs at minimum cost.

There are two ways in which you can make your distribution network more cost effective:

- You can improve your stock replenishment service from the factory by providing a rapid response and by making sure that you never let them down; having to say 'Sorry, we're out of stock at the factory' should be so unusual that top management will want to know why it's happened.
- You can improve stock control procedures at the distribution centres so that stock levels are better balanced.

You will probably have to do both.

Making sure that your factory can satisfy customers' requirements quickly (with minimum dependence on stocks) is a key objective of just-in-time. The various techniques that can help you achieve this objective are described elsewhere in this chapter.

Providing a more rapid response is usually easier than you might think. Factory distribution departments are normally geared to minimizing distribution costs because that's what they believe to be their mission. That may mean waiting until they can make up a full vehicle load or, more likely, servicing each distribution centre just once a week. In recent years there has been a significant increase in the number of specialist carriers, many of them offering a daily service regardless of destination; their charges may even be less than it costs you at present because they can keep costs down by consolidating deliveries with those for other customers or by organizing return loads to improve vehicle utilization.

Making sure that stocks at distribution centres are properly balanced becomes very much easier once you have improved your stock replenishment service. You will usually find that stock levels have become distorted in the past because distribution centre staff have learnt to live with 'difficult' items by over-ordering, ending up with far too much stock of such items once the problem has been overcome. They will be suspicious of promises from remote Head Office staff that 'everything's going to be all right in future' because they will have heard that before. So, if you want to reduce the level of stocks at distribution centres you first have to convince the staff there that the problems they've had to live with in the past really have been overcome, and this will take time. One way of speeding up the confidence building process is to arrange a series of open days at the factory, so that distribution centre staff can see for themselves all that's being done to make the company world-class, and so that they can meet the people involved face to face. It's worth putting some effort into this, involving top management in the open days to demonstrate their personal commitment to providing a truly world-class service to customers through the distribution centres: if you can get the right balance of stocks at distribution centres you can expect sales to increase as a result, and total inventory to reduce by as much as 50 per cent.

Once all concerned are satisfied that you can provide a rapid and reliable stock replenishment service, you can start on the process of reviewing what stocks should be held. Such decisions are likely to have been influenced in the past by a desire to have as many items in stock as possible 'just-in-case' they were asked for by a customer and, because of financial constraints on total inventory value, this inevitably meant that stock levels of the more popular items had to be restricted. In other words, the stock profile was a thin covering over a wide range of stock lines. This made sense at a time when it took a week or more to get supplies from the factory, but that situation has changed: now that you can be confident of satisfying requests for slow-moving items from stocks held at the centre within two to three days, you can concentrate on holding just the faster moving items (for which competition is probably fiercest) at the distribution centre.

The procedure for reviewing inventory parameters, described in Sec. 11.4, will help you decide which items should be stocked at the distribution centres and how much stock to hold of each item. The principle is to *maximize sales* by making sure that you don't run out of popular items at the distribution centres, and at the same time to *minimize total inventory value* by having just one central stocking point for slower moving items. The total inventory value, i.e. that at all the distribution centres and central stockholding point combined, can be controlled through the inventory policy review technique described in Chapter 11.

Having completed the procedure described above you will end up with a list for each stockholding point, showing which items should be stocked in future and how much of each item should be held. These lists may well differ because of the different mix and volume of sales in each region. But however confident you are that you've got it right, you're sure to get resistance from local staff, and if you want their cooperation you should respect their opinions and give them the opportunity to suggest amendments. After all, they are the ones who have to live with the effects of your planned stockholding policy and they should have a better understanding of the competitive pressures they face locally. At the same time you don't want to give them too free a hand, or you'll soon be back where you started.

A 'stock-capping' approach is a useful compromise which gives a degree of freedom to local management while ensuring that overall control is maintained. Suppose, for example, that you have decided on a list of 80 items to be stocked: you can tell them that they can, if they wish, elect to stock an additional 10 items of their choosing, on condition that they do not increase their inventory value by more than 10 per cent and that they do not reduce the planned stock levels on your list. If, at a later date, they wish to add a new item to their 'optional extras', they must deselect one of their previous additions so that they maintain the stock-capping conditions. These additions won't have too much affect on your overall inventory policy, and in any case the cost can be allowed for when you are preparing the initial lists. Their main value is psychological: it allows local management to feel that they are still in charge.

Having agreed which items are to be stocked in future, you should arrange for all other items to be returned to the central stockholding point, together with any excess stocks of the remaining items. These returns will need to be carefully checked before they are put back into stock at the centre: you will probably find that some have been damaged in storage or transit, and others may be obsolete.

Finally, you may need to let the distribution centres have additional supplies of some items in order to bring their stocks up to the agreed levels.

Archilighting GmbH have used the techniques described here to improve the efficiency of their distribution network. They were able to reduce the number of stock lines held at distribution centres by more than 80 per cent and the total value of stock by a third, and yet were able to satisfy a higher proportion of customer requirements than ever before. Further details of their experiences can be found in the case study in Sec. 11.4.

3.5.3 Obsolete Stock

When you carry out an analysis of inventory you may discover that obsolete stock is a problem that needs to be tackled (Sec. 11.4 includes some suggestions for improving how you identify stock as obsolete). Hopefully, you will have taken action to avoid accumulating much more of this in the future, for example by tightening up your Engineering Change procedures, but you will need to find ways of getting rid of what's already there. You may well find that the value of obsolete stocks is still included in the company's assets because, until you started looking in detail at inventory problems, no one had really known which items *were* obsolete. This puts particular pressure on you not to just throw it away, since you will have to write off the lost asset against profit for the year. Since most of the obsolete stock will have come about because of design changes, it's well worth getting your design staff and production engineers to look at each item, to see if the obsolete items can be used up (with careful control and supervision) on existing products. Alternatively, it may be possible to modify them in some way to turn them into items which conform to current specifications; of course, this is only worth doing if the cost of re-work is less than the manufacturing or purchase cost of the new item. In some instances you may be able to persuade the original supplier to take some of the items back, or you may be able to sell them off to the trade or another manufacturer at a discounted price, where safety and commercial considerations permit.

A significant part of the value of obsolete stock can often be realized, *provided that those involved are adequately motivated.* You may well find that the main hurdle you have to overcome is not so much *how* to dispose of obsolete items, but in getting your people to actually *do* something more imaginative than simply writing it off as scrap. The problem is that it usually means a lot more work for people who are usually kept pretty busy, so that they're not motivated to do anything about trying to use up obsolete stock – it's a lot less hassle for them if the new designs are used instead. The most effective solution I've found is to make this a key strategic project and set up a team with a clear target and date by which it must be achieved.

For example, in an inventory reduction project at Archilighting GmbH, the team identified the total value of obsolete stock to be in excess of DM2 million. Management responded by setting up a special team to tackle this problem, involving representatives from Design, Production Engineering, Production, Quality Management, Accounts and Sales. The team were given the specific target to 'Dispose of DM1.5 million of finished goods stock classified as obsolete by 31 December (i.e. within six months), and collect a minimum of DM450 000 in cash from that disposal'. Since the whole team were required to make a presentation to the Board early in January, setting out what they had achieved, management were confident that something really would be done to solve the problem, as indeed happened. The team also improved Archilighting's Engineering Change Control procedure to reduce the risk of obsolete stock accumulating in the future whenever current products were replaced by new models. To smooth the path from 'current' to 'obsolete', design and marketing staff now classify products or components as 'Dying', 'Dead' or 'Buried'. 'Dying' means 'consult Marketing before re-ordering', 'Dead' means 'do not re-order, but retain stocks in case of future demand (e.g. for spares or specials)', and 'Buried' means 'dispose of all stocks'. Their New Product Development procedure now includes a check-list to ensure that a systematic review of existing products is carried out before new products are launched, with the appropriate Obsolete classification recorded on the stock file.

3.5.4 The Next Step

Having identified the probable reasons why things are going wrong, you may well need to carry out more detailed investigations to help you decide on priorities for action. The methods described in Sec. 11.4 should help you do this. You may also want to arrange for a physical stock check to be carried out in order to correct the inaccuracies that have accumulated in the records. Avoid doing this too early. A physical stock check is a significant undertaking for most companies: if you do it too early you will probably have to repeat the process later.

Some of the changes that you will want to introduce may involve changes to your computer systems. But this will take time, probably longer than you can afford to wait if you are really serious about achieving your world-class objectives. If this is the case, saying 'we're waiting for the computer people' is just passing the buck: if you can't get your computer system to do what you want it to do, you have to find some other solution that will enable you to get on with your world-class improvements. You may be able to develop a temporary solution, using a spreadsheet program on a desktop computer, or you may have to fall back on manual systems. But whatever you do, you have to make sure that you stop using and relying on procedures that you now know are the ones that have got you into trouble in the past. That might seem to you such an obvious statement that you wonder why I trouble to say it. But it needs to be stressed, because in most manufacturing companies today people have become so used to using computers to generate requirements and schedule production that they find it difficult to think of operating without them, even for a limited period. Fortunately, these same people can be very resourceful at finding ways of solving the short-term problems that involve the minimum of extra work, once you persuade them that there isn't time to wait for the ideal solution and that, somehow, the problems have to be overcome *now*.

Finally, remember that although the steps outlined in this section will make a direct contribution to reducing inventory, their *primary* purpose is to provide a sound basis to enable you to introduce the other JIT techniques smoothly.

3.6 IMPROVING LABOUR FLEXIBILITY

Few manufacturers are fortunate enough to have a consistent level of demand day after day, week after week. Most have to cope with variations both in overall volume and in the mix of products ordered.

The usual way of dealing with these short-term 'peaks' and 'troughs' is to quote a long enough lead time to allow variations in demand to be smoothed out; or to hold enough stocks of part processed or finished products to cope with typical peak demand levels, using the spare capacity in slack periods to replenish these stocks; or to vary capacity by altering the number of hours worked, for example through overtime.

JIT changes all that: we want to offer shorter lead times, but at the same time we want to reduce stocks to the absolute minimum. And we want to avoid authorizing overtime in some parts of the factory if there is spare capacity elsewhere, because that would be an avoidable 'waste'.

Smaller batch sizes will help to increase flexibility (because they don't tie up production machinery for so long), but that's not enough. We also need to improve the flexibility of our human resources, so that we can move people quickly from areas where demand is slack to those which are under pressure. You may already have ways of coping with short-term overloads, which are appropriate for your particular type of operations, but make sure that you have at least considered all the following (I've listed them in order of preference):

- Move people around within the workgroup
- Move people around between workgroups in the same department
- Move people around between different departments of the factory
- Authorize overtime
- Call in casual workers from an established register of trained part-timers, e.g. for a 'twilight' shift
- Take on additional temporary workers, if the increased demand is expected to continue for more than a few days (you can put the temporary workers on to the simpler, easier to learn tasks, moving the people who normally do those tasks on to more difficult ones for which they've been trained as 'reserve resources')

Don't forget that you may have to make similar arrangements for administrative functions, particularly order processing, planning and purchasing. If you've raised customers' expectations by promising them a quick response to their requirements, these departments too have to be able to cope with variations in workload.

This need to switch people around at short notice means that the resource base has to be managed more effectively than ever before. We need to know precisely what skills are available and where additional skills can be obtained at short notice. And we need to make sure that the available skill base is developed effectively. In other words, the world-class 'continuous improvement' concept should apply as much to the skills of the workforce as it does to the production processes. The skill development aspects are beyond the scope of this book; this present section is concerned primarily with how to maintain up-to-date information on the skills available, and how to use that information to improve labour flexibility. You can use the method described below in a factory or in an office, and the procedures will be identical; for the sake of clarity I'll base the explanation which follows on a manufacturing unit consisting of machining and assembly operations.

The first step is to draw up a grid or 'matrix' chart for each workgroup, showing all the skill categories (machines/processes/tasks) across the top, and with the names of all employees in the workgroup listed in the left-hand column; supervisors, foremen etc. should normally be included, since they are often the ones who train new operators, or help out in emergencies. You then need to take each row in turn and put some sort of mark under each column/task for which that person has some level of skill.

You may find that some such analysis already exists, but beware! It's most unlikely that it will be up-to-date, and even more unlikely that it's used on a regular basis as a resource planning tool. I've found that the resource/skills matrix is used in most companies for two specific purposes: when planning for a major project or a new range of products; or, when business is poor, for deciding who should be made redundant. While an existing matrix will provide a useful starting point, it will probably only indicate 'who can do what' by means of a tick in the appropriate square; if you're lucky it will show a skill level rather than a simple tick, but even this is unlikely to be sufficient for JIT purposes, since in most cases only a simple skill grading will have been used and this will probably have been done by the supervisor without consulting the person concerned.

I prefer to use a skill grading system with six categories of skill, as illustrated in Fig. 3.7; the symbols shown have been designed to make it easy for skill levels to be amended as higher grades are achieved (by simply adding another dot), without having to redraw the chart. Figure 3.8 shows an extract from a resource/skills matrix using these symbols. When the chart is first compiled, it's important that people are consulted about their current skill grade for each task: once you've completed the 'where are we now' matrix, you will want to consider what training each individual needs, and it's

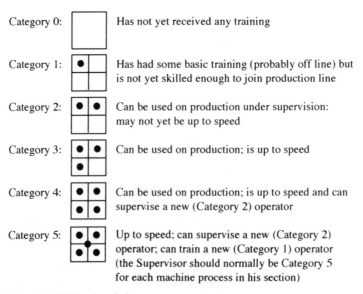

Category 0: Has not yet received any training

Category 1: Has had some basic training (probably off line) but is not yet skilled enough to join production line

Category 2: Can be used on production under supervision: may not yet be up to speed

Category 3: Can be used on production; is up to speed

Category 4: Can be used on production; is up to speed and can supervise a new (Category 2) operator

Category 5: Up to speed; can supervise a new (Category 2) operator; can train a new (Category 1) operator (the Supervisor should normally be Category 5 for each machine process in his section)

Figure 3.7 Skill level symbols.

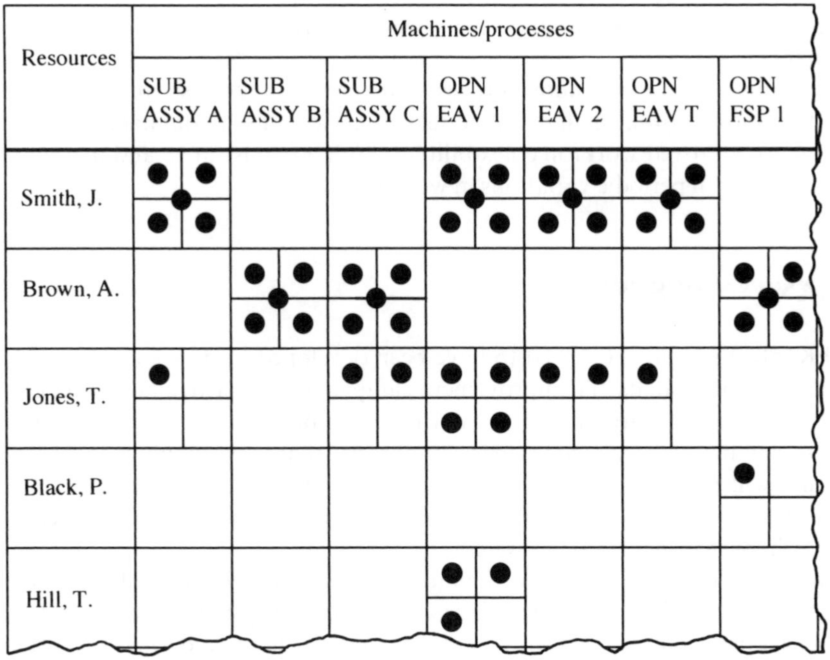

Resources	Machines/processes						
	SUB ASSY A	SUB ASSY B	SUB ASSY C	OPN EAV 1	OPN EAV 2	OPN EAV T	OPN FSP 1
Smith, J.	●●●●				●●●●	●●●●	●●●●
Brown, A.		●●●●	●●●●				●●●●
Jones, T.	●			●●	●●●●	●●●●	●
Black, P.							●
Hill, T.				●●●			

Figure 3.8 Extract from resource/skills matrix.

important to make sure that both parties agree on the starting point for this. You should also take the opportunity to find out whether they have any strong ideas about their future role: would they like to be trained in new tasks and, if so, are there any in particular that interest them? Or would they prefer to be left as they are?

The completed matrix can be viewed in two ways. Firstly, by looking at each column in turn, you can review whether you have enough people who can do the task and whether you have a reasonable balance of skill levels; you can also review whether you have adequate cover for holidays and sickness, and who could be drafted in from other areas when there's a temporary overload. This first part of the review process, looking vertically, enables you to assess *management's* needs. Secondly, by looking at each row in turn, you can decide whether you have sufficient flexibility to move people around to suit the workload, and whether each individual is being given sufficient opportunity to learn new skills. This second part of the review process, therefore, takes into account the *employees'* needs as well as management's. The final stage is to consult each individual in order to agree proposed skill upgrades which satisfy the needs of the business and, as far as possible, the employee's personal development aspirations.

A training plan can then be drawn up, showing the priorities for each person. Special arrangements may need to be made for training, but it's surprising how much can be fitted in to the normal work schedule by taking full advantage of slack periods or interruptions to production: that's only likely to happen when there's a clear plan prepared in advance so that everyone concerned knows who has to be trained, in what task, to what standard, by when, and who is to do the teaching. Once such a plan has been prepared, agreed and publicized, you can usually leave it to those concerned to make sure it happens.

A practical application of the above process is described in the case study included in Sec. 11.5. This shows how a small manufacturing business (a self-contained Division of Vokes Limited) improved workforce flexibility in both administrative and manufacturing areas to cope with periodic variations in workload.

3.7 THE KANBAN SYSTEM

The original Kanban system is believed to have been developed by Toyota in the early stages of what we would call its JIT improvement campaign. The particular feature of a Kanban system is that it short-circuits normal ordering procedures: as supplies of a Kanban-controlled material are used up, new supplies are requested simply by releasing a re-order card which is sent direct to the supply point (i.e. the manufacturer or stockist). It is often described as a 'pull' system, in contrast with traditional ordering procedures which 'push' orders into the system.

The term 'Kanban' comes from the Japanese language, in which Kanban simply means 'card'. Somehow, the word Kanban seems to have caught the imagination of manufacturing people in the Western world, even on the shop floor, and today it is often used to describe simplified ordering systems which a Japanese manufacturer wouldn't consider to be true Kanbans. I personally don't see any problem in that: if using the Kanban label helps to get the idea of simplified ordering procedures accepted, then I'll put aside my usual aversion to using Japanese terminology in manufacturing companies in the Western world, even if the interpretation isn't quite true to the original! However, in this section I shall stick to the true meaning of Kanban, the other types of application being covered in the next section, on improving the performance of suppliers.

To explain the Kanban concept, consider the case of an assembler who is drawing a particular component from a pallet which, when full, contains 100 pieces. As the last piece is drawn, the assembler takes an identifying card from the empty pallet and sends it back down the line to the earlier work centre where that part (among others) is made. On receiving the Kanban card, the work centre responsible for supplying the component makes a new batch of 100 and sends it to the assembly post (so that the assembler isn't kept waiting, there will probably be an extra pallet in the system to maintain the supply while the new batch is being made). This means that there is a minimum of paperwork, and the order cycle is generated on a 'pull' basis, the components only being made when there is an immediate need for them, thus keeping work-in-progress to a minimum. If you are familiar with the 'two-bin' method of stock control you will recognize the similarity.

Since the procedure was first introduced at Toyota, a number of variants have been introduced (the explanation in the previous paragraph was based on the second variant, the 1 card Kanban):

- *The 2 card Kanban*: this is the original Toyota method, developed at a time when replenishment supplies were routed through a component or parts store (though it can also be used when no stores intervention is involved). The card released by the user authorizes the stores to 'move' a replenishment supply to the user. When they do so, a second card, which is found on the pallet they are about to supply, is removed and sent to the component supplier as authority to 'produce' another standard quantity.

- *The 1 card Kanban*: similar to the 2 card system, but a single card acts as both 'move' and 'produce' authority. This method is typically used where the supply point is close to the user point, so that the supply and user operatives move the empty and full pallets between the two work centres themselves without the intervention of a stores function. It is also commonly used where the movement of pallets is automated.

- *The container-based Kanban*: in this variant the Kanban card is dispensed with altogether. Instead, there are a predetermined number of containers or pallets in the system, all uniquely identified to a particular part number or component: if the maker of the component has an empty container waiting he or she fills it; if there is no empty container waiting, then the operator must stop production of that component and switch to some other task. This procedure is often used when special-purpose containers or pallets are provided, so that there is no doubt as to which components have to go into them. However, it is also possible to use multi-purpose containers in what is in effect a cross between the container-based and the 1 card systems, by painting the appropriate part number and standard quantity on the container itself. Another useful technique is to paint containers for similar parts in different colours, so that operators can identify the right container easily.

- *The shelf-space Kanban*: anyone who has used a motorway cafeteria will be familiar with this method. At the cafeteria counter, a range of dishes is provided to the customer via a display/dispensing cabinet which is subdivided into a number of 'pigeon-holes', each providing one compartment for each type of dish. The instructions to the kitchen staff are 'ensure that there is always at least one and not more than three of each type of dish available in the cabinet. If there are three dishes available of all types of dish, stop producing and find something else to do (like cleaning your equipment)'. The same principle, applied to the factory, takes the form of shelf spaces marked up with the part number/description of different parts. Someone is given the task of making sure that empty shelf places are filled. When all spaces are filled, production of the items stops.

- *The floor grid Kanban*: exactly the same as a shelf-space Kanban, but typically used for bulky or heavy components which are unsuitable for putting on shelves.

In all the above examples of Kanbans, an essential feature of the system is that the number of containers or locations is systematically reduced by management to the point where supply is kept just in balance with the rate of use, so that the replenishment supply arrives 'just-in-time' for the user. The usual way of doing this is to keep taking away one more container each day (or week) until you reach the point where production is interrupted because the next full container doesn't arrive in time (i.e. it's 'just-too-late'!); replacing one container should then bring the supply back into balance with the rate of use. If you use this method, make sure you keep one or two full containers somewhere out of sight, ready to slip into the line quickly so that the interruption to production doesn't cause a problem. This trial and error method of finding out how many Kanban containers are needed is popular because in practice Kanbans are usually introduced gradually, in parallel with the old method of supply; if the same containers are used as previously, some will become surplus to requirements anyway when the faster Kanban supply is implemented, so you might as well take advantage of this to reduce the number in use gradually, in the way described.

If this trial and error method worries you, or if you've decided to buy a new type of container for your Kanbans, there is a way of working out in advance exactly how many containers will be needed: using a 'simulation' model will enable you to test the effects of different demand levels and a different mix of production with a high degree of confidence. You can find more information about simulation techniques in Sec. 3.11, and a case study illustrating the use of simulation in Sec. 11.10.

From the above you will realize that Kanban is not just another name for just-in-time, as some people have suggested: it is only part of a JIT implementation. The 'true' Kanban system is normally only suitable for high turnover components which are in regular use, and you should generally avoid using Kanbans on high-cost components. However, you can get some of the benefits of a Kanban system, even with high-cost components, by using the shelf-space or floor grid method in conjunction with the 'scheduled contracts' method, described in the next section: the example of a fax call-off form, referred to there and illustrated in Fig. 3.9, is used by Vokes Limited in conjunction with a floor grid Kanban system for arranging twice-weekly deliveries of large rolls of filtration material. This method has enabled them to simplify ordering procedures, cut lead time from four weeks to a few days, and do away with the bulk stores previously held.

If you decide to use the Kanban concept in your own factory, don't constrain yourself by trying to conform too rigidly to what I have referred to as the 'true' Kanban system. Be flexible: adapt the basic concept to your own circumstances in whatever way you think appropriate, remembering that the prime considerations are minimizing material and work-in-progress stocks, simplifying re-ordering paperwork, and empowering the actual users of the material to call for supplies as and when they need them.

3.8 IMPROVING THE PERFORMANCE OF SUPPLIERS

3.8.1 The Need

There has been a noticeable trend in recent years for manufacturing companies to cut back on peripheral activities and concentrate on those core activities where technologically or commercially they have an advantage over other manufacturers.

Generally available services, such as straightforward machining or presswork, have been farmed out to specialist subcontractors who are better equipped, have lower overheads, and can often provide high-quality work at lower cost. Commonly used items, such as fastenings, that were previously manufactured in-house to the company's own design, have in many cases been replaced by proprietary items.

In other cases, advancing technology has lead to the development of specialist component manufacturers who have become leaders in their industry, supplying most of the users of their type of products. A typical example is the manufacture of seats for commercial vehicles, where a specialist seat manufacturer uses an automated 'carousel' plant, costing in excess of 1 million; this produces seats by injecting the latex foam base into a mould in which the fabric cover has been previously inserted, allowing a fully finished seat to be produced in one integrated process. No commercial vehicle

REF: PART NO. 3-708743-04
FAX

FROM	VOKES LTD
TO	J. SMITH & CO
ATTN	SALES DEPARTMENT
FAX NO.	0344 23649
DATE	
PAGES	1 ONLY
MESSAGE	VERY URGENT

VOKES

VOKES LIMITED

Henley Park
Guildford
England GU3 2AF
Tel Guildford (0483) 69971
Telex 859235 VOKES G
Fax (0483) 235384

THIS IS TO BE CONSIDERED AS A CALL-OFF ORDER AGAINST
PURCHASE ORDER NO: 104803
VOKES MATERIAL PART NO.: 3-708743-04
DESCRIPTION: MS COIL 22SWG CRI 364.5 ± 0.5MM WIDE
BS 1449 PTI CRI I/D = 20-24 IN, O/D =48 IN

QUANTITY ORDERED = ... TONNES

= .... x 1721 SQFT

WRITE NO. OF TONNES HERE

= ....SQFT

DELIVERY REQUESTED ....

SIGNATURE OF SUPPLIER: (ORDER REQUEST)..

SIGNATURE OF STOREMAN/FOREMAN ....

NOTE: (1) A SEPARATE DELIVERY NOTE MUST BE RAISED
AGAINST THIS CALL-OFF.

(2) C OF C REQUIRED WITH MATERIAL.

(3) DELIVERY NOTE MUST CLEARLY STATE OUR PURCHASE
ORDER NO., DATE OF REQUEST, MATERIAL PART NO. AND
TOTAL MATERIAL DELIVERED IN TONNES AND CONVERTED
TO SQFT.

Filtration Technology

Figure 3.9 Example of a fax call-off form.

manufacturer is likely to have the necessary design and development capability or the technical process skills required to manage such a development in-house and, in any case, the huge investment required could only be recovered by producing in volumes greater than any one commercial vehicle manufacturer could justify.

In many companies this increasing trend to cut back to core activities can mean that outside purchases now account for more than 70 per cent of their total manufacturing cost; reducing the cost of external purchases by just 1 per cent could well have the same effect on profits as increasing sales by 10 per cent – and it could be a lot easier to achieve. Suppliers have consequently become a key part of the company's total manufacturing resource: they are an essential part of the processes which enable the company to achieve a competitive advantage and, as such, they need to be managed just as effectively as the company manages its own manufacturing facilities.

3.8.2 Appraising Performance

This implies that, just as you regularly and routinely monitor the performance of your *production* facilities, you should also regularly and routinely monitor the performance of your *suppliers*. And there's more to this than simply keeping a check on price and delivery: if you want to be a world-class company, you need to develop your supplier resource as effectively as you would expect to develop your own production facilities. To do this, your appraisal of supplier performance needs to include a wide range of evaluation criteria, such as:

- Are the supplier's corporate culture and its vision and strategy for the future compatible with your own?, i.e., does it look as though you could develop a good and mutually satisfying relationship over the longer term? Is there a degree of mutual dependency, or is retaining your business not particularly important to the supplier?
- Is it financially sound, or is there a risk that the business might collapse or be the subject of a take-over bid? That is, are its managers likely to be so concerned with problems of day-to-day survival that they might fail to give you the attention and support you deserve?
- Does it have effective control systems to ensure that you will consistently receive the quality, cost and delivery performance you require?
- Does it have the necessary level of technical, design and product development capability, and the appropriate manufacturing skills and equipment, to enable it to satisfy your requirements? Does it look as though its management is fully committed to the continuous development of all these facilities in the future (illustrated, preferably, by a history of doing so in recent years)?
- Does it have an organized approach to achieving continuous improvement in its performance, with particular emphasis placed on quality and customer service? Are all its employees encouraged to contribute to this improvement process? Is a multi-disciplinary team approach used for this?

In other words, if *you* want to be a world-class company, you ideally want all your suppliers to follow the same world-class principles as you do yourselves.

3.8.3 Improving Performance

If you and your suppliers are travelling towards the same destination, it makes sense to see if you can help each other along the road. Many Japanese companies provide assistance to their key suppliers, particularly where these are relatively small companies, by lending them specialists from their own staff to help with management training and in introducing world-class techniques, such as are described in this book. They set tough improvement targets for these key suppliers, requiring a specified price reduction each year (often as high as 15 per cent continuously, year after year), but they help the supplier to find ways to achieve them and they try to make sure that the benefits of the cost reductions achieved are shared between supplier and customer.

A larger supplier would probably resent this approach, but there is still an effective way in which you can bring about a steady reduction in material costs, with both you and your supplier benefiting. Get your designers and production engineers to work together with their opposite numbers in your supplier's organization, in order to find ways in which *your* requirements can be modified to make it easier for your supplier to satisfy your needs: you'd be surprised at how effective such a joint value engineering approach can be in finding ways to overcome your supplier's problems without affecting the material from your point of view, with consequent improvements in quality and delivery performance, often accompanied by a reduction in costs. This is particularly the case when you are trying to get your supplier to deliver smaller quantities more frequently, to meet your new JIT requirements.

3.8.4 Forging Strategic Alliances

This process of working closely with suppliers, to mutual advantage, is increasingly being referred to as 'Forging Strategic Alliances' or 'Partnership Sourcing'. It involves much more of a commitment to your suppliers than you may have been used to in the past and a drastic reduction in the number of suppliers you deal with, many items being switched from multi-source to single-source as part of the process of developing a worthwhile relationship with the best suppliers. This may well be resisted by people in your organization who have memories of being held to ransom in the past by single-source suppliers who have taken advantage of their position to put up prices unreasonably, or where strikes at a supplier's factory have crippled their customers' production. I've also heard objections from some accountants who are in the habit of delaying payment for goods received as long as they can get away with it – they prefer to have alternative suppliers in case late payments lead to them being put on a stop-list. However, those companies which have gone down this path (and this includes virtually all companies which have successfully pursued a world-class strategy), have found that the benefits of a closer relationship with their key suppliers have far outweighed these perceived disadvantages. But a prerequisite of forging successful strategic alliances is to select your suppliers with great care and to make clear what *both of you* expect to gain from the partnership. The objective is to agree on a set of common goals as the basis for developing a business relationship which will benefit both parties over a long period.

This relationship needs to be formalized, so that both parties fully understand what they are committing themselves to. Figure 3.10 shows some suggested guidelines for such an agreement.

3.8.5 Selecting Preferred Suppliers

As a first step in selecting preferred suppliers, you will need to start monitoring suppliers' performance, along the lines described above. You can then use the results of key performance measures, such as quality performance and delivery reliability, to produce

1. STATEMENT OF PRINCIPLE
The title 'Statement of Principle' should be included in any major partnership approach. For example, Partners A and B agree in principle to work together in an open and trusting style in partnership deliberately to create a business relationship which is ethical and progressive, delivering tangible, measurable benefits to both partners over a long period.

2. SCOPE
The scope of the partnership extends to the following materials, components and services: *list*.

3. COST
Each partner will work year-on-year to ensure that the total acquisition cost of items or services supplied will go down.

4. SERVICE
The supplier will work to ensure achievement of customer performance and service levels of not less than x% timeliness of delivery, y% quantity of delivery, z% quality of delivery.

5. FORECASTS
The customer will ensure that it will provide accurate forecasts regularly. Such forecasts will provide x months firm orders and y months forecasted business volume.

6. TECHNOLOGY IMPROVEMENT
Each partner will work to improve the technology and process of manufacture of the materials and items supplied and will regularly review specifications to ensure maximum effectiveness of items supplied. As appropriate, technology improvement projects will be defined, agreed and implemented.

7. CONTINUOUS IMPROVEMENT
Both partners will start a continuous improvement programme in their own business, apply it to the items supplied, and meet regularly (at least quarterly), to assess potential improvements.

8. OBJECTIVES
Each partner will agree and set specific agreed annual objectives and obligations of task performance and will review these in quarterly meetings.

9. HARDSHIP
In the event that either partner gets into difficulty under the terms of this Partnership Agreement, they will have the right to approach the other partner requesting relief from hardship. At this point, both partners will meet to openly discuss the issues involved and the pro-active positive solutions to them.

10. COST STRUCTURE
For each of the items or services supplied, an agreed open book cost structure will be created (consisting of a formula containing materials, labour, manufacturing overheads, general overheads, profit, plus other categories, e.g. return on investment). These will be agreed at the initiation of the partnership and reviewed regularly in the light of the continuous improvement programme, cost reduction objectives and technology improvement objectives of the Partnership Agreement.

11. MATERIALS
The customer will work with the supplier to minimize the cost of the supplier's material purchases, for example offering joint agreements for similar materials used in its business and offer to hold joint negotiations with material suppliers to minimize end-product costs.

12. CAPITAL INVESTMENT
Where expenditure on capital is required to be undertaken by the supplier to manufacture items on behalf of the customer, these will be identified at the beginning of the partnership. The criteria for investment and pay-back and return from that investment will be clearly agreed and defined between the partners before any investment is made.

13. CONFIDENTIALITY
The nature of the partnership will involve the passage of sensitive information between both partners. It is an absolute obligation of this agreement that any information is not passed to any other third party of any kind.

14. EXCLUSIVITY
Where investment is made in proprietary tooling or specialist technology is developed between the two parties, supply may not occur under any circumstances to any third party unless specific explicit agreement is made in writing between the partners.

15. TERMINATION
In the event that all other avenues are exhausted, and both partners come to a conclusion that the partnership must be dissolved, a notice period of x months must be given prior to termination.

16. MANAGEMENT, EDUCATION AND PUBLICITY
Each party will undertake to brief its management and staff regularly: initially on the nature of the agreement and subsequently on the status of development of the relationship between the two partners.

17. KEY CONTACTS
The key contacts in this partnership, who initially have the responsibility of managing the critical key relationships between the companies, are x and y.

a 'league table' in which suppliers are listed in descending order of 'goodness'. If you use a coded supplier reference, you can then show this league table to your suppliers' representatives and let them see how their company's performance compares with others, and highlight the degree of improvement needed. Those suppliers which respond positively and are prepared to work with you to improve their position in the league table are likely to hang on to your business. Those which don't respond are unlikely to figure in your long-term plans – even if you can't do without them at the moment you should be actively looking for alternative suppliers that *will* cooperate, or you should be getting your designers to find ways in which you can reduce your dependence on them.

Once you have eliminated the unreliable suppliers, you may still be left with more suppliers than you really need for some types of material. Resist the temptation to spread your work round more suppliers than you really need, 'just in case', since this will reduce the importance to each of them of holding on to your business. In order to select which should remain on your list of suppliers for key equipment, you will now need to look at the other factors in the supplier appraisal criteria listed above; for example whether the supplier's corporate culture, and its strategy for the future development of its business, fit well with those of your own company. Your aim must be to identify the most dependable, cooperative suppliers, which you feel comfortable working with, and with which you feel you have a good prospect of developing a good long-term working relationship.

Communications can be an important factor: if a supplier is just down the road, people can visit each other's factory easily whenever there's a problem to sort out, and the short distance will make it easier to deliver small batches at frequent intervals, with less risk of transportation delays, for example from bad weather. If you have to use a supplier located some distance from you, for example because of a specialist manufacturing capability, it may be worthwhile using other suppliers at or near to that location, so that several can be visited in one trip and so that advantage can be taken of consolidating several small deliveries from these different suppliers into an economic load. One company I know of did precisely this when reviewing supply sources for certain specialist materials previously obtained from several suppliers located in Germany, France and Italy: the most important source was one of the manufacturers in Italy, and by re-sourcing most of the other purchases either to this supplier, or to one of the three other potential sources nearby, communications were improved significantly. There was also an unexpected benefit: because despatches from each of these Italian manufacturers were consolidated into one load, and the companies involved were used to doing business together, they tended to look after the chasing up of deliveries to make up the load between themselves.

Figure 3.10 (*opposite*) Partnership sourcing guidelines for management. (*Source*: These guidelines are reproduced with the kind permission of Partnership Sourcing Limited, a non-profit-making company established to promote the concepts, application and benefits of partnership sourcing. This project, which evolved through collaboration between the UK's Department of Trade and Industry and the Confederation of British Industry, brings together a wide range of bodies concerned with the profitable competitiveness of UK companies. Its brief is to encourage knowledge about partnership sourcing and how it can serve the interests of companies of all sizes. Details of booklets published by Partnership Sourcing Limited, which draw heavily on the experience of companies who are using partnership sourcing as a key part of their business, are included in the Bibliography.)

Some manufacturers, particularly in the motor industry, have taken this a stage further. They have overcome the problem of persuading smaller suppliers to deliver on a just-in-time basis by organizing a 'milk round' collection service. A distribution services subcontractor makes regular calls on a group of suppliers at set times, ranging from once a week to several times a day, and delivers the materials collected at the specified time, day or night, to suit the manufacturer's just-in-time schedule. This significantly reduces the total mileage costs incurred in the supply chain and, even more importantly, it frees the smaller suppliers from having to make their own haulage arrangements, often for uneconomic loads. This development introduces yet another consideration to the process of selecting preferred suppliers, particularly where the volumes involved are small: would the supplier welcome inclusion in the 'milk round' service and, if so, does the supplier's location fit readily into one of the existing rounds? These questions need to be answered during the negotiation stage, since the saving to the supplier and the additional cost incurred by the purchaser need to be reflected in the price agreed.

3.8.6 'Suppliers' Day' Briefings

Having selected your list of preferred suppliers, a useful first step in the process of forging strategic alliances could well be to host a 'Suppliers' Day' to brief them on how you want to develop your relationship with suppliers (you may also have to hold individual briefing sessions for a handful of suppliers with whom you expect to place a significant part of your business). A Suppliers' Day typically starts off with an introduction by your top management in which they first explain about your world-class objectives and then go on to present their views on market trends, your competition, the opportunities ahead, and how you need to develop a closer long-term relationship with suppliers if you are going to make the best of the available opportunities. Your Purchasing and Technical staff will then explain the approach you are taking in evaluating suppliers and your wish to work more closely with them in order to identify areas of potential improvement in their quality, cost and delivery performance, and to involve them in future at an early stage in the introduction of new products. It is usually very helpful if you then take them on a tour of your own factory, so that they can see for themselves the improvements you have already achieved as a result of your world-class programme and talk directly with those involved from your workforce. Finally, you should aim to open the door for your staff to make return visits and establish this type of interaction as the norm for the future.

3.8.7 Developing New Supply Methods

Developing a closer relationship with your suppliers opens up opportunities for you to introduce new methods of supply which short-circuit delays and cut down on administration. Here are three possibilities for you to consider, if you are not already using them:

- *Scheduled Contracts*: you will probably be familiar with call-off schedules and already used to using them; your buyers will probably negotiate price and delivery for, say, a year's estimated supply of materials, and the buyer will then issue a call-off schedule on a monthly (or perhaps weekly) basis. You can improve on this method with strategic alliance suppliers by curtailing the buyers' responsibility just to the annual negotiation of the contract. Call-offs can then be on an 'as required' basis, probably using Kanbans, with the *production operatives* responsible for sending a fax to the supplier direct whenever a delivery is required (an example of a fax call-off form is shown in Fig. 3.9). Materials ordered on this basis can normally be delivered within 24 hours of the requirement having been identified and, if you use the 'quality at source' approach, described in Sec. 3.8.8, they can be delivered direct to the production line, bypassing Goods Inwards.

- *The 'Supermarket' Method*: you arrange for the supplier to take responsibility for keeping stocks of regularly used materials (typically located alongside the production area) topped up through regular daily or weekly visits. The usual method is for the supplier's delivery person to check how many Kanbans are empty at each visit, and that determines the quantity to be delivered on the next visit. The supplier invoices on the basis of quantities delivered, so that you need to set up reliable systems to cross-check this against quantities used each day.

  The Supermarket method is also frequently used for ready-use stocks of small items such as fasteners, although for these you will need to have one of your own staff accompany the supplier's representative when topping up, since it would otherwise be difficult to confirm that the quantities supplied matched the quantities actually used. The stocks of material not yet used may belong to you, or you may negotiate for the supplier to let you have the stocks on an 'on consignment' basis, in which case the supplier retains ownership until the material is actually used.

- *Contingency Stocks*: when you first arrange for a supplier to deliver on a JIT basis, you may well be nervous about continuity of supplies, and the risks to your business if the supplier lets you down. A solution adopted by many companies during the transition to JIT is to arrange for the supplier to deposit several days supply of key materials as a contingency stock, either in your own plant or at some other location nearby. This sort of arrangement also provides protection against transport delays during bad weather and, possibly, industrial relations problems at your supplier's factory.

  As you will, I hope, realize, contingency stocks are not in the true spirit of the JIT philosophy, since *any* type of stock is a waste. However, we have to be realistic: unlike in Japan, most of our suppliers aren't yet used to supplying on a JIT basis, and we can't therefore afford to trust them completely until they have proved their reliability over a period – otherwise we may put ourselves in the position of letting *our* customers down. Holding contingency stocks and never touching them (except as part of a planned stock rotation process) will give us the confidence we need eventually to get rid of these consignment stocks – but not until we're sure!

3.8.8 Quality at Source

Under the JIT philosophy, inspection is a waste. Ideally, therefore, you should arrange for materials received from outside suppliers to be delivered direct to your production department and used by your operatives without prior inspection. Contrast this with what actually happens in most factories! I give as an example an actual case I came across recently.

Archilighting GmbH, who are the subject of a later case study, manufacture lighting fittings, some of which incorporate a polished aluminium reflector purchased as a finished component from a specialist manufacturer. The components were 100 per cent inspected at the supplier's factory immediately after the spinning and polishing process, at which point they were inserted in individual protective wrappers and then placed in a cage pallet which, depending on the size, held between 50 and 100 reflectors. The cage pallet was then partly unpacked at the supplier's factory before despatch, in order to allow statistical sampling inspection to ensure the batch conformed with the Acceptable Quality Level (AQL) specified in the supply contract. On arrival at Archilighting's factory, the cage pallets were completely unpacked by Goods Inwards, so that the quantity of reflectors in the pallet could be checked against the quantity on the advice note. They were then held for two or three days until the Goods Inwards Inspector got round to dealing with them, at which point the same sampling procedure, to ensure AQL, was gone through as when the batch was about to leave the supplier's premises. The cleared batch was then moved to Stores (in some cases the parts were removed from the protection of their cage pallet so that they could be stacked more compactly in the overcrowded Stores). As rather large batches were ordered, which took several months to use up, the parts were sometimes further unpacked and repacked during stock checks. Eventually they were packed into kits for assembly (still in their individual protective wrapping, but often put into the assembly cage with other parts piled on top) and a few days later arrived on the assembly line. You will not be surprised to hear that, at that point, the assembler would often have to reject an expensive reflector because the highly polished surface had been damaged during one of the many handling operations. (In fairness to Archilighting, I should, perhaps, add that this is typical of procedures carried out by manufacturers throughout the world – very possibly in your own company. It simply reflects the fact that we've been let down so many times in the past by suppliers who have short-delivered or sent us materials that aren't quite up to standard.)

After discussions with the supplier, and the design of an improved individual protective sleeve, Archilighting arranged for the part to be delivered direct from the point of production in the supplier's factory, on a JIT basis, to a holding area in Archilighting's assembly shop, *without intermediate inspection*. The supplier undertook to deliver on a 'certificated supply' basis, i.e. it guaranteed that there were no defects and that the quantity was as stated on the advice note. To achieve this without intermediate inspection, the supplier took steps to improve quality control at the point of manufacture of the reflectors, and the design of the protective sleeves made it easy to count the quantity delivered.

The principles of quality at source don't just apply to materials obtained from outside suppliers. They can, and should, also be applied within your own production departments. The objective to aim at is for each operator to take responsibility for the quality of his or her own work, and for this to be backed up by 'neighbour' inspection, i.e. each operator checks that the preceding operation has been carried out correctly. If an error is detected, it should be returned *immediately* to the previous operator, so that no more parts are produced with the same error. This is the ideal – it may take some time to achieve, and it may not always be feasible, but it should certainly be aimed at wherever possible.

3.8.9 Assessing The Scope For Your Company

Some readers may be tempted to say 'That's all very well for the big boys, but we don't have enough clout with our suppliers, many of whom are much bigger than us'. My experience is that even where this is the case you are likely to get a very positive reaction from the larger suppliers, many of whom will already have reached partnership sourcing agreements with some of their key customers and can see the benefits in it *for themselves*. Not least will be the reduction in their administrative costs as a result of simplified ordering procedures and not having to provide quotations each time you wish to place an order. If you *do* find that some of your suppliers are unwilling to cooperate, you may be able to re-source the materials to another supplier, which will help achieve the objective of reducing the number of suppliers used; or, where this is not feasible (for example because a proprietary item is specified), you may be able to overcome the problem by getting Design to change the specification. You can also increase your purchasing 'clout' by grouping similar items together, and negotiating agreements for packages of materials. These and other techniques for improving purchasing effectiveness are illustrated in the Archilighting case study, which can be found in Sec. 11.7.

Before launching a campaign to improve suppliers' performance you need to find out just how well (or how badly) you are managing your supplier resource at the moment. I've defined seven levels of development of the purchasing function, ranging from little more than 'order placing' at Level 1, to full 'world-class purchasing' at Level 7. These are explained in Sec. 11.6, together with some suggested questions that you should ask your Purchasing managers to help you assess how far you have to go to become truly world-class.

3.9 DESIGNING FOR MANUFACTURING EFFICIENCY

3.9.1 Flexibility In Design

A key element in JIT is making your production facilities more flexible, so that they can adapt quickly to changing customer requirements. If you want to achieve this objective, you will probably need to make your designs more flexible first.

In a world-class environment, designers need to take into account not just function, appearance and cost, but flexibility for production as well. For example, there are now so many options available on cars that, in theory, for all except the very largest manufacturers the number of different possible combinations of options is greater than the total number of cars they sell in a year! This means that they can no longer make standard batches against forecast sales, as in the days of Henry Ford; they now have to be able to make to specific customer orders in a time that is short enough to be acceptable to the customer, i.e. a matter of a few weeks between receipt of order by the dealer and delivery of the 'customized' car. The development of JIT techniques, together with modern telecommunications and computer systems, have all helped make this possible, but it could not have been achieved without the development of designs aimed at improving flexibility and speed of response. The modern approach to design typically allows for different combinations of standard modules to be slotted together to meet the particular requirements of a specific customer. Some parts may be designed to enable different modules to be connected without having to change the design. For example: a whole range of lighting fittings may have identical 'works' (buried out of sight in the suspended ceiling), with only the decorative part which shows being different; a family of computers, varying widely in facilities offered (and price) may differ only in which of a range of circuit boards are included at the final stage of assembly; a standard wiring harness may be used in a particular model of a car, enabling whatever accessories are ordered to be fitted without changing the harness.

The secret is to offer the customer a wide range of options which all look different, or behave differently, but which have most of the components common to the whole range.

3.9.2 New Product Development

So much for improving the design concept. The next stage, developing the concept into a detailed design, ready for production, offers even more opportunities for improving the design process. Here are a few ideas for you to consider:

- Try to design components in such a way that they can be manufactured in cells: if you don't yet have cells, you should – they are usually a key element in a JIT environment, enabling manufacturing cycle time to be cut dramatically and making it easier to introduce small batches and the quality at source concept. More details on cell manufacturing can be found in Sec. 11.9.
- Consider how the detail design might be altered to make it easier for production operatives to change machine set-up between batches. This might, for example, involve making it possible for Production Engineering to use modular fixtures, or standardizing on a range of 'preferred' external and internal dimensions and hole sizes in order to reduce the number of tool and material changes required, and to make it more economic to invest in more sophisticated tooling and gauging equipment.
- Many companies still use far too wide a range of fasteners. You should get your Design Department to draw up a list of 'preferred' fasteners, with special authorization needed before a draughtsman is allowed to specify any non-preferred items.
- Challenge any 'Make vs. Buy' guidelines you may have: make sure that your 'Make vs. Buy' decisions aren't distorted too much by the way overheads are recovered in your estimate of in-house manufacturing cost: you'll probably find that the overhead element included in the in-house cost will still be incurred by the factory even if you decide to buy the item from an external source.
- Don't re-invent the wheel: many companies can quote examples of where they go to the trouble of making items in-house when an equally good standard proprietary item could be obtained ex-stock from an outside supplier. Making in-house might save a few pence on the direct cost, but rarely enough to compensate for the additional planning and indirect costs, let alone the impact that the in-house manufacturing time can have on finished product lead times.
- 'Focused factories' are becoming increasingly popular, taking this 'leave it to the experts' concept a stage further: in-house manufacturing is limited to those core operations which are central to the company's end products, typically those which involve specialist skills or 'high risk' components; everything else is sourced outside the company. Apart from releasing management to concentrate on those aspects of the manufacturing process that are central to the company's experience and reputation, focused factories provide a much greater flexibility in responding to changes in demand, and make 'tooling up' for new designs much less of a problem.

- On the other hand, there are times when it *does* make sense to bring the manufacture of components in-house, in order to overcome long lead times or delivery problems with outside suppliers. Typically this is worthwhile when the supplier is manufacturing key components to your particular requirements, i.e. as far as the supplier is concerned it's a 'special'.
- Make sure that tolerances on your production drawings are appropriate both to the end use and to the capability of the manufacturing process. I've seen many instances where 'standard tolerances' have been specified for dimensions that, when assembled, are not in contact with any other part, so that Production are spending time in producing a degree of accuracy that is not needed. I've also seen instances where Production are struggling to hold tolerances which are really beyond the capability of their equipment. If the tolerances were right, alternative production arrangements should have been made when the design was first agreed.

All this implies that there needs to be a much closer link between design and manufacture, and it needs to start much earlier in the design cycle than is traditionally the case. This process, which is the norm for Japanese companies (in their factories in the West as well as in Japan), is increasingly being referred to as 'simultaneous engineering' or, by some advocates, as 'concurrent engineering'. I like these terms because they sum up the essence of what is involved, that *engineering* the manufacture of a product is undertaken in parallel with the development of the design. Production Engineering, Tooling Design, Production Management, Quality Management, Purchasing and, in some cases, outside suppliers all contribute to the process of developing a design which not only satisfies the customer's requirements, but is also 'manufacturing-friendly'. Problems such as the handling of bulky or heavy components during the production process, or components which could be manufactured more easily in two pieces rather than one, or changes which make it easier for a part to be made 'right first time', can all be examined and good ideas from the relevant experts incorporated in the design *before* this gets set in tablets of stone. The net effect is that a new design goes into production for the first time avoiding most of the teething troubles we are accustomed to: it really does work (ask any Japanese manufacturer!).

There's a further refinement of the simultaneous engineering process which I think will become increasingly popular in the future among world-class manufacturers, based on the 'Failure Modes and Effects Analysis' (FMEA) process. FMEA is described in more detail in Sec. 11.8; it is used to identify *at the design stage* ways in which a product or component might fail in the field, and is used particularly when failure of the product could have serious economic or safety consequences, such as in the design of aircraft. An adaptation of the FMEA process can be used when the design stage is reaching its conclusion, by getting all the relevant experts together and asking them to 'brainstorm' two questions:

- 'What quality problems could arise during the manufacturing process?', i.e. 'What are the most likely production errors that will occur?'
- 'What set-up changes will be required during the manufacturing process, which ones are significant, and what features of the design are responsible for the complexity of these set-up changes?'

Ideally, one or two operatives should be included in the team of experts for the brainstorming session: they are, after all, the 'experts' at the actual process of manufacture.

If you can anticipate potential production problems in this way, the designers can then re-examine their original ideas to see if they can find a more manufacturing-friendly solution.

3.9.3 Improving Existing Designs

Manufacturers put a great deal of effort into finding ways of improving *how* a component is made, but all too often the question of *what* is being made is ignored. If the component design is treated as sacrosanct, then the opportunity for reducing manufacturing cost can be severely limited. The methods suggested above should ensure that any new designs are challenged while they are still at the design stage, but what about existing designs? Many of these may well continue to be manufactured for some time ahead; this is particularly true at the component level, since new products often incorporate components from previous product designs.

Value Analysis, or Value Engineering, has long been used in manufacturing as a technique for re-examining existing designs in order to make them more cost-effective. Many of the ideas suggested above can be applied successfully to existing components, using the value analysis approach, *provided that the review team includes representatives from the Design department*, in addition to those from Engineering, Production and Purchasing. Without the active participation and commitment of the Design department, many of the best ideas either won't be considered or they'll end up in the pending basket, with priority always being given to work on new products.

The two case studies included in Sec. 11.7 illustrate what can be done to improve design efficiency. The first describes how Cincinnati Milacron used the simultaneous engineering approach to develop a new range of world-class machine tools in rapid time, completely replacing their existing range of products. However, most companies only introduce new products gradually, retaining part of their existing range. In such cases, ensuring that just the *new* products are designed for manufacturing efficiency is not enough: if you want to make your manufacturing truly world-class you also need to apply the same approach to redesigning *existing* products or, at least, those of them that will continue to form a significant part of future manufacturing operations. The second case study describes how Archilighting GmbH tackled just such a problem.

3.10 MAINTENANCE

3.10.1 The Need – Or Not?

Some experts insist that 'Total Productive Maintenance' is an essential part of JIT, almost on a par with Total Employee Involvement. Others ignore the subject of maintenance completely. You might think it strange that clearly knowledgeable people should differ so fundamentally in their views.

In fact it all depends on where they've gained their expertise. Suppose this was in the steel industry for example, where maintenance costs at an integrated steel mill can run into hundreds of millions of dollars a year, and where a breakdown of a significant item of equipment could bring the whole of the continuous process to a halt; or in the automotive industry where stoppage of a highly automated assembly plant can quickly lose production of hundreds of cars and cause havoc to the JIT component delivery schedules; and there are many other instances where keeping vital equipment working is of critical importance. However, there are also many industries which are *not* so dependent on machinery or process plant, where the maintenance function is just a minor irritation, its main role being thought of (however unfairly) as little more than changing blown light bulbs and clearing blocked drains.

Your view on the importance of maintenance, just like that of the experts, will reflect how dependent you think you are on machinery and process plant. But, whatever your view in the past, you may well have to reconsider your approach to maintenance if you want to achieve world-class performance.

There are two ways in which you can do this: by getting greater effectiveness and better value for money from your maintenance activities, through the application of 'Reliability-Centred Maintenance' (RCM); or by reducing the 'waste' associated with equipment either breaking down or performing below par, through the application of 'Total Productive Maintenance' (TPM).

TPM will *always* be relevant, regardless of how much, or how little, you depend on machinery. Even hand tools and simple handling equipment can cause 'waste' if there's something wrong with them which affects either quality or the time taken to perform a task.

The formal application of RCM, in contrast, is more relevant to those manufacturers for whom improving plant performance, and getting better value for money from their maintenance activities, can have a significant effect on overall operating performance: in other words, where the rewards are high enough to justify the amount of work involved. Even so, the basic concepts of RCM are of relevance to everyone, whether or not they are applied in detail, because they challenge some of the fundamental principles of traditional preventive maintenance. The description of RCM, below, is limited to an explanation of these basic concepts; a more detailed description of the RCM decision process, including the initial FMEA (failure modes and effects analysis) stage, is given in Sec. 11.8.

But first, let's look at *why* RCM was developed.

3.10.2 Challenging Traditional Maintenance Practice

Everyone understands the basic concepts of preventive maintenance:

- Mechanical parts gradually wear out
- The longer they are in use, the greater the wear
- Eventually, the point is reached where the machine ceases to operate properly because one or more of the parts has worn too far (point A in Fig. 3.11)
- The objective of preventive maintenance is to replace the part *just before* the point where failure is increasingly likely to occur (point B in Fig. 3.11)
- The operating age at which the probability of failure starts to increase significantly can be estimated by analysis of past failures, or by comparison with similar parts in other equipment

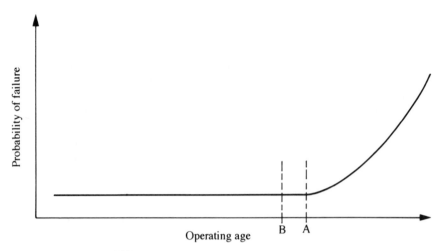

Figure 3.11 Age-related failure pattern.

- Any difficulty in estimating the age at point A can be compensated for by increasing the frequency of maintenance inspection

Unfortunately, for all except the simplest items, the assumption that failure is normally age-related is simply not valid. Doubts were first raised in the civil aviation industry in the early 1960s, the lead being taken by maintenance specialists at United Airlines of California, USA, where maintenance costs then represented approximately 30 per cent of total direct and indirect operating costs.

Maintenance theory in the aircraft industry at that time was firmly based on the belief that 'more scheduled maintenance leads to more reliable equipment'. It's understandable that, in the days when unreliable equipment could have a direct impact on passenger safety, estimates of the safe working life of parts, and hence the frequency of preventive maintenance, were usually very conservative. However, by 1960 the application of FMEA techniques at the design stage had effectively broken this dependence on scheduled maintenance, with potentially critical failures either designed out completely or rendered non-critical through the use of comprehensive instrumentation and back-up systems. In these circumstances, the airline operators argued, there was no longer a need to be so conservative in estimating the safe life of items, and consequently preventive maintenance activities could be scheduled at longer intervals.

The US Federal Aviation Authority agreed to trials in which, in stages of not less than three months per step, the overhaul intervals would be progressively eased, with more dependence being placed on 'on-condition' inspections. These involved much less work than the usual complete 'teardown' inspections: subject to specific checks being carried out periodically, the equipment was allowed to continue in service for the longer overhaul interval *on condition* that these checks were satisfactory.

As the overhaul intervals were cautiously extended, step by step over a number of years, it became increasingly clear that the whole concept of there being a predictable safe life was suspect. After extensive research and examination of maintenance records going back many years, United Airlines produced the results shown in Fig. 3.12. These clearly demonstrated that, for the vast majority of items, the probability of failure did

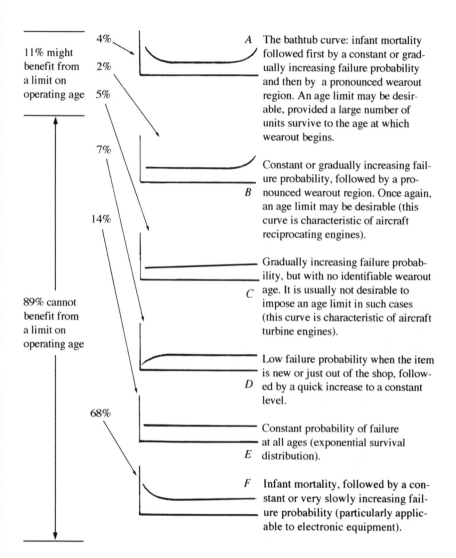

11% might
benefit from
a limit on
operating age

4%

2%

5%

7%

14%

89% cannot
benefit from
a limit on
operating age

68%

A The bathtub curve: infant mortality followed first by a constant or gradually increasing failure probability and then by a pronounced wearout region. An age limit may be desirable, provided a large number of units survive to the age at which wearout begins.

Constant or gradually increasing failure probability, followed by a pro-
B nounced wearout region. Once again, an age limit may be desirable (this curve is characteristic of aircraft reciprocating engines).

Gradually increasing failure probability, but with no identifiable wearout
C age. It is usually not desirable to impose an age limit in such cases (this curve is characteristic of aircraft turbine engines).

Low failure probability when the item is new or just out of the shop, follow-
D ed by a quick increase to a constant level.

Constant probability of failure at all ages (exponential survival
E distribution).

F Infant mortality, followed by a constant or very slowly increasing failure probability (particularly applicable to electronic equipment).

Figure 3.12 Age–reliability patterns. In each case the vertical axis represents the conditional probability of failure and the horizontal axis represents operating age since manufacture, overhaul or repair. These six curves are derived from reliability analyses conducted over a number of years, during which all the items analysed were found to be characterized by one or other of the age–reliability relationships shown. The percentages indicate the percentage of items studied that fell into each of the basic patterns. (*Source*: Reproduced from F. S. Nowlan and H. F. Heap: 'Reliability-Centered Maintenance', US Department of Defense Report No. AD-A066-579, December 1978.)

not increase with age (these patterns are not peculiar to the aviation industry – analysis of failures in many other industries in recent years have shown broadly similar patterns). This analysis by United Airlines forced a complete re-think of maintenance theory, leading to the development of the modern RCM approach, now used in all types of industry around the world.

'Very interesting', you might say, 'but what does it mean for *me?*' Section 3.10.3, on the RCM approach, will explain this in more detail but the key points to remember are:

- Some items, such as tyres, brakes, or cutting tools, *do* wear out with age, but most items don't.
- It's usually a waste of time to do preventive maintenance on complex machinery in the hope that this will reduce the risk of breakdown; you may actually *increase* the risk, because of errors in the maintenance process (you may have experienced this personally last time your car was serviced!).
- Other techniques must therefore be used to improve the reliability of production equipment.

These other techniques can be found through the application of RCM and TPM.

3.10.3 Reliability-Centred Maintenance

The traditional approach to scheduled maintenance starts by defining a list of maintenance tasks, consisting of both inspection and repair or replacement activities; these are then built into schedules, the frequency with which they are applied being specified in terms of either elapsed time or time in use.

RCM, in contrast, starts by considering what would happen if you *didn't* undertake such tasks, i.e. what could cause a failure of the equipment, and what would be the consequences of each of these possible failures. This means that you can get better value for money from your scheduled maintenance activities, since with RCM these are carefully targeted: if the initial failure modes and effects analysis indicates that the consequences of failure are minimal (as is often the case), then no preventive action is justified; in other words, RCM accepts that there are occasions when the old 'if it ain't broke, don't fix it' policy can be the most cost-effective approach. You could well find that this results in getting on for half your previous scheduled maintenance tasks being eliminated: this saves not just the labour cost involved, but also the cost of all the spare parts that would have been fitted 'just-in-case', as part of the scheduled maintenance routine.

To illustrate the point, consider what scheduled maintenance would be required on a simple water pump. The old way would be to get a drawing of the pump and make a list of parts such as bearings and seals which need to be checked regularly and replaced periodically; if there are several identical pumps used in the factory, that makes the task easier, because *the same list of maintenance tasks is used for each pump*. The RCM way, in contrast, is to say, 'Hang on a minute, where's the pump going to be used?' If the answer is 'In the nuclear reactor cooling system', then the effects of failure could be so serious that some form of protective maintenance would be considered essential. But suppose the answer was 'To keep the water circulating in the ornamental pond outside the main reception area', then it would probably be cheaper to leave it alone and accept the risk that it might fail. In other words, *an RCM schedule takes full account of the operating context of the equipment and of the consequences of failure.*

That raises another question: what constitutes 'failure'? Suppose your car works perfectly well in all respects except that every time you exceed 80 k.p.h. it has a tendency to jump out of gear: but the car will still get you to your destination. Is this just a sign of a *potential* gearbox failure that could eventually lead to an actual failure at some future date so that you don't reach your destination; or has it already failed because you are unable to use the car to its maximum potential? This sort of problem happens all too often in a factory, when production equipment is routinely operated at less than its rated output speed, because the operators know from experience that problems will occur if they try to run the equipment any faster.

In world-class terms, a 'waste' occurs if you are unable to use equipment to its full potential and, as you know by now, you should endeavour to eliminate or, at least, minimize any form of waste. Accordingly the RCM definition of failure is:

- A *failure* is an unsatisfactory condition; in other words, a failure is any identifiable deviation from the original condition which is unsatisfactory to a particular user.

RCM further defines two types of failure:

- A *functional* failure is an inability of an item (or the equipment containing it) to meet a specific performance standard.
- A *potential* failure is an identifiable physical condition which indicates a functional failure is imminent.

With these underlying principles explained, I can now summarize the key stages in the RCM procedure:

1. Start by defining, for each piece of equipment, *how it might fail and what effects each failure mode might have* (this is the FMEA stage, described in more detail in Sec. 11.8).
2. Use the RCM Decision Diagram to assess *how critical* these effects are. Do they affect personal safety, so that the risk of failure must be avoided altogether, if necessary by redesign? If personal safety isn't affected, what would be the economic consequences of failure? Does the cost penalty if failure occurs justify the cost of preventive measures? (For a more detailed explanation of the RCM Decision Diagram, see Sec. 11.8.)
3. For each safety-critical failure mode, decide what action must be taken to overcome the risk of such a failure occurring.
4. For each failure mode with significant economic consequences: decide whether the failure pattern is age-related, so that a 'scheduled discard' task can be planned; if not, what 'potential failure' signs could be used to indicate when corrective action is needed, or what condition monitoring techniques or on-condition maintenance tasks might be appropriate.
5. For the remaining failure modes, i.e. those defined as 'tolerable', decide what action can be taken to minimize the risk of them occurring (for example, by getting operators involved in TPM in order to improve equipment reliability).

To sum up: RCM enables you to target your maintenance resources precisely in order to minimize waste, whether this be the waste of equipment breaking down, or the waste of equipment working below par, or the waste implicit in carrying out 'preventive' maintenance work that has no real effect. Whether the amount of work involved in a full

RCM application is worthwhile will depend on your particular circumstances. However, it will nearly always be worth applying the basic concepts to at least one or two key machines; sufficient information to enable you to do this, and to decide what degree of detail is appropriate, is included in Sec. 11.8. Readers interested in pursuing the subject further will find information on where to obtain in-depth reading in the Bibliography at the end of the book.

3.10.4 Total Productive Maintenance

The application of TPM means getting *everyone*, particularly operators, involved in the task of improving the performance and reliability of production equipment. In effect, it is the application of total quality principles to getting the best out of your equipment: the total quality concept of 'zero defects' is adapted here to 'zero machine trouble'.

At the heart of TPM philosophy is the belief that equipment failures can be dramatically reduced if the people who *use* the equipment can be taught to recognize signs that something isn't quite right: in other words, getting them to react to any *potential* failure condition, and take corrective action before the related *functional* failure actually occurs (remember that the definition of a potential failure is 'an identifiable physical condition which indicates a functional failure is imminent'). You've probably been applying the TPM principles yourself for years, for example with your car: if your brakes start to squeal loudly every time you slow down, and the car pulls a bit to one side, you recognize that this isn't normal and treat it as a *potential* failure condition; you probably get your garage to check what's wrong, and put it right, long before the related functional failure of the braking system has a chance to develop. In a factory, even if the failure modes and effects analysis identifies a particular functional failure as non-critical, it still involves a *waste* if it occurs, because planned production is interrupted and operators will lose productive time while they are being switched to other tasks.

Traditionally, failure has been thought of only in terms of the equipment failing to the extent that production is actually interrupted. If the production operators can still manage to keep production going, they are often loath to stop in order to give the maintenance staff a chance to do any repairs or adjustments needed to get the equipment working to its full potential again – even if this means that quality or output suffer in the meantime. But in world-class terms it's a waste if the equipment isn't working to its full potential, and TPM aims at overcoming such waste.

There are a number of ways in which operators can be involved in reducing equipment failures, either during the production process, or while they are waiting for a set-up to be changed. For example:

- Keeping working surfaces clean to minimize contamination and wear
- Reporting oil leakages, and making sure that something is actually done about them
- Using their senses to recognize unusual noise, temperature, vibration, smell etc., which can often give advance warning of failures
- Checking bolts for tightness (considered by some maintenance experts to be the single most important cause of machine failures)
- Reporting any deterioration in quality before this becomes serious
- Keeping an eye on condition-monitoring instruments, instead of relying on maintenance staff checking them periodically

- Maintaining process control charts and taking corrective action *before* a control level is breached (i.e. as soon as a trend towards the control level is established)

No doubt you can think of others, depending on the equipment you use. But don't forget that operators will need to be trained in what to look out for, so you'll need to get the cooperation of your maintenance specialists, for example by involving them in a brainstorming session to identify what needs to be done, and then getting them to discuss directly with the operators what they can do to help. Their first instinct may well be to say that only a skilled engineer can do certain tasks, but it's often possible to find a way round that. For example, consider the question of lubrication, where several different types of oil and grease have to be used on a particular machine, and the engineers are afraid that an untrained operator might get it wrong: you may be able to overcome the problem by getting the engineers to prepare a procedure sheet, with each step numbered, and then paint the number alongside the lubrication point on the machine; painting the lubrication points with a colour code will make it quite clear which oil can or grease gun should be used for each point.

With the advent of increasingly complex process plant the distinction between mechanical, electrical and instrument technicians is necessarily becoming blurred, a process usually referred to as 'multi-skilling'. Typically, skilled technicians are trained by the equipment supplier in whatever skills are needed to enable them to look after a particular piece of equipment. Recognizing that with more complex equipment there is a limit to what TPM tasks a production operative can undertake, some world-class companies have taken multi-skilling an important step further, and include a skilled technician as a member of the production team. Like the other members of the team his primary task is production, but he has an additional responsibility for monitoring the condition of the equipment as it operates. Because of his technical skills he is more likely to pick problems up quickly and so be able to nip them in the bud; if problems *do* occur, he is on the spot and can deal with them immediately. When his production duties allow he looks after routine maintenance tasks such as lubrication.

I said earlier in this section that 'TPM will always be relevant, regardless of how much, or how little, you depend on machinery. Even hand tools and simple handling equipment can cause waste if there's something wrong with them which affects either quality or the time taken to perform a task'. However, *don't* try to introduce TPM until you've succeeded in changing the culture of your operations to one where involvement of the whole workforce in continuous improvement is the norm. If you try to do it too early you are likely to increase the degree of conflict which so often exists between production and maintenance staff. TPM on its own is unlikely to appeal sufficiently to those involved to enable you to break down these barriers. My advice is to wait until you have successfully introduced 'continuous improvement groups', described in Sec. 4.3, and in Chapters 5 and 13.

3.10.5 Design Implications

No form of maintenance can yield a level of reliability beyond that inherent in the design. Inevitably, the design of complex equipment has to be a compromise between the lightness, compactness and cost factors required for high performance and value for money, and the weight and bulk required for durability and reliability.

Those readers whose companies are involved in the design and manufacture of complex equipment, particularly in the defence and public sectors, will be aware that customers are increasingly concerned about lifetime costs. RCM is particularly valuable in these cases because it provides a mechanism for anticipating possible types of failure, so that you can either design them out, or introduce back-up systems to make the equipment more failure-tolerant, or incorporate condition monitoring equipment to prevent failure occurring. It will also provide the basis for preparing the 'manufacturer's recommended maintenance schedules' that most customers insist on having (although, if you stick to the RCM philosophy, these need to reflect the future operating context).

You can also apply the same RCM principles when you are *buying* complex equipment. Make sure that the suppliers have used the FMEA method to improve reliability, and for any significant failure modes that haven't been designed out make sure that they really understood the implications of failure *in your particular operating context*. Maintenance, in world-class terms, is a waste because it doesn't add value. The more you can reduce the need for maintenance in any new equipment you buy, the less waste you will be committing yourself to over the lifetime of the equipment.

3.11 REDUCING THE RISKS OF CHANGE

We're used to things going wrong in manufacturing – it's a fact of life that we've all got used to living with. I've even heard it said that manufacturing industry's greatest strength (in the UK at least) lies in its ability to respond to a challenge and overcome adversity!

One of our prime defensive weapons is stock. We hold stocks of raw materials in case a supplier lets us down; we hold work-in-progress stocks at various points in the production sequence, in case something happens to interfere with planned production; we make larger batches than needed, just in case something goes wrong, such as defective work on a subsequent operation; we hold stocks of components and of finished products in case our sales forecasts are wrong; and we make sure that there is a good stock, in the form of a queue, in front of as many machines or processes as possible so that, if there's a delay earlier in the production sequence, the machine or process won't run out of work. This defensive policy offends two basic principles of JIT:

- All stock is a 'waste', so that action needs to be taken to reduce it.
- Problems should be brought out into the open, so that corrective action can be taken to avoid them recurring.

That's all very well in the longer term, when we've been applying the JIT philosophy for long enough to have got most of the bugs out of our operating systems, but in the early stages we have to cope with teething troubles in our new JIT methods *and* still deal with all the traditional problems in the areas we haven't tackled yet. So, particularly in the early stages of a JIT programme, we really need to do all we can to prevent problems arising by anticipating them and then taking avoiding action.

Here are some suggestions on how you might reduce the risk of problems arising:

- *Simulation*: re-arranging production facilities; planning the introduction of cell manufacture; deciding how many operators are required in such new arrangements;

estimating how many fixtures or items of tooling are required; replacing traditional ordering systems with Kanbans; deciding what new handling equipment will be required: all these depend on estimates and assumptions which may well be 'informed' or calculated guesses, but inevitably they also depend on variable factors that cannot be determined accurately. All too often, mistakes in these estimates and assumptions can be very expensive either in terms of lost production or unnecessary investment. If a lot depends on getting the answers as near right as possible, you would do well to consider testing out your guesses on a simulation model before 'going live'.

There are quite a few simulation programs available today, some of which can be run on desktop computers. A user-friendly simulation program (such as HOCUS) is best because it allows you to draw up a simple model manually, in the form of a diagram on a large piece of paper, and then test it out to prove the logic before transferring it to a computer. This means that a team of experts in the manufacturing process can be involved at the start to help you get the logic right, even if they have no knowledge of simulation techniques. Once the logic has been proved you can transfer it to a computer and test various arrangements of facilities over equivalent 'weeks' or 'months' of production time, until you are satisfied that you've got the right balance of all the required resources. (The Bibliography, at the end of the book, includes details of where you can obtain further information about the HOCUS simulation package, and a case study in Sec. 11.10 describes a practical application of the simulation technique.)

- *Sensitivity analysis*: make a list of all the assumptions you've made. Take each one in turn and assess what would happen if your assumption is wrong; for example, decide what would be the 'worst case' scenario, and see what difference this would make to your conclusions. When you've finished working through the list of assumptions you'll probably find that only a few of them would significantly affect your conclusions: you can then concentrate all your efforts on these, and see what you can do to improve the accuracy of your initial assumption, if necessary by carrying out trial runs before finalizing your plans.
- *Reverse brainstorming*: even when you *think* you've thought of everything, take the final precaution of reverse brainstorming before implementing your planned changes. Get all the experts together, *including* the operators and others who will have to make it all work, and brainstorm answers to the question: 'This is what we are proposing to do – what could possibly go wrong?'.
- *FMEA*: similar to the reverse brainstorming approach, but more formalized. Use the failure modes and effects analysis concept to analyse in detail each step in the manufacturing process. Ideally, the reverse brainstorming process should be applied systematically to each of the steps in the FMEA type analysis.
- *Contingency stocks*: as proposed for outside supplies, in Sec. 3.8. Keep emergency supplies of part-processed materials away from the production area until you are confident that the new procedures are working well. It's also useful to plan well within theoretical capacity at first, so that you may need to have some contingency supplies available to make up any consequent shortfall during the run-in period. *Remember*: contingency stocks are a precautionary measure for the short-term only; on no account allow them to become institutionalized as part of the system.
- *Traffic lights*: this is an ongoing technique for nipping potential problems in the bud. Each operating post has a 'traffic light' mounted above it, or in the gangway along-

side, consisting of an amber light and a red light. The operator switches on the amber light when things aren't going quite right or when help is needed, and the red light if production has to be halted due to a breakdown or quality problem. In some production departments switching on the red light also sets off a klaxon. Repeater signals of both amber and red lights are sometimes provided on a panel in the foreman's office. The idea is that the amber light will give sufficient advance warning for the foreman or maintenance operative to take corrective action *before* the red light stage is reached. Traffic lights seem such a simple and obvious idea that you may be tempted to dismiss them as naïve. Don't: virtually all Japanese manufacturing companies use them, and would feel lost without them, and yet how often have you seen them used effectively in factories in this country?

- *Disaster planning*: don't wait until a disaster happens before considering what you need to do about it. The effects are felt so much more quickly in a JIT environment that you can't afford to waste time in deciding a plan of action on the spur of the moment. Draw up a list of the various 'disasters' that you think might happen (reverse brainstorming again), and then decide what is the best way of dealing with each of them. For example, notifying JIT suppliers and JIT customers immediately is likely to be high on your action list. As a result of this process you may well find ways of reducing the risk of some of the potential disasters ever arising. (This subject is dealt with in more detail in Sec. 11.10.)

A final word of advice: implementing JIT rarely goes as smoothly as you would like, however thoroughly you prepare for it. So don't go shouting to the outside world about what you're doing until you're sure you've ironed out the teething problems. If you've taken all the precautions I've suggested to lessen the risks, the chances are that no one will ever know about the mistakes you made before you went public!

FOUR

TOTAL QUALITY

After explaining the total quality concepts and the process for developing a quality creation culture across the whole company, this chapter goes on to describe the procedure for assessing how much you are really spending on quality-related costs; it then briefly reviews the key quality improvement techniques; explains the benefits and shortcomings of 'Quality Assurance Standard' accreditations; and ends with a review of the main reasons why attempts to introduce total quality sometimes fail to achieve expectations. Further guidance on implementing total quality can be found in Chapter 12.

4.1 THE TQ CONCEPTS – A QUALITY CREATION SYSTEM

When I first started work in manufacturing industry, 'quality' meant making sure that you supplied products to your customer which were in accordance with an agreed specification. This specification frequently permitted a small percentage of defective parts, provided that the overall 'Acceptable Quality Level' (AQL) for the batch was satisfied. You could say that the philosophy was to accept in principle that defective work would be produced: the task of filtering out the faulty products afterwards was entrusted to inspectors.

The snag about this approach is that even if every defective product is caught before it can leave a supplier's premises, this has only been achieved at a cost: as I explained earlier, rejects and rework are a waste, as are the inspection costs incurred in order to avoid shipping defective products, and these wastes lead to customers ultimately having to pay more as a result of the failure to 'make products right, first time, every time'. The total quality philosophy, in contrast, is based on *defect prevention* in place of the traditional *defect detection and correction*, the concept being that customers will only get full value for money if this hidden cost of quality is eliminated.

This means developing what is sometimes referred to as a 'quality creation system', where every member of the workforce takes personal responsibility for the quality of his or her own work. The goal of 'right first time, every time' applies to every employee and to every aspect of the company's operations, not just to the manufacturing process. Inspection systems will never achieve this – it requires an attitude of mind right across the company, in all jobs at all levels. That, in essence, is what total quality (TQ) is all about. I should, perhaps, add that many 'experts' prefer the term 'total quality management' (TQM), because this emphasizes that responsibility starts at the very top of the company. There's no difference between the two terms (other than the actual name used); it's just that some of us believe that including the word 'management' acts as a barrier because people tend to think it means it's up to *management* to do something: leaving out the 'management' reinforces the TQ message that it involves everyone in the company, in everything that they do.

I don't propose to go into the history of the total quality concept here, or the pioneering work done in Japan with the help of 'gurus' such as Juran and Deming. If you are interested in this I suggest you get hold of Richard J. Schonberger's book *Japanese Manufacturing Techniques: Nine Hidden Lessons in Simplicity* (see Bibliography): Chapter 3 gives an excellent description of both why and how Japan adopted the teachings of these American experts who couldn't (at that time) gain a hearing in their own country.

Personally, I prefer to describe the total quality concept in terms of the four 'Eras of Quality', which shows how we have virtually come full circle: the concept of total quality isn't really new – all it does is to ask us to apply once more the standards and working practices of the original master craftsmen, as they were before the days of mass production.

4.2 THE FOUR ERAS OF QUALITY

The first era of quality lasted throughout the history of manufacturing right up to the beginning of the twentieth century. A craftsman was taught not just his craft skills, but also the concept of self-inspection, so that when he completed a task he would ask himself 'Does the work I have done satisfy my craft standards?' and 'Have I achieved what I set out to achieve (i.e. have I fully satisfied my customer's requirements?)'. The concept of independent inspection was virtually unknown other than when he was learning his craft skills under the supervision of a master craftsman, and even then it was thought of as part of the teaching process. Once he'd finished his apprenticeship and qualified as a craftsman he was expected to uphold the standards of his craft and accept personal responsibility for the quality of his work.

The second era of quality came with the advent of mass production. Manufacturers such as Henry Ford believed that manufacturing would be more efficient if production workers concentrated primarily on maximizing the volume of production, leaving it to a separate inspection function to weed out any defective work. The cost of this defective work was, they felt, more than compensated for by the benefits of mass production. As long as there was still a degree of the old craftsman culture remaining this was undoubtedly true, since the production worker would still strive to produce good work – particularly if, as was then the case, he was heavily penalized in his pay packet for work subsequently found to be defective.

During the years between the two world wars this process continued. Although there was an increasing tendency for production operatives to let defective work go on to the next operation in the hope that it might slip through inspection, the financial penalties, coupled with the threat of losing one's job during years of high unemployment, continued to make the reliance on separate inspection a cost-effective way of managing production.

The Second World War brought about the need to produce high-quality arms at high production rates. At the same time, many of the skilled workers left the factories to join up and they had to be replaced by workers, many of them women, who had no previous manufacturing experience. The last remnants of the craft culture disappeared, there was no longer a threat of losing one's job, and it became patriotic to produce as much as possible: if someone complained that quality standards were slipping the answer would be 'Don't you know there's a war on? Anyway, the inspector's the best judge of whether it will do or not'. This led to a new emphasis having to be placed on quality: the solution adopted was the introduction of what were termed 'quality assurance' systems.

This third era of quality, based on quality assurance (QA) systems, had a strong military pedigree. Indeed, the current QA standards BS 5750 and ISO 9000 have a lot in common with the original military standards on which they were based. Many companies over the last few years have achieved certification to the new QA standards; in many parts of the world those which have not will probably have to do so before long if they wish to remain in business. However, there is a great deal of scepticism as to how effective QA standards are in actually improving a manufacturer's quality performance. In theory, they emphasize the need to replace defect *detection* with defect *prevention*, but in practice many people find that there is little that is done to change people's attitudes to quality across the company: QA is still seen in far too many companies as just something the Quality Manager has to worry about, instead of something that affects the way in which everyone works (as the originators intended). The acid test is what happens at the end of the month when you're trying to reach your output targets, and you're held up by some material or components which you know are faulty, but you also know that your customer will probably accept (particularly if you're so late on delivery that the customer is getting desperate!). I'm afraid that in most companies the answer will probably be 'Let it go through, we'll make sure we get it right next time' (but, of course, they don't).

This brings us to the fourth era of quality, which is the introduction of the total quality philosophy across the company. Here the emphasis changes from *systems* to *attitudes*. The aim is to get everyone to take personal responsibility for the quality of their own work. There is no one else you can blame if you let defective work go through: the buck stops with you. Consider the example above: suppose management insist that, in spite of a company-wide commitment to total quality, in this instance the faulty work should be passed (I hope they wouldn't, but I'm not so naïve as to think it couldn't happen). The difference with total quality is that, if you've succeeded in changing attitudes, the people concerned let the work go through against their better judgement; it's an action that is completely alien to the new total quality culture, so they make it a priority to *do something* about whatever caused the fault so that they aren't put in that position again. The fourth era of quality effectively returns to the attitudes of the crafts-man in the first era of quality: each individual is responsible for the quality of his or her own work; if something goes wrong the people concerned accept that it is their personal responsibility to see that something is done to stop the fault occurring again, calling on some other person for help if necessary. Problems must not be swept under the carpet: they must be exposed and dealt with.

4.3 DETERMINING COMPANY-WIDE CUSTOMER–SUPPLIER RELATIONSHIPS

It's all very well talking about 'changing attitudes', but how do you actually go about getting people to think and behave differently? Explanatory seminars, top management involvement in Quality Steering Committees, articles in the company's internal news-letter (if one exists) and widely distributed publicity material, such as posters, all these can help, *provided* that they are accompanied by a firm public commitment that the Boss, personally, intends to drive the total quality campaign. Even so, all that these things will do will be to attract people's attention: something more is needed before they will believe that it is anything other than their management's latest fad which will soon blow over (and they may well be right!).

Fortunately, deep down most people don't like doing work that isn't quite up to scratch; they would much rather be proud of what they do and of the company they work for. Nor do they usually like to be just a cog, isolated from the end product to which they contribute. They will welcome change if they can see that the new approach offers them some improvement in these two factors, which are important to *them*. Total quality does indeed provide this, if you follow the usual practice and get everyone involved, right at the start, in carrying out what is generally referred to as either a 'function analysis' or a 'department purpose analysis'. I don't really like either of these terms – they're too academic for me because they don't make it immediately clear to the average person what they actually mean. I prefer the term 'What are we here for analysis' – it's not very grammatical, nor very 'learned', but at least its meaning is pretty clear to all. Even so, I shall use the term 'department purpose analysis' here because it's the most commonly used term and it's easy to abbreviate (to DPA). In this section I'll concentrate on explaining the DPA process and how it is used; further guidance on how to introduce the process in your own company can be found in Sec. 12.3.

The first stage in a DPA is to write down what the department does, who it does it for (i.e. who are the customers for its outputs), and where it gets its materials or instruc-tions from (i.e. who the suppliers of its inputs are). The process can best be understood with the help of the diagram in Fig. 4.1:

- The chain represents what the department does. Several chains may be needed to represent the full range of a department's work: if there are very many, concentrate at first on the most important half dozen or so.
- Each link in the chain represents the contribution of one individual; if the department is very big, you may have to use one link to represent the work of a whole Section or subgroup, in which case you will then need to draw a 'second level' chain for that 'first level' link.

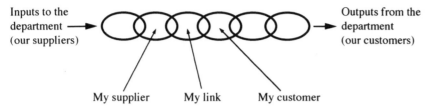

Figure 4.1 The department's 'chain'.

Preparing a DPA should be a group activity; get everyone concerned together so that everyone who works in the department ends up with a good understanding of:

- The reason for the department's existence (and, therefore, for the individual's own existence within the department)
- Who the 'suppliers' are, on whom the department is dependent for inputs of good quality material and information
- Who the 'customers' are, who are dependent on the department's output as a source of their material or information, and who depend on its quality
- What are the various links in the chain, which enable the department to convert its inputs into the desired outputs
- Which link is 'mine', which other links provide 'my' inputs, which receive 'my' outputs

The idea is that the process should involve everyone and make them think about their job and how it is linked to other people's jobs. It helps people to appreciate how everyone is dependent on someone else and so encourages identification with a team and an increased sense of responsibility to other members of that team. It also forces people to think more carefully about what inputs they want (both for their department *and* for their individual link), so that they can pass this information to their suppliers; similarly, their customers will think more carefully about what *they* want, and so on. Of course, it isn't sufficient just to *think* about who your suppliers and customers are, and what your inputs and outputs are. But once people know what to expect, *and have agreed these with the suppliers and customers concerned* (the second step in the DPA process), then everyone has a standard against which to monitor what actually happens. As soon as something falls short of the required standard, *any* individual can now go to the person responsible for the immediately preceding link (i.e. the supplier) and say 'Hey, this isn't what we agreed: what's the problem? What can we do to put things right?'. Instead of there being some separate and distant Inspection or Quality Control Department who have to decide what isn't right, we've changed to a situation where the supply of the 'right' material or information has now become almost a personal contract between the two individuals concerned. Individuals now have personal responsibility for making sure that everything goes right at their link in the chain: they are no longer just a cog but a vital part of the chain – if their link breaks down they now know that means the whole chain will break – so they have responsibility as part of a team, with others depending on the quality of their work. If you've got this far, you're well on the way to changing attitudes to quality in your company.

The final step in the DPA process is concerned with quality improvement. By comparing the agreed requirements of all the 'customers' with what their 'suppliers' currently provide, you can identify what improvements are necessary in order to fully satisfy the 'customers'' requirements; you may well also identify tasks currently undertaken which don't add value, and which are therefore targets for removal. The results, therefore, provide the basis for an improvement programme, although priorities will still need to be established which take into account not just the department's needs, but also those expressed through the company's mission statement, its longer term strategic objectives and its business goals and targets for the shorter term.

DPA is a structured method of getting people involved in a company-wide quality improvement process; its emphasis on teamwork encourages everyone to take responsibility for improving the quality of service they give to their customers and which they in turn receive from their suppliers. However, it can involve a great deal of work and, if you're not careful, some of the departmental managers who have to put it into practice can get so overwhelmed with the task that it can become counter-productive: before embarking on the DPA process, therefore, you should first consider carefully whether you might be able to get people involved effectively through other means. You can often achieve this by starting your campaign with key strategic projects, taking the opportunity at a later stage to allow these to develop into *continuous improvement groups* in response to pressure from the shop floor: this process is described in Chapter 13.

However, if the conclusions of your strategy review were that emphasis should be placed on total quality, and that everyone should be involved right from the start, then you won't be able to wait for the response to come naturally from the shop floor; in that case DPA will probably be the best approach, and you will need to find a way of reducing the risk of the process overwhelming some of the participants.

The most effective way of virtually eliminating the risk of things going wrong is to enlist the help of external consultants. They should have the experience (and ready-for-use material) that will enable them to look after any training that's needed, and they will have the skills to guide departments in applying the DPA process. However, it will cost you money, in some cases a great deal of money; but against that, you will be far more confident of success in your quality improvement campaign and you can expect to get results much more quickly than if you tried to do it on your own.

If you decide on a do-it-yourself approach, try to start with a pilot project; this should be used as a learning process, both to finalize details of how you are going to apply the DPA process elsewhere, and to train two or three carefully chosen people who will act as facilitators when the main process is launched. The first task will be to decide which part of the company you are going to use for the pilot project; while it helps if the area chosen is 'typical', it's far more important to choose one with which the trainee facilitators are familiar and in which one of them actually works (they'll have quite enough on their plate learning about DPA, without having to learn about the department's processes as well). Once they've completed the pilot project and made any necessary amendments to the documents and procedures, the next step is to hold a briefing session for managers and supervisors in which those who conducted the pilot scheme will explain the procedures. Finally, each department should be asked to apply the process in its own area, with the pilot scheme 'experts' acting as facilitators to guide them through the procedures.

Before leaving the subject of DPA I should, perhaps, mention the development of an alternative methodology, generally referred to as '*Business process engineering (or re-engineering)*' which has become increasingly popular in the last year or two. In practice the underlying concepts behind this approach are very similar to those of the DPA process and both are closely related to various other techniques that have been fashionable in previous years. All these are concerned with undertaking a fundamental re-think of what people do, why they do it, whether it's necessary and, if so, how it can be done better. My reason for preferring the DPA process to these alternative 'packagings', and for including it in the chapters on total quality, is that its central theme is getting the whole workforce involved in improving the service that they, as 'suppliers', provide to their 'customers'. I have said that total quality can be effective in changing people's attitudes *provided that you can get them involved*, the DPA process is, I believe, the best of these techniques for achieving this. However, if you do decide to follow the business process engineering approach, be careful not to go over the top with it – it's all too easy to end up identifying so many desirable changes to your organization, and then to spend so much time implementing these (and the new computer systems that go with them), that you lose sight of that key objective of a world-class company – improving things that are important to *customers*.

4.4 COST OF QUALITY ANALYSIS

4.4.1 The Components of Quality Cost

I referred earlier to the underlying philosophy of total quality: that the customer will only really be getting full value for money if the hidden cost of quality is eliminated. This implies that you need to identify where quality costs arise, so that you can take whatever action is necessary to eliminate (or at least to reduce) them.

British Standard 6143 (see Bibliography) classifies quality-related costs under four headings, as follows (words in italics are quoted from the Standard):

- *Prevention Costs: The costs of any action taken to investigate, prevent or reduce defects and failures.* Examples include the cost of any quality management, quality assurance and quality engineering functions and activities; vendor assessment; quality training; design improvements aimed at reducing the risk of errors in production; and the maintenance and calibration of test and inspection equipment. The cost of hiring external consultants to assist you with assessing quality costs or with your quality improvement projects is also included under this heading, as is the time spent in preparing a department purpose analysis.
- *Appraisal Costs: The costs of assessing the quality achieved.* This consists mainly of the cost of inspectors and their equipment, but also includes costs associated with activities such as conducting field performance tests, carrying out periodical product quality audits, evaluating field stocks of spare parts, and producing computer reports of inspection and test results.
- *Internal Failure Costs: The costs arising within the manufacturing organisation of failure to achieve quality specified (before transfer of ownership to the customer).* Examples include scrap; rework and repair; troubleshooting or defect/failure analysis; re-inspection or re-testing; modification permits or concessions; and downgrading of products.
- *External Failure Costs: The costs arising outside the organisation of failure to achieve quality specified (after the transfer of ownership to the customer).* This includes

handling customer complaints; product or customer service activities; product liability claims, insurance, or protective measures; product recalls or allowances granted; and warranty costs and costs associated with replacement. It also includes a proportion of the Managing Director's, Technical Director's, or Sales Director's costs, if they get involved with dealing with after-sales complaints from customers!

Some people combine the two types of failure cost under one heading; I prefer to keep them separate as the Standard suggests, because a quality problem that the *customer* has to tell *you* about is potentially far more damaging than one that you identify yourself and can rectify while it is still hidden from the outside world.

The proportion of quality costs you might expect under each heading varies significantly from one company to the next. Generally speaking, prevention costs tend to be less than 10 per cent, until management realize the significance of the overall cost of quality and start to take corrective action. Spending more on prevention invariably more than pays for itself in terms of the three other types of cost, once the preventive measures introduced start to take effect. Examples of the results of a cost of quality analysis at four different companies are shown in Fig. 4.2. Note that Company D, which has the lowest total cost of quality (in terms of percentage of sales turnover), is the company which spends proportionately most on prevention; it has also eliminated most of its external failure costs (but it still has some way to go in reducing internal failure costs). Note also that Company C, which spends proportionately least on prevention, has the highest overall quality costs. I promise I haven't doctored these figures: they are reproduced just as they were!

Type of cost	Total quality cost (percentage)			
	Company A	Company B	Company C	Company D
Prevention	12	14	5	21
Appraisal	8	20	5	15
Internal failure	35	55	54	58
External failure	45	11	36	6
Total quality cost	100	100	100	100
Quality cost as percentage of sales turnover	15	11	25	5

Figure 4.2 Cost of quality analysis: comparison of results at four companies.

One of the objectives in assessing your cost of quality is to draw everyone's attention to the need to take action to reduce the 'waste' currently being incurred: if you want your workforce to pay more attention to 'getting it right first time', it helps if you can show them how much it's costing *in their particular department* because they're *not* always getting it right first time at present. However, there's another important reason for carrying out the analysis: it shows you where the heaviest costs are being incurred at present, so that you can identify where the priorities for improvement lie.

4.4.2 Assessing the Cost of Quality

Unfortunately, assessing the true cost of quality is notoriously difficult. Should it, for example, comprise solely those quality costs which are traditionally reported in many companies: the value of labour and material lost through non-recoverable process waste and components or finished products scrapped and costs incurred from customer returns or in providing field service during the warranty period? Or, at the other extreme, should it encompass *all* the costs associated with ensuring that all the company's operations (including administrative procedures such as invoicing) are carried out correctly; *plus* a 'lost opportunity' cost to reflect the profit you would have made on those additional sales you might have won if you had a better quality reputation in the market-place?

This is why you might read authoritative statements, such as in publications issued by the UK's Department of Trade and Industry, claiming that 'The cost of quality in many manufacturing companies in the UK varies between 15 and 25 per cent of sales turnover, and in some cases can be as high as 40 per cent'; while your Quality Manager, backed up by your Accounts Department, insists that *your* cost of quality is less than 5 per cent. It all depends on what you include in the calculations. In the example quoted, your Quality Manager is including only those costs which are shown under a separate heading in the monthly management accounts: all the other costs of quality are buried under other headings. The total quality philosophy requires that the calculation of your cost of quality should include *all* costs associated with ensuring that you fully satisfy your customers' quality requirements. This means, for example, that if 50 per cent of a senior manager's time is spent in 'fire-fighting', because of problems due to some errors which occurred previously (perhaps in planning or specification procedures), then 50 per cent of the manager's cost (including secretarial support and office accommodation etc.) should be included in the cost of quality calculations. However, I don't, personally, agree with including 'lost opportunity' costs: I suspect that these have crept into some people's calculations in order to help justify expenditure on an ambitious total quality campaign!

Whatever you decide to include in your cost of quality calculations, if you do it realistically the results are likely to be quite frightening. Suppose, for example, that you worked out that a reasonable assessment for your company was 20 per cent of sales turnover – fairly typical in my experience for a company which is only just starting its world-class initiatives. Imagine the horror in the Boardroom when they first hear this, if they had previously believed (on the basis of what the management accounts showed) that 'scrap' was less than 3 per cent: if their profit before tax was, say, between 10 and 12 per cent of sales turnover, what reaction are they likely to get if major shareholders hear that almost 50 per cent of potential profit was being lost due to quality problems! Faced with figures like these, only the genuine world-class believers in your management ranks will raise a cheer, because they see a tremendous opportunity for improvement. The rest will probably be very unwilling to accept figures which they will see as challenging their competence as managers: they will therefore want to know how you arrived at the figures, and they may well search for ways to discredit them (this is another reason why I don't like to include lost opportunity costs, which are so easy to challenge).

Fortunately, there is a way you can overcome this problem and produce figures that are realistic and yet which will stand up well to challenge. There are three requirements to achieve this:

- Follow the procedure laid down in British Standard 6143: *Guide to the determination and use of quality related costs*. Don't be tempted to improve on the procedures set out in the standard, because you want to be able to say to anyone who challenges the results: 'We have kept strictly to the procedures and guidelines laid down in the British Standard'.

- Arrange for the cost of quality analysis for each department to be carried out by a team consisting primarily of people who work in that department, including key managers. This ensures that those involved understand the department's processes and procedures, and the sort of quality problems that arise. It also makes it very difficult for the director responsible for the department subsequently to challenge the results, since they have been prepared by his own staff, who probably know a lot more about the detailed working of the department than the director does.
- Include a senior member of the Accounts department in each team. This ensures that the results are published with the authority of the Accounts department, again making it difficult for the results to be challenged subsequently (in addition, most people, looking at the figures, will believe them to be erring on the conservative side, since this is the nature of accountants!). If at all possible, the same member of the Accounts department should serve on all the teams, both to increase the individual's understanding and expertise, and to ensure that the figures for all departments are seen to be prepared on the same basis and that any inter-departmental implications are properly taken into account.

Although the British Standard is very helpful, it would be unrealistic to expect departments to undertake the cost of quality analysis without having someone in their team with the appropriate specialist experience. For this reason, I strongly recommend that you get expert assistance from an external consultant on the first occasion that you undertake this task. In addition to giving some introductory training to those involved, the consultant should act as facilitator for each team, ensuring that the outcome represents a fair balance between the views of the departmental members and the accountant member, and that the team as a whole accept and give their authority to the results.

Assessing the cost of quality involves a lot of work. For this reason, it is usually advisable not to go into too much detail on the first assessment. Your objective should be to get an idea of where the key areas of quality cost are in your company, so that you can see where it would be worthwhile examining the costs in much more detail. This is usually a sensible approach since the cost of quality in most companies follows the Pareto Principle, i.e. the bulk of the costs can be traced back to a relatively small number of root causes – these are the ones which you want to start with in your improvement campaign.

Generally speaking, it's not worth carrying out a cost of quality analysis across all departments more than once or twice a year, because of the work involved. However, when you do undertake a full review, the results will show you which are the key areas of quality cost, and you should certainly set up some sort of procedures for monitoring these specific areas on a regular (i.e. weekly or monthly) basis. You will never be able to eliminate all the costs of quality: at the beginning you may even increase them as a result of your additional expenditure on correction and prevention. A reasonable target in most cases would be to reduce the total cost of quality by two thirds over a period of eighteen months to two years. Repeating the analysis at, say, six monthly intervals, backed up by regular weekly or monthly reports on key cost areas, will show whether you are on course for achieving the overall target.

Finally, if you are considering undertaking a cost of quality analysis in your company, I suggest that you first read the following publications:

- BS 6143: *Guide to the determination and use of quality related costs*: you may well have a copy of this already, as it is included in the hardback BS publication *BSI Handbook Twenty Two, Quality Assurance*. As well as explaining the four main components of quality cost, the standard provides a suggested report layout and gives examples of different ways of breaking down the figures to make them more meaningful. There is also a useful check-list provided in the appendix, to help you in remembering what costs to include.
- A publication in the UK Department of Industry's Enterprise Initiative series: *The Case for Costing Quality*; details of where this can be obtained are included in the Bibliography. This 40 page publication first explains what quality costs are and why they are important and need to be measured; it then goes on to give 15 case studies from a good cross-section of companies; and finally, it offers some 'Dos' and 'Don'ts' to '... help companies avoid some of the difficulties and traps typically encountered in a quality cost collection exercise'.

Further guidance on how to conduct a cost of quality investigation in your own company can be found in Sec. 12.2.

4.5 QUALITY IMPROVEMENT TECHNIQUES

The first stage in any improvement process is to find out where things are going wrong. Apart from normal inspection procedures, which from time to time will throw up a specific quality problem that may be localized and transitory, your main source of information should be the cost of quality analysis. This is because any existing routine quality reports you may already be producing will probably only include the results of the various inspection operations that are included in the manufacturing process, or information relating to customer returns and warranty claims. You will remember that this is the '3 to 5 per cent' type of quality cost reporting. The cost of quality analysis, in contrast, will show where the real costs are being incurred, and this should enable you to identify areas for priority action.

Most of the more important quality improvement techniques are described elsewhere in this book; they are summarized briefly below:

- *Teamwork*: don't try to solve a major problem on your own; you need a team, including the various 'experts' who own any part of the process, backed up perhaps by some 'non-owners' with appropriate technical expertise and by one or two 'outsiders' to encourage the introduction of new thinking. The subject of quality circles, a specific application of the teamwork concept, is covered in more detail in Secs. 5.1 and 13.1.
- *Process flow analysis*: the most important technique of all; finding out what is actually happening at present, writing it down, drawing diagrams, taking photographs or making video recordings, collecting data, trying out the various steps in the process yourself – whatever is appropriate for making sure that you understand the process(es) thoroughly; examples of using the process flow analysis technique are included in Secs. 8.3 and 11.1.

- *Pareto analysis*: when you analyse the various causes of quality problems you will normally find that a very few problems account for most of the overall defect level. Plotting a Pareto graph helps you to identify which these are, so that you can target them for corrective action (another way of expressing Pareto's law in this context is: 'Unless the *main* cause of a problem is identified and remedied, no significant improvement can be achieved').
- *Brainstorming*: free-ranging generation of ideas by the improvement team (supplemented for the brainstorming session by the actual operators concerned); more information on 'improved' methods of brainstorming is included in Chapter 8.
- *Fishbone diagrams*: (also known as 'cause and effect diagrams' or 'Ishikawa diagrams'); a logical approach to analysing potential causes of a quality problem – useful during brainstorming sessions to make sure that attention is paid to every aspect of the process or problem; methods of applying fishbone diagrams are explained in Chapter 8.
- *Statistical Process Control (SPC)*: SPC monitors batch or continuous production by sampling at set frequencies, in order to identify whether there is a trend towards a control parameter being broken (for example, the external diameter of successive items in a batch moving closer and closer to the maximum tolerance level). The idea is to give advance warning so that corrective action can be taken (such as sharpening or replacing the tool), *before* the problem reaches the point where defective products are produced. More information on SPC can be found in Sec. 12.5.
- *Traffic lights*: similar in concept to SPC, and can be used in conjunction with it; the operator switches on an amber light to summon help as soon as the process shows signs of a potential quality problem developing, and a red light (stopping the process) if the control parameters are exceeded. Further details are given in Sec. 3.11.
- *Mistake proofing*: (often known by its Japanese name, 'Poka-Yoke'); this approach, developed by Shigeo Shingo, uses a combination of production engineering and design modifications to reduce the risk of something being done wrong in the manufacturing process (particularly at the assembly stage). Shingo has written an excellent book on the subject: *Zero Quality Control: Source Inspection and the Poka-Yoke System* (for further details see Bibliography).
- *Rapid feedback*: TQ encourages the concept of everyone being responsible for the quality of his or her own work; this 'self-inspection' concept needs to backed up by 'neighbour inspection', in which everyone checks, as far as they can, that the previous operation has been carried out correctly – if it hasn't, the most effective way of getting the error corrected *and* of making sure that it is not repeated, is for the neighbour to pass the defective work back immediately (or, if return isn't feasible, give appropriate information feedback as rapidly as possible.
- *Taguchi methods*: Taguchi (a Japanese statistician and quality expert) has developed a number of quality improvement techniques which are usually referred to collectively as 'Taguchi methods'. These all reflect his belief that the quality and reliability of a product is to a large extent fixed at the design stage; his methodology is therefore concerned primarily with 'the routine optimization of product and process *prior* to manufacture'. Taguchi is probably best known for his method of analysing the causes of a quality problem, using an adaptation of the factorial experiment design (FED) approach; the technique is used typically when you believe that there are a number of possible factors that are causing the problem (for example temperature, processing

method or material), and that there is probably some degree of interaction between these factors. The only effective way of finding a solution to the problem is to adjust each of the factors both individually and in combination; however, the number of 'experiments' that you would have to undertake in order to examine all the different combinations of feasible variations would be prohibitive. Taguchi's method enables an effective solution to be derived with only a small number of experiments. Further information on Taguchi methods can be found in Sec. 12.4.

- *Multivariate analysis*: this is a statistical method of assessing the interaction between a number of possible causes of a problem, provided that you have the appropriate data available; although programs are available for use on desktop computers, I wouldn't advise using multivariate analysis unless you have someone in your team who really understands statistics!
- *Failure modes and effects analysis (FMEA)*: this is a process used by designers to identify *at the design stage* ways in which a product or component might fail in the field; it can also usefully be used to anticipate potential quality problems *before production starts on a new design*, so that the design or tooling can be changed to avoid the problem. In both cases the objective is to anticipate a potential problem and then find a way of avoiding its occurrence. You will find more about FMEA in Sec. 11.8.

This is not intended to be a fully comprehensive list of all the recognized techniques that you are likely to need in a quality improvement campaign, but it should certainly be enough to get you started.

4.6 DESIGNING FOR ZERO DEFECTS MANUFACTURE

'Zero defects' is the ultimate objective of total quality. Even if you are convinced that you will never fully achieve this objective, nevertheless it should remain as your ultimate goal.

I suspect that when you start your world-class initiatives you will be a long way from achieving zero defects. But there are still some useful steps that you can take to start creating this ideal, in particular when you are designing new products and introducing them to production. Most of this has already been covered in Sec. 3.9 and I don't propose to repeat it here. The rest is covered very effectively in Shigeo Shingo's book on the Poka-Yoke system, referred to above, which describes techniques for 'making it easier to manufacture it right first time than wrong'. You should also consider under this heading getting zero defect deliveries from your suppliers: this is dealt with in Sec. 3.8.

A manufacturer's ability to maintain zero defect deliveries to customers will often depend very much on the quality and reliability of the raw materials and components provided by the manufacturer's own suppliers. Fortunately, the increasing use of national and international standards for products and materials, particularly in Europe and the US, is making it easier to achieve the desired stability of supplies. But it also means that a world-class company has to take proper account of these standards, particularly when supplying to parts of the world where the standards may differ from those in their own country, or where special conditions are imposed to satisfy local environmental or health and safety regulations.

4.7 QUALITY ACCREDITATIONS (BS 5750 ETC.)

I said in Sec. 4.2 that '... there is a great deal of scepticism as to how effective QA standards are in actually improving a manufacturer's quality performance'. This does not mean that you can ignore them. In the first place, there is increasing pressure from customers for their suppliers to have the appropriate QA accreditations or approvals, and it is unlikely that a company wishing to be considered world-class could resist these pressures. In the second place, while obtaining QA accreditations might not *in itself* have other than a short-term benefit in terms of improving quality performance, it certainly does provide a most important foundation for the total quality approach to build on. If you want your company to place the right emphasis on quality, it is, after all, important for everyone to have a clear understanding of what *are* the organizational responsibilities and approved procedures covering all the company's operations that are intended to both produce and monitor achievement of the required quality performance. This is what QA standards such as ISO 9000 provide.

There are quite a number of different QA standards, but the most widely used today are BS 5750 and its International and European counterparts, the ISO 9000 and EN 29000 series. (With effect from 1 August 1994, the BS 5750 standard has been replaced by the International Standard ISO 9000. However, I shall continue to refer to BS 5750 here since it is the term many manufacturers are more familiar with.) Other QA standards generally apply to specific industries, such as defence (e.g. NATO's AQAP) and those used by the pharmaceutical industry, and by the UK's National Health Service and its equivalent in other countries.

The QA standards are divided into several sections; for example:

- **ISO 9001** and **BS 5750 Part 1** cover the specification for design and development, production, installation and servicing.
- **ISO 9002** and **BS 5750 Part 2** cover the specification for production and installation.
- **ISO 9003** and **BS 5750 Part 3** cover the specification for final inspection and test.
- **ISO 9004** and **BS 5750 Part 0** provide a guide to quality management and quality system elements.

If you operate in the UK and need help in deciding which standard is relevant to your own company's activities, and what you might have to do to satisfy the requirements for accreditation, you can get free advice under the Department of Trade and Industry's Enterprise Initiative. To find out more you should contact your local DTI office.

4.8 REDUCING THE RISK OF FAILURE

Many companies have tried to introduce total quality, and all too often the results have failed to live up to their expectations. Don't let any such experiences you may have heard of put you off: invariably the fault lies not in the total quality concepts, but in the way they have been applied. Some of the most common mistakes are summarized in this section.

Probably the most important reason for failure is delegating responsibility for total quality to the wrong person, most commonly the Quality Manager. All that does is to confirm people's instinctive belief that total quality is just a refinement of quality control, and that makes it 'someone else's job'. The objective, you will remember, is to develop a *quality creation culture* across the company, and there's only one person in the organization who is responsible for something as fundamental as the company's culture: the Chief Executive. If he (or she) isn't seen by all to be driving the total quality campaign personally, then it's doomed to failure. That doesn't mean that he has to get involved in the detail of what's done, but he should make sure that his presence is felt, through chairing the total quality steering meetings, through making an appearance at as many of the briefing seminars as can be managed (particularly in the early stages) and, most important of all, through personal intervention when advised that progress in a particular area is unsatisfactory.

I've said that Chief Executives don't have to get involved in the detail of what's done, provided that their influence is felt and that they occasionally wave a big stick to demonstrate their personal commitment. However, don't take this to mean that someone else should be appointed as the total quality boss, because if someone else is the boss then people will assume that the Chief Executive isn't and you'll be back to square one. Instead, the Chief Executive should make sure that all Board members realize that they are personally responsible for the total quality campaign in their part of the company; the Board members in turn will hold their direct reports responsible for the total quality campaign in their parts of the company, and so on through the different levels of the management structure. What you are doing through this approach is to institutionalize total quality as part of your normal management processes, rather than as an add-on: managers can, and often will, neglect something which they see as being outside their day-to-day responsibilities, and probably transitory, but managers cannot afford to neglect something which they know their boss, and their boss's boss, consider to be part and parcel of their 'normal' responsibilities.

All this implies that you will need to review your existing quality organization. The need for effective quality control and quality engineering will continue, but should become the responsibility of the teams in each department who actually carry out the operational tasks. If specialist technical skills are required, then the person who has those skills should be a member of the operating team, not of some central function. The role of the Quality Manager, on the other hand, may well continue to be a central function, in many cases at a higher level in the organization than previously, but the emphasis should be primarily on providing support to the teams in each department and, in particular, advising them of developments in national and international quality procedures and standards that are relevant to their operations.

A common practice with total quality implementations is to cascade training, as well as responsibility, down through the organizational structure. This approach has its attractions (because it reduces the dependence on external consultants and gets the company's own managers personally involved) but it can often prove another reason for failure. What typically happens is that external consultants are used to explain the total quality message to higher levels of management but, to keep costs down, those attending the consultants' training sessions are required to pass the training on to their own areas of responsibility. In a large company this process is sometimes repeated through several layers of management; not surprisingly, by the time it gets to the final level, where most of the action will take place, the message can sometimes get rather distorted! The argument in favour of this cascading approach is that groups are given instruction by their own bosses, so that they are seen to be the owners of their part of the total quality campaign. Unfortunately it doesn't work very well, because the people you are relying on to put the message across are for the most part not very good at that sort of thing. It's far better to use an expert, who has the thorough understanding of the concepts, and has the skills to put the message across well; you can get round the problem of ownership very easily by requiring managers to be present at the training session for their people, and by getting them to express their personal commitment through making the opening and closing remarks. The expert can be an external consultant, or someone within the company who is known to have good presentation skills and who has been specially trained for the task (probably through attending external courses or seminars).

What you can, and in most companies should, do is to appoint someone as total quality facilitator, making it clear that his or her role is not to run the campaign, but simply to provide technical support and guidance to departments. Part of this support can be the training role, referred to in the previous paragraph. Where people often go wrong is to send their Quality Manager on appropriate external courses, and then tell everyone that he or she is now the Total Quality Adviser. Back to square one again! It's hard enough as it is to get people to understand that total quality isn't the same as quality control (which is one reason why I prefer to use the 'world-class manufacturing' banner); tell them that your former quality expert is now your total quality expert and you are inviting a response of 'same difference'! So, however suitable such an individual might seem, the last person I would recommend appointing as facilitator is someone who is currently identified in your people's eyes with the existing quality functions; since total quality has so much to do with people and their attitudes, someone from the Personnel function, for example, would probably be more suitable than a former quality specialist. In short, anyone who is reasonably familiar with the manufacturing processes will be capable of doing the job once the necessary training has been given, provided that the person selected has good communication skills and the charisma to portray the appropriate degree of enthusiasm.

Another cause of failure can be taking too long over the initial planning stage, something which is particularly likely to happen in large organizations. Thorough preparation is, of course, both commendable and advisable, but you need to be careful that you don't overdo it. One large multinational organization decided to introduce total quality management and were advised by their consultants to do their groundwork thoroughly; so they did. They spent the next two years reviewing strategy and setting improvement objectives, first at the corporate level, then at divisional level, then cascading down through the various layers of management at their many locations around the world. Throughout this time they were scrupulous about involving people in the review process and kept the whole workforce informed of what they were doing, so that when the time came for their level in the organizational structure to get involved they would know what it was all about. Unfortunately, the process took so long that by the time it came to the turn of the shop floor and administrative staff they had lost interest: management's initial enthusiasm had raised their expectations and prepared them for change, but having to wait two years while only managers were involved convinced them that it was the *managers* who would be expected to find ways of meeting the improvement objectives; calling the campaign total quality 'management' simply reinforced that view. Perhaps I should add that it wasn't the consultants' fault that so much time was spent on the initial planning stage; they were only involved at the corporate planning level, after which the company decided they could manage on their own.

The final cause of failure that you should beware of is management sending the wrong signals. The Chief Executive will know how determined he is to change attitudes to quality across the company; the top management team, because they are so close to the Chief Executive, may realize how determined he is; but the rest of the company will at first have no means of knowing whether this is a real change, or whether it's just another 'flavour of the month'. And since they will have seen many different 'flavours' in the past, but little or no instances of real fundamental change, they may well assume that total quality is just the latest fad and they will be looking for signs that management's initial enthusiasm is waning. Actions that *you* may think irrelevant to your total quality campaign can all too readily be interpreted, by middle management in particular, as the signs they've been watching out for. For example, the Chief Executive, after chairing the first two or three total quality steering meetings personally, then misses three successive meetings; or, at the end of a month when output is low, management overrides quality control and allows work that is not quite up to scratch to go through in order to meet budget; or, no one makes a fuss when progress on implementing the total quality plan falls badly behind schedule, because those responsible 'were, after all, under rather a lot of pressure due to production difficulties last month'. There may well be good reasons, in management's eyes, for all of these, but they are just the sort of signs that your people will be looking for as indications that total quality is, as they suspected, just another of management's latest fads. Some such actions will be unavoidable, particularly in the early stages when the benefits of your total quality campaign haven't yet been realized, but you should be on the look-out for them and, at the very least, make sure everyone understands the reasons why they were thought necessary in this instance, and that it hasn't affected management's commitment to continuing down the total quality path.

Running a business often involves learning from past mistakes. If a new product fails to sell as you expected you can cut your losses, find out where you went wrong and rush out a replacement. If a new distribution or marketing initiative doesn't work, you can change it. If a production process causes problems, you can try different manufacturing methods or install new equipment. Even with just-in-time, because it has so many facets, you can often change course and start again on a different tack. Total quality isn't like that: you only get one bite of the cherry; mess it up and you will have difficulty in convincing your people that it's different when you try and start again. The potential rewards of total quality are so great that you shouldn't take any chances. If this is the path you've chosen for your company, my advice is to hire expert assistance; choose external consultants who can demonstrate that they've successfully helped companies that are similar to yours, and stick with them for long enough to make sure that your company too succeeds.

FIVE

TOTAL EMPLOYEE INVOLVEMENT

To become a world-class manufacturer you will need to make better use of your people than ever before: this chapter explains how you can do this. It starts by stressing the key role of teamwork in achieving world-class goals; suggests ways in which resistance to change can be overcome; and explains how to involve people in both step change and continuous improvement type activities. It goes on to consider the arguments for and against introducing quality circles; organizational implications such as 'empowering people' and 'restructuring' to reduce the number of management levels are also considered. The chapter ends with comments on the relative merits of different ways of recognizing and rewarding success. Further guidance on 'getting people involved' can be found in Chapter 13.

5.1 TEAMWORK

Have you ever considered why, when there's a crisis, the 'impossible' often seems to happen? Why is it that productivity performance can achieve an order-of-magnitude improvement overnight – and, unfortunately, slip back again to 'normal' levels once the crisis is over?

Two examples at the national level will illustrate what I mean. The first happened in the UK in 1974, during a long-running strike by coal miners: in order to reduce energy consumption, companies throughout the country were only allowed to operate for three days a week; and yet, even though average hours worked dropped by about a third, gross national product (GNP) during this period fell by only 5 per cent and in many manufacturing companies *output actually rose* – only to revert to the usual daily output levels as soon as normal five-day working was resumed. My second 'crisis' example also occurred in the UK, in this instance shortly after the outbreak of the Falklands war, when there was an urgent need to transport men and equipment to the battle zone: a hastily commandeered passenger liner was converted into a troopship, complete with helicopter deck, *over a weekend*; just think how many weeks or, more likely, months a typical ship repair yard would have quoted for carrying out such a task in normal times! Most companies can think of similar instances when a crisis within their own company has been overcome and previously unheard of levels of productivity achieved, usually for a tantalizingly short time. And in all these cases the 'impossible' was achieved without new machines, without new computers, without even the introduction of JIT or TQ methods – there simply wasn't time. What made things possible was the willingness of people to work as a team, temporarily discarding traditional barriers and suspicions, with everyone involved completely committed to finding the best ways of overcoming the crisis.

The lesson is clear: the best opportunity for achieving a major breakthrough in manufacturing performance will come not so much from investing in new equipment or computers, nor from improving incentive payment schemes, but from making better use than ever before of the skills and experience of your whole workforce. And you'll come to the same conclusion, I believe, if you look behind the scenes at what Japanese manufacturers actually did that has made them so decisively world-class.

Numerous studies of Japanese factories have been carried out by Western manufacturing experts and various theories have been developed to explain why Japanese industry has been so successful in recent years: the development of the just-in-time 'system'; the total quality concept; investment in 'automated' factories; better market research before launching new products; or better product design; each of these has been identified by one expert or another as *the* answer.

Most observers have missed the point altogether: all of these were indeed important, but they were only the *tools*. What has made Japanese manufacturers so successful is the way in which they have consistently harnessed the skills and experience of their whole workforce in the task of 'continuous improvement', while at the same time giving them clear guidance on which sorts of improvement should be given priority. The JIT approach, for example, was developed in response to management stressing the need to achieve an order of magnitude reduction in throughput time and inventory; management philosophies such as 'The Nissan Approach', emphasizing total quality aspects, were developed because companies like Nissan wanted to eliminate the high levels of waste generated in traditional manufacturing organizations, which could be traced back to a failure to 'get it right first time'. But these were only the tools: what made it work, time after time, was the way in which these tools were used by the numerous Kaizen improvement teams set up in every workplace, these teams being made up of the people who owned the problem to be studied, regardless of their respective rank, department or job skills. Japanese managers recognized that those who actually carried out the work on a day-to-day basis were the people who, *as a group*, not only understood every aspect of the problem better than anyone else, but would also be the ones who would have to implement any new ideas, whether these were to do with the production process, or whether they involved administrative procedures or more fundamental changes, such as to the design of the product. Their active involvement was, in short, vital if they were to succeed in their endeavour to eliminate waste and provide an ever-improving quality of service to customers.

The idea of workers getting together in a group to find better ways of doing things fits in well with Japanese culture: in Western culture we place much more emphasis on the individual, so that the process of involving everyone in a team effort to find better ways of manufacturing our products doesn't come so naturally to us. But it *can* be done, as is illustrated by the summary of results included in Chapter 1 and the various case studies throughout this book.

The Japanese concept of 'Total Employee Involvement' encompasses:

- The setting up of teams to tackle both 'strategic projects' and 'local projects', in order to achieve specific performance improvement targets *set by top management.*
- Establishing quality circles within departments to tackle quality or productivity problems *identified by the circle members.*
- Encouraging individuals to set their own personal improvement goals.

In each case the objective is to harness the skills and experience of every member of the workforce in attacking waste and providing an ever-improving service to customers.

The remainder of this chapter is concerned with how this Japanese style of teamwork can best be adapted to suit a Western manufacturing environment. Don't be put off if you've tried teamwork before and it didn't work as well as you hoped: Chapter 13 explains what you can do to make your teams more effective in the future. But first we need to consider *why* attempts to introduce new ways of tackling problems will probably be resisted: if we can understand the underlying reasons for this resistance, we should be able to find ways of overcoming it.

5.2 OVERCOMING RESISTANCE

Unfortunately, in most organizations there is resistance to change, particularly when 'increased productivity' is interpreted by employees as 'fewer jobs'. Generally speaking, the larger the organization, the greater the resistance to change – perhaps because channels of communication from management to shop floor are so much longer and more complex. Certainly, involvement of the workforce and strenuous efforts on the part of management to improving communications can do a lot to enhance the success of any improvement project. The key to this is the need to try to anticipate likely obstacles and conflicts.

Techniques such as brainstorming can be used to identify such roadblocks to success in advance, so that action can be taken to avoid them or, at least, to reduce their impact. However, many potential problems can be readily identified even without any formal analysis. Typical examples, found in many organizations, are:

- The effect on value-added bonus calculations during the period when work-in-progress is being reduced.
- The longer term effect on earnings from incentive schemes as a result of new operating methods.
- Current performance measures, by which the efficiency of operations is judged by management; for example, 'number of standard hours produced', which ignores whether you can actually sell what has been produced; and the conflict between the traditional concepts of 'labour utilization' versus the new concept of 'cash utilization'.

- The effect on the role of foremen and union representatives if workers are involved more directly with improvement projects, which effectively challenges the traditional procedures for authorizing or negotiating new working methods.
- Fears of the shop floor workers when they see their 'bank balance' of work awaiting process reducing.
- The 'not-invented-here' syndrome, particularly among long-serving employees.
- The attitude of 'we've seen it all before – it's just management's latest craze – if we keep our heads down for a few weeks/months it will go away'.
- The conflict of work priorities among those involved in improvement projects (both project staff *and* those they must consult): 'we've still got to produce our planned production – don't have time to help you today'.
- The problems of lack of flexibility between trades, and between jobs within trades, and the learning curves and training requirements brought about by changing working practices.

All these potential problems arise either from *fear* or from *attitudes*.

Fear comes, for example, from a shop floor worker that if productivity improves, fewer people will be required to do the work, and why should employees help management to find ways of destroying their jobs? There may be a fear that earnings will fall, either because over-generous bonus allowances will be eliminated, or because elimination of production problems will reduce the opportunity for overtime work. And there may be fear, in some cases, from skilled workers, that they will lose their 'specialist' skill status when others learn to do tasks which previously only they could do, and they in turn have to learn new tasks for which they may have difficulty in acquiring the necessary skills. Supervisors may fear that they will no longer be in control of their sections, because the new world-class projects will bypass their authority; and, particularly if they became 'top dog' because of years of experience, they will probably be afraid that if things change too much they will no longer be able to cope.

These fears will generally be unspoken and will often not even be recognized consciously by those concerned. But whether they are brought out into the open or not, they will certainly be there and need to be tackled positively if you want to win the cooperation of your workforce. It's not enough for management to say 'Don't worry, we understand the problems and we'll make sure we deal with them if the need arises' because the sort of problems summarized above are so fundamental, and seen by those concerned as so threatening to their personal security, that you have to be very specific about the action you are taking if you want to overcome their concerns. Just how you do this will depend on your particular circumstances, but here are some suggestions, based on what others have done:

- Make it clear that an increase in productivity is essential in order to respond to an expected increase in customers' orders; this may be because you have won a major new source of business, or it may be because you have made sure that one of your first 'key strategic projects' is aimed at increasing sales; whatever the expected source of additional sales, you'll need to have a convincing story if you want to allay fears of job losses – when it comes down to a question of personal security, 'trust me' isn't likely to be enough.
- Give a formal undertaking, preferably in writing, that no one will suffer financially as

a result of any changes implemented under the 'world-class' banner. If the thought of 'guaranteeing' earnings worries you, think of it from their point of view: if *you* were a shop floor worker and suggested to management ways of improving productivity, only to find that your personal bonus earnings dropped as a direct result of them introducing your ideas, what would *you* think? You might not be quite so inclined to come up with any more ideas, and you'd probably pass the word around your fellow workers about how unfairly you'd been treated! If you're not prepared to give your employees an open-ended guarantee that no one will suffer financially, at least consider giving one for a limited period of, say, six months. But be careful to make it clear that you are only protecting bonus earnings against the effects of world-class improvement initiatives (from which the company will gain benefit) and not against any loss of bonus due to a temporary reduction in sales which is not connected with your world-class initiatives.

- If you are intending to streamline your organizational and reporting structure, for example by introducing the 'team leader' concept, before you start talking about the concept with those involved make it a priority to consider what you're going to do with the foremen and supervisors whose roles will disappear. They will probably be long-serving employees with a deep knowledge of your products and manufacturing methods; even if you no longer want to use them in a supervisory role, you may well be able to make good use of their accumulated knowledge, for instance by switching them to the development of new products or new manufacturing methods, or to strengthening your customer support services. If any of these are a possibility, knowledge of what you have in mind would help to allay their fears and so win their cooperation – or, at least, make them less inclined to resist the changes you want to introduce.

- Above all, you need to make it clear to the whole workforce that you believe the company has a long-term future, provided that the changes you are proposing are implemented. This is particularly necessary if you are unable to absorb productivity increases sufficiently through increased sales, so that some redundancies become unavoidable. Over the years many workers have got used to the idea that periodic reductions in the workforce are inevitable; they will resist them, because even if they're not personally on the list this time, they may well be next time. They will also be unwilling to cooperate in productivity improvements, because they believe this would only bring that 'next time' closer. However, if you really *are* going to make your company world-class, you should be able in the future to reverse the decline and get back on to a steady growth path which will provide long-term job security for your workforce. Once they believe that, you shouldn't have any difficulty in gaining their cooperation.

Attitude problems, when people persistently fail to give the commitment and co-operation expected by management, will often have their roots in fear, but there can be other causes which need to be recognized and tackled. The three most commonly found are a resentment of criticism because 'I know best how to do my job'; a deep rooted commitment to traditional priorities, so that overcoming today's problems always takes precedence over efforts to improve future performance; and a feeling that any improvements achieved will primarily benefit 'management' – often expressed as 'What's in it for us?'.

The essence of the world-class concept is to continually challenge the way in which tasks are carried out, to try to find better ways of doing things. Few people would argue against that in principle, but when it comes down to challenging the way they do their own jobs they are less easy to convince: it always seems to be someone else's job that can be done better, not their own. People resent others criticizing how they do something; and in case you're nodding your head and saying 'Yes, they do, don't they', you (and I) are just as bad – just think how you reacted last time anyone said something that was in any way critical about your driving! And that's not even your professional job expertise that's being criticized. We need to create a climate where everybody is looking all the time for better ways of doing their job and welcomes ideas that will help them achieve this. I find it helps to get this message across if you remind people about someone like Nick Faldo. Even while he was officially ranked as the world's best golfer, he still enlisted the help of a coach, David Leadbetter, to find ways of improving his technique, and his 'job performance' improved as a result, demonstrating that however good you are at your job, even if you're the best in the world, it's worth getting someone else to see how you might do things better. The department purpose analysis procedure, described in Sec. 12.3, suggests how this attitude problem can be tackled by considering internal customer–supplier dependencies and getting everyone to ask themselves 'what can be done to make it easier for me to do my job more effectively?'.

The second attitude problem, a failure to recognize that priorities have changed, applies particularly to middle management levels. The problem arises because these are the people who have the prime responsibility for keeping the company running on a day-to-day basis: if customers complain, or if production targets aren't met, they are the ones who are called to account. And they usually have so many things to do that when they leave work each day there's still a long list of uncompleted tasks that they haven't had time to deal with. Then along comes top management with a new idea called 'world-class'; little wonder that their first reaction is often 'Oh no, yet more work for me and I'm still left with all my normal responsibilities. How am I going to find the time?'. In most cases, when they fail to turn up for 'world-class' team meetings, or hinder the team's progress in other ways, they're not being deliberately obstructive: they genuinely believe that their assessment of priorities is what's best for the company. They're unlikely to change their views until they see step change improvements happening as a result of the world-class projects and see the day-to-day problems they have to deal with reducing as a result, but that will take time – longer than you can afford to wait, particularly since without their support progress may be very difficult. This may well mean that, to start with, you will have to do a certain amount of 'arm twisting', so that it becomes less trouble for them to swim with the world-class tide than to resist it:

- Start by explaining the Chief Executive's personal commitment to the world-class initiatives, and reinforce this by getting each member of the top management team to tell their managers that they too are personally committed.
- Reaffirm this commitment each month by putting 'world-class progress reports' at the top of the agenda for your company and departmental management meetings.
- Hold an inquest whenever anyone fails to attend a meeting or complete a task connected with the world-class projects because they're 'too busy'.
- Set time management targets for managers, with the proportion of their time that should be spent on world class initiatives clearly specified (further details on this

are included in Sec. 13.1); having set targets, actual achievement should then be monitored regularly, and those concerned may well need guidance on how to manage their time better.

• Above all, *be careful not to send out the wrong signals*: middle managers are used to their top management going hot and cold over new ideas and will interpret any action that they perceive as backsliding on your part as a sign that your so-called commitment is waning; postponing a planned 'world-class' progress meeting with top management, or diverting a key member of the team to another unrelated task, or overriding 'marginal' quality rejections in order to meet production targets are all typical of the misleading signals that you should try to avoid.

The third type of attitude problem commonly found, that only 'management' will benefit from performance improvements, usually disappears of its own accord as people start to take pride in what they have been able to achieve when given the chance. The concept of 'empowering people' (explained in Chapter 13) is the key to this, but you can help psychologically in the way in which you talk about your company's strengths. For example, Vokes Limited, who are the subject of a case study in Chapter 1, can rightly claim to be 'one of the top filtration equipment manufacturers in the world' but that's essentially a *management* or *customer-oriented* view, which employees at the sharp end won't necessarily relate to; with the increasing success of their world-class teams, the message within the company has been changed subtly to 'our people are the best filter makers in the world'; in other words, what their people are now beginning to say is 'It's not just Vokes that is the best, it's *us*, our team, that keeps Vokes in front'.

Conflicts and obstacles will *always* be present when one tries to bring about fundamental change. This is why management as a whole needs to be seen to be fully committed to achieving the objectives of any changes proposed. If success is to be achieved it has to be made more painful for those directly involved to *resist* change than it is for them to *cooperate* in bringing about the change. This message will need to be reinforced continually, particularly during the first year or two, until *pride* in what has been achieved, *pride* in the company and *pride* in the individuals' roles take over as the driving force. If the message is *not* continuously repeated in the early stages then the inherent inertia, present in any large organization, will win in the end.

The remainder of this chapter is concerned with the different ways in which you can get people throughout your company involved in both step change and continuous improvement activities: further details are provided in Chapter 13.

5.3 STRATEGIC IMPROVEMENT TEAMS

Chapter 2 explained the procedure for developing a world-class strategy, culminating in Sec. 2.6 in the selection of action priorities. These action priorities provide the basis for specifying a number of key strategic projects, and a team needs to be set up to tackle each of these.

Becoming a world-class manufacturer usually involves a change of culture right across the company. I believe strongly that such a fundamental change cannot be achieved simply through a programme of continuous improvement based solely on the accumulation of many small improvements. A step change improvement is necessary in some area (or areas) which everyone recognizes will have a real impact on the company's competitive edge. This means that the improvement targets for your strategic projects need to be ambitious: for example, if you decide that a key task should be the reduction of lead time from the current level of, say, 15 weeks, then a target of 6 to 8 weeks would concentrate everyone's minds much more effectively than a target of 12 weeks. Everyone would realize that fundamental changes would have to be made, so that all existing practices would have to be challenged – *nothing* would be sacred.

I referred earlier to a difficulty that nearly always has to be faced when you are trying to bring about a change of culture: that the people who are most able to achieve the required improvements will probably already have a heavy workload. Their natural instinct will be to give priority to their traditional tasks of day-to-day management, i.e. fire-fighting and overcoming immediate problems; they will normally put a lower priority on tasks aimed at improving manufacturing efficiency as being 'tomorrow's problem'. This is another reason why you need initially to select key projects that will clearly have an important impact on your company's competitive edge, so that senior managers will willingly provide the commitment (and enforce the discipline) to ensure that the initial momentum is maintained right through to final achievement of the objectives.

Once you have selected your key strategic projects, and top management have agreed the objectives, you need to prepare terms of reference for each of them; these should be set out clearly on a Project Briefing Sheet. Ideally you should try to get the whole of the briefing on to one sheet of paper, so that everyone concerned (including the directors) is encouraged to read it properly, without being tempted to skip over the detail. The typical contents of a project briefing sheet are:

- **Project name**
- **Background** (explaining the reasons for the project and why achievement of the objectives is important to the company)
- **Improvement objectives** (with quantified objectives to be achieved on a specified time-scale)
- **Reporting arrangements** (saying which director will act as the team's 'Champion', providing whatever support and top level authority the team may require)
- **Project group members** (and which of them will act as facilitator to the team)

Some examples of project briefing sheets are shown in Sec. 13.2.

You will usually find that your selected projects cross traditional departmental boundaries – if they didn't they would probably have been solved before now. This means that project group members need to be drawn from several departments. I've found that this is a very important part of achieving a change in culture: team members, often for the first time, start seeing what is happening from an overall company point of view, instead of just in terms of how it affects the work of their own department. They get to know 'outsiders' from other departments through working with them in the project group and find to their surprise that they are not the incompetent, obstructive 'enemy' that they've considered them to be in the past! New relationships develop and contacts of the 'Old Boy' type are built up between individuals from different departments who have worked together on key projects: these are used to break down the old barriers between departments long after the project is finished.

In addition to crossing departmental boundaries, the members of each project group may well be drawn from a variety of disciplines, ranging across the company structure. However, they will all have one characteristic in common: they are the people who 'own' the problem that the project team have been asked to tackle. For example, a group charged with the task of reducing the assembly time of a portable compressor unit would probably include a process planner, a production engineer, a production supervisor, a designer and, most importantly, the fitter who actually assembles it. These are the people who, *as a group*, understand every aspect of the problem *and* have to implement any new ideas, whether these are to do with the production process itself, or whether they involve changes to the design or the tooling. Between them they own the problem; they are the best equipped to develop the solution to the problem; they are the *only* ones who have the ability and the authority to make the solution work: *they* are the ones who need to own the solution and be personally committed to making it work. Ignore them at your peril! If you leave them out of the group (for whatever reason), don't be surprised if they get in the way of a successful project.

In addition to those who own the problem, every improvement team should also include a couple of members who are not involved in the problem as part of their normal day-to-day responsibilities. Their role is to challenge existing practices and pre-conceived ideas, introducing 'wild' ideas without risk of losing face, which may well stimulate the experts to develop more realistic and innovative solutions themselves from the original wild idea. One of these 'outsiders' should be nominated as facilitator, to coordinate the group's activities: if you ask one of the owners to act as facilitator, the other owners will usually be less committed to the project because they will see it as a takeover bid.

Further guidance on the selection of team members, and on how to make the work of their team more effective, can be found in Sec. 13.1.

Finally, when setting up your improvement teams, don't forget to make sure that the majority of those involved have had appropriate training in group working and problem solving techniques. This is dealt with in Sec. 5.7.

5.4 LOCAL IMPROVEMENT TEAMS

Resist the temptation to set up too many strategic improvement teams. I've found that three or four projects at any one time are about right for most companies. Fewer than this may fail to make a sufficient impression across the company and, in any case, not every project succeeds (although most do): if you start with only one or two projects and one unfortunately fails to live up to expectations, you won't have created the sort of impact that's necessary to stimulate enthusiasm for your world-class campaign. On the other hand, if you try to tackle more than about four projects at the same time you may well find that management effort is dissipated, there is too much interference with the day-to-day running of the company's operations, and as a result the commitment of top management to the work of the project teams could start to slip.

However, once you've started to get results from your initial projects, you can start building on these foundations by spreading the involvement in teamwork to as many of your workforce as possible, *but not through involvement in key strategic projects*, for the reasons explained above. The way to achieve this is to encourage teams to be set up to deal with problems which are mainly confined within one department: you will usually find that little encouragement is needed – once you start to get good results from your key strategic projects you will usually find that others want to get involved and come up with their own ideas for projects; the problem is making sure that these fit in with your world-class improvement objectives. A local improvement project should be authorized at the departmental level and the team should report periodically to the department's own management team, although the Head of Department should keep the company's top management team informed of progress so that they have an overall view of the various world-class initiatives that are taking place across the company.

When approving a local improvement project you will need to consider whether the departmental team will need some outside specialist support from one or more central service functions such as Design, Accounts, Engineering or Computing. It is also useful to include one or two non-experts from other departments to ensure that preconceived ideas and existing practices are properly challenged. Make sure that the person nominated as facilitator is one of the independent members of the group and not a principal owner of the problem.

Finally, to ensure that work on the local improvement project doesn't interfere too much with day-to-day operations, allow a longer elapsed time before the team is asked to report (compared with the time-scale of a key strategic project). However, if you want results, having agreed to a longer elapsed time *make sure that the team sticks to the agreed target completion dates*.

An example of a local improvement project is shown in Sec. 13.3.

5.5 QUALITY CIRCLES – PROS AND CONS

Quality circles are used extensively in Japan, where they are an essential element of the continuous improvement programme in most manufacturing organizations. The usual procedure is for each department (across the whole company, not just in manufacturing) to organize its own quality circle, with membership being *on a voluntary basis*. All workers are encouraged to bring any ideas they have for improvements to their quality circle's facilitator, who ensures that it receives proper consideration – this is important: *every* idea is considered. Although the team is called a 'quality' circle, it is actually used to consider any ideas for improving the efficient use of the department's resources, since in Japan a central feature of quality improvement is *the elimination of waste*.

The concept of quality circles has been introduced in a number of companies in the West, sometimes under the name of 'productivity circles' to ensure that ideas are not limited to purely quality problems. However, in most cases quality circles in the West have not lived up to expectations. The usual explanation for this is 'lack of management commitment'. If we look at the pros and cons we can perhaps see why.

5.5.1 The Pros

- Everyone who wants to be involved can be.
- *Employees* select improvement tasks which *they* consider to be important.
- Because *they* have selected the tasks, they will put more effort into making the solutions work.

- The ability to bring problems to the attention of management, and know that they will be properly considered, acts as a safety valve to avoid the build-up of frustrations which could otherwise develop into an industrial relations problem and 'them and us' attitudes.
- There is a chain reaction in making the whole workforce more conscious of the need for continuous improvement and, hopefully, greater customer awareness.

5.5.2 The Cons

- There is a tendency for teams to concentrate on ways of improving 'personal comforts', such as environmental, welfare or health and safety aspects, which are seen by management as incurring costs with no direct or quantifiable benefits to the company.
- Even where quality or productivity matters *are* considered, a lot of time and effort may be spent on investigating problems and implementing solutions that don't have any great impact on the company's competitive edge (i.e. its profitability, or improvements that encourage a potential customer to want to buy from you instead of from your competitors).
- Because ideas are often less significant, there is a danger that management support will slip, with a knock-on effect to the credibility of the whole world-class initiative.

This latter point explains why so many quality circle initiatives in the West have failed to live up to expectations. It is so important that personally I do not favour the 'bottom-up' quality circle approach until you are at least a year into your world-class programme and have already completed the bulk of your initial step change projects. In other words, I suggest that quality circles are *not* suitable when you are trying to *become* a world-class manufacturer, but are only appropriate in the later stages as part of your efforts to *maintain* your world-class status through a continuous improvement programme which will involve your whole workforce; by then you will usually find that management doesn't actually need to initiate the concept – the initiative will nearly always come from one or more groups of workers who have seen the results of the step change projects and want to get involved themselves. Management can then respond by agreeing to them forming a 'continuous improvement group' (a much better name in my view than 'quality circle'). Once the first continuous improvement group has started to get results, you can get *them* to talk to workers in other departments to explain what they've done; all management will have to do is to provide encouragement and whatever training may be appropriate (Sec. 13.4 includes guidance on what training might be needed).

5.6 PERSONAL COMMITMENTS

It's the task of top management to decide where the company is going, and what needs to be done to get it there, but it's the managers and supervisors across the company who then actually make it happen. If these managers and supervisors spend all their time on 'fire-fighting' and the day-to-day running of the company *without* devoting part of their time to 'moving the business forward', then the company will stagnate – and in time it will die.

If you want your company to be world-class, you *have* to ensure that every one of your managers and supervisors realizes that it is not sufficient for them just to carry out their day-to-day operational tasks efficiently, they must also reserve part of their time for improving the company's competitive edge: indirectly, through finding ways of carrying out the operations of their department more cost-effectively; or directly, by improving some aspect of customer service.

To get them into the habit of doing this I suggest that you should get each of them to agree with his or her boss a 'personal commitment' task. This need not be a major undertaking – in fact it *shouldn't* be something that will take up too much of the individual's time. I usually suggest a task that will require on average not more than two hours per week, and possibly as little as half an hour per week. Here are some examples of personal commitments I've seen specified:

- **A Production Manager**: 'I know I spend too much time fire-fighting short-term problems and so never have enough time left to stop the same type of problem recurring repeatedly. I *have* to break out of this vicious circle: I propose to start using a simple form of time management to force myself to delegate some of my routine work and reserve at least some of my time to plan *preventative* measures.'
- **An Inventory Manager**: 'We have a problem with customer returns – there is no control mechanism to check if the goods are returned because of some fault on our part, or simply because customers have changed their minds. If it's the latter, our standard terms of business allow us to make a handling charge, but because we're never sure why the goods are returned we have to assume it's our fault – I estimate this has cost us over £50,000 in the last twelve months. I propose, as my task, to design and implement a new customer returns system.'
- **A Site Manager**: 'I propose to investigate ways of reducing the site telephone costs through the use of call logging and reporting equipment, and trunk call route optimizing via Mercury's "smart box". I've set myself a target reduction of between 15 and 20 per cent within six months.'
- **Sales Forecasting Manager**: 'The team working on stock reduction has identified that over £500,000 of our current inventory is obsolete. In order to stop the build-up of obsolete stock in the future, I propose to design and implement an effective obsolescence procedure, to ensure the proper communication of information to enable the efficient run-down of stocks when the decision is taken to make a product obsolete.'

You won't always get such positive thinking when you ask your people to propose their individual personal commitment towards 'moving the business forward', and you may find that you need to provide some training in basic management skills to help them adapt to new ways of working.

To make sure that those involved do more than just pay lip service to their personal commitments, I suggest that you introduce a formal structure as follows:

- Once every three months, bring all your managers and supervisors together, in groups of about 15 to 20, with the directors present.
- In the first meeting, get each manager and supervisor in turn to state his or her proposed personal commitment task for the next three months; the directors should either approve or suggest amendments to the task, and whatever is agreed

should be written down there and then and read back, to ensure that there is no misunderstanding.

- At the next three-monthly reporting session, each manager and supervisor should be asked to report on progress to date, and then agree with the directors present whether he or she should continue with the same task for a further three months or undertake a new personal commitment.

Those of you who are familiar with 'management by objectives' (MBO) will recognize the similarities. The differences are that a personal commitment is concerned solely with moving the business forward, whereas MBO is often concerned with day-to-day operational targets; a personal commitment target doesn't have to be quantifiable, with actual achievement against target measured, as is usually the case with MBO; personal commitments are usually limited to just one task at a time and updated quarterly, while MBO usually involves several targets which are only reviewed annually. There's no reason why you shouldn't use MBO in parallel with the personal commitments method, provided that you recognize their different purposes: use MBO as a means of managing the way in which people carry out their duties, agreeing a range of improvement goals for the next 12 months and then periodically measuring progress towards achieving those goals; use personal commitments as a way of involving managers and supervisors *publicly* in the continuous improvement process, as part of your world-class initiatives, ensuring that the tasks can be completed on a short enough time-scale to demonstrate *achievement* (i.e. not just good intentions), as an example for others to follow.

Changing a company's culture is never easy. Most consultants who work in this field will tell you that the key to success is to get the company's *middle management* to change: if you can do that, the rest will follow. I've found that getting every one of the company's managers and supervisors involved in the personal commitment process, reporting formally to the top management team *in the presence of their peer group* once every three months, can play an important part in bringing about change. Even those most prone to resisting change usually give way rather than having to report 'no progress' in front of their peer group!

5.7 TRAINING AND DEVELOPMENT

5.7.1 The People Plan

I said in Chapter 1 that 'people are the key to achieving and then maintaining your world-class goal'. If you are to succeed in making better use of your people than ever before, then you will need to pay as much attention to investing in training and staff development as you do to investing in areas such as your manufacturing facilities and your sales and marketing activities: training in job skills, to improve quality and productivity performance and to increase flexibility; training in management skills, so that managers and supervisors are properly equipped to make the best use of their people; and training in the world-class approach, so that everyone fully understands the concepts and knows how to use the world-class techniques to improve operating methods and procedures.

Towards the end of 1991, as part of the British Government's initiative to raise the political profile of training, their Department of Employment launched a new 'National Standard for Effective Investment in People'. The main points of this standard are:

- 'An Investor in People makes a public commitment from the top to develop all employees to achieve its business objectives.'
- 'An Investor in People regularly reviews the training and development needs of all employees.'
- 'An Investor in People takes action to train and develop individuals on recruitment and throughout their employment.'
- 'An Investor in People evaluates the investment in training and development to assess achievement and improve future effectiveness.'

The Investors in People standard is very relevant to any company that intends to become (and then remain) world-class, wherever it is located; if your company is based in the UK there's the added bonus of obtaining the government's seal of approval for your achievements in the form of an Investor in People award, enabling you to use the official logo on you stationery and publicity material. If you comply with its requirements, you will include the preparation of a People Plan as part of your corporate planning cycle, linking the training and development needs of your workforce to the requirements for achieving your business plan. This should include consideration of whether each individual is in the most suitable post to enable the best use to be made of his or her experience, talents and ambition. Removing square pegs from round holes and putting them where they fit better will usually benefit the company as much as the individual, particularly at a time when you are making major changes in the way in which you operate. It's an obvious opportunity for improvement, but one so often overlooked. However, to make the most of this opportunity you will probably first need to train the managers concerned in the necessary interview, selection and testing techniques. Some managements have gone so far as to invest in psychometric testing as an effective way of revealing hidden talents, but useful as this testing can be, many employees are likely to be suspicious of a technique of this type and I would be concerned, therefore, that it might prove counter-productive at a time when you are trying to improve cooperation and understanding between management and workforce.

Some specific human resource aspects that you will need to consider when preparing your business plan are covered in Sec. 13.5. The Bibliography includes details of where further information can be found on the Investor in People standard.

5.7.2 Training in Job Skills

I referred in Chapter 3 to the need for moving towards a more multi-skilled workforce in order to improve manufacturing flexibility. This helps to overcome the problem often experienced when JIT is introduced and you can no longer cope with fluctuations in demand by simply drawing from stock: instead, you must plan to move people around, both within and between departments, to match capacity more effectively with load. The resource/skills matrix, described in Sec. 3.6, is a good way of identifying where training in operational skills is needed in order to improve performance and provide the degree of flexibility you require. The results of a resource/skills analysis for each part of the company can then be consolidated into a company-wide training plan and estimates of cost prepared for consideration by management. You will probably find that the total cost involved when you do this for the first time is more than even the most enlightened management would be prepared to authorize, so that inevitably decisions will need to be taken on priorities, *taking into account the company's strategic plans*: the People Plan will then show the training programme approved for the current year.

5.7.3 Training in Management Skills

You will also need to consider how best to improve the basic management skills of your managers and supervisors, to help them become better 'professional' managers. You could arrange formal in-plant classroom sessions for this, but I find that this approach isn't usually very successful, particularly since their individual needs are likely to be different. External courses may be appropriate in some cases, but would be expensive and would be dependent for their usefulness on the ability of the people concerned to translate what they have learnt on the course into practical application in their particular environment. I prefer to use a tutorial approach, tailored to suit individuals or small groups, using a structured self-improvement process based on check-lists. Suggestions on how to do this are included in Sec. 13.4. As with training in job skills, management will need to consider costs and priorities for training in management skills and the agreed programme should then be incorporated in the People Plan.

Before leaving the subject of management training, for the benefit of readers in the UK I should mention the Management Charter Initiative (MCI); formed in 1988, its objective is 'to improve the performance of UK organisations by improving the quality of UK managers'. MCI is the officially appointed 'Lead Body' in the UK for developing National Standards of Performance for managers and supervisors. Although at an early stage of development, there are already a number of Management Standards agreed which are closely linked to the National and Scottish Vocational Qualification frameworks (these provide NVQ/SVQ qualifications for virtually all jobs and professions). Although the NVQ/SVQ schemes are specific to the UK, the standards which are being laid down by MCI for assessing the professional competence of managers and supervisors, and the associated 'Management Standards Implementation Pack' and 'Computer Based Assessment System', will be relevant wherever your company is located. Contact details for MCI are included in the Bibliography.

5.7.4 Training to be World-Class

Many readers will be familiar with the types of training considered so far: some may even be putting them into practice! The main differences will lie in the increased emphasis on training and in the way in which training needs are linked to the strategy review to ensure that the workforce as a whole have the necessary skills to achieve the company's corporate objectives.

To complete the process you will also need to train people so that they become a truly world-class workforce. The first task will be to make sure, through 'awareness' seminars, that everyone understands the world-class concepts; those who will be involved in the initial key strategic projects will then need specific training in the appropriate techniques and in problem analysis and problem solving methods. These will eventually need to be extended (in a less detailed form) to the whole workforce, but I suggest you leave this until you are ready to launch the continuous improvement groups referred to above. Let the key project teams act as pioneers: leave the training of others until they are ready to put the training into practice; if you do it too early they may have forgotten what they have been taught when the time eventually comes for them to apply it.

5.7.5 Target-Oriented Training

A final word of caution: most people will welcome an increased emphasis on training, seeing it as a tangible sign of management's confidence in the company's future and a commitment to its employees. However, all too often the benefits of training are lost because those receiving it either don't have the opportunity to put it into practice while it's still fresh in their minds, or are unable to see how to apply it to their day-to day activities. If you want to get full value from your investment in training you should try to ensure that it is 'target-oriented', with people being given training to equip them to achieve specific improvement targets; alternatively, the training should be structured as 'action learning', where part of the training plan includes carrying out tasks in which they have to put into practice what they have just learnt and then discuss the outcome with their instructor. Always remember that training starts off as a cost: the *benefit* comes from applying the training successfully.

5.8 ORGANIZATIONAL IMPLICATIONS

Once the teamwork approach is well established, and you've found that empowering people actually gets things done, you may well want to reconsider the whole question of your management structure. Does it make sense any longer to have quite so many layers of managers – people who have to be consulted before anyone can do anything, people who often find it easier to say 'No' than 'Yes' to new ideas? If the teamwork approach can be so successful in bringing about major improvements of the step change type, why not apply it to the management of day-to-day operations as well?

Many companies have already gone some way down this path in recent years, breaking their organization down into a number of business-oriented divisions, and giving much more autonomy to divisional management in how they run their day-to-day operations. However, the traditional hierarchical management structure usually survives, even if the pyramid is rather smaller than before; as a result the overall number of middle managers probably hasn't changed much. Perhaps it *would* be better to go the whole hog and turn the divisions into separate teams such as 'the machine shop team', 'the widget assembly team' and 'the technical support team'. The management structure could then be very flat because each team would have just one boss, who would report directly to the Divisional Manager; or perhaps you could do away with the Divisional Manager as well and have the Team Leaders all reporting directly to an Operations Director (or even to the Chief Executive)? One company that has done just that is Barr & Stroud: their story is told in Sec. 13.6.

Reducing the number of management layers follows naturally from the empowering people principle that often goes with effective teamwork. Once people get used to the idea of using their initiative instead of relying on others to give them orders, then the need for so many managers starts to disappear. That's when you can really start to make progress, because the managers and supervisors who are no longer needed for day-to-day decision-making can be switched to tasks such as developing new products or processes, or providing technical support to customers – tasks that will make full use of the skills and experience they have accumulated over the years. Each of the individual operating teams, meanwhile, will be free to develop the family spirit of a small business while still retaining all the financial and marketing advantages of being part of a larger organization. That, surely, should be the ultimate goal of total employee involvement.

5.9 REWARDING SUCCESS

Many companies have some form of payment linked to effort or achievement, ranging from shop floor incentive schemes, through commission for sales people, to profit-related bonuses for top management. So it's not surprising that people working on key strategic projects sometimes ask if they will receive a special bonus if they achieve their project objectives. After all, they say, the company will benefit greatly as a direct result of our work and we deserve some recognition for all the extra hours and effort we will have put in, *in addition to continuing to carry out our normal duties*.

It's a persuasive argument, but personally I'm against making any directly related extra payments. There are several reasons for this:

- A majority of the members of the team are there because they are 'owners' of the problem, and as such they should not be paid extra for doing something which is part of their normal duties – even if they *have* had to put in more hours.
- If, for this reason, you don't pay a bonus to the members of the team who are 'owners', it wouldn't be fair to pay one to the two or three team members who are not.
- Some project objectives are easier to achieve than others; some can be achieved quickly, others may take a year or two to complete: this makes it very difficult to make any rewards system fair.
- I've suggested that you should not tackle more than three or four key strategic projects at a time; this means that there will be people in other departments who might want to be involved in projects, but can't because management don't want to start another project yet – they might well resent others getting a reward that was not open to them.
- Finally, and most importantly, being world-class requires the involvement and co-operation of the whole workforce across the company, working together to find ways to improve operational efficiency and customer service; paying rewards selectively to specific groups would be divisive and therefore contrary to the spirit of your world-class initiative.

In practice, I've found that most people readily accept that there will be no direct reward (even when they've asked for one!). They recognize that it is the long-term future of their company, and therefore their own job security that is at stake. In addition, for many of them it is their first chance to be involved in a high-profile activity that enables them to demonstrate their abilities to senior management. I've seen many instances where involvement in a key strategic project has led to individuals being promoted to greater responsibility as a direct result of their having become more 'visible'. To most people, recognition for a job well done is actually more important than a monetary reward, so make sure you show your appreciation, and do so publicly (perhaps through a quarterly *World-Class Newsletter*). If you feel you must go further, consider celebrating a successful project with a team dinner or family outing.

A related problem arises in companies which already operate a suggestion scheme. Should they allow the scheme to continue and, if so, how do they stop it conflicting with their various world-class initiatives? I had an interesting example of this some years ago in one of my first world-class projects. The team worked late one evening, brainstorming ideas for reducing lead time. First thing next morning, someone who at first sight had no connection with the team put in a suggestion identical to one of the ideas developed in the brainstorming session. Further investigation brought an admission from one of the team members that the person who submitted the suggestion was his wife's brother: they had both expected that the suggestion would be disqualified, but they thought it worth a try! Ever since that experience I have made a point of warning managements to make a policy statement on how their suggestion scheme will be affected *before* launching their world-class projects. My usual advice is to suspend the scheme until they are two or three years into the world-class campaign, i.e. wait until they are ready to launch 'continuous improvement groups' and then consider re-launching the suggestions scheme as an alternative way of involving the whole workforce. Even then, I'm rather against the idea, since the experience of most companies is that the majority of suggestions come from only a small percentage of the total workforce (an excellent example of the Pareto Principle!).

Finally, don't forget to look at what sort of incentive schemes are in use in your factory. If these are based on individual performance measures, such as piece-work or 'standard hours produced', you will almost certainly have to change them: firstly, because the changes you will be introducing as a result of your improvement projects will usually affect the measures of standard performance on which the incentive payments are based and secondly, because individual bonus arrangements are likely to get in the way of introducing greater flexibility of labour. Group schemes may still be relevant, particularly if you change your organizational structure along the lines described in the previous section, but you may also need to consider introducing company-wide or divisional bonuses based on some measure of overall business performance, or the achievement of specific world-class performance objectives.

WORLD-CLASS INFORMATION SYSTEMS

A world-class manufacturer needs world-class systems. This chapter explains how tradi-
tional information and control systems may need to be modified to suit the differing require-
ments of a world-class environment, suggests which elements of existing systems will still
be needed and what new types of information reports may be necessary. Further details on
activity-based costing and on the monitoring of world-class performance can be found in
Chapter 14.

6.1 ADAPTING TO WORLD-CLASS NEEDS

Manufacturing companies in the West have always placed a lot of emphasis on developing new and better computer systems as a means of improving manufacturing performance – far more so than has been the case in Japan. If better computer systems were
indeed the answer, we would expect to find that manufacturing performance in the West
was therefore much better than in Japan. Of course it isn't, and that fact alone should
be sufficient to make us reconsider our faith in systems as a prime tool for improving
efficiency.

By now I am sure you will have realized that a far more effective approach is to start
by reducing the number of things that can go wrong in your manufacturing processes,
simplifying them by eliminating wasteful activities and shortening process times, instead
of developing systems which expect complexities and try to cope with them. You need to
treat some of the advice you'll get on this subject with extreme caution: serious money
is involved and a whole industry exists to 'help' companies find the best solution to
their systems problems; hardware manufacturers, software developers and consultants
who specialize in advising clients on selecting and implementing systems have all made a

considerable investment in using the power of computers to bring order out of chaos. Inevitably, much that has been written reflects these vested interests, either directly by those whose livelihood is at stake, or indirectly by those who have been converted by the propaganda. However, don't be too cynical: you probably *will* need the help of all of them at some point if you want to make your systems world-class, but try to hold them off until you have a better understanding of what *you* need to support your world-class initiatives: systems should *support* the changes you are introducing; don't try to use them to *drive* the process of change.

Once you've cut out much of the wasteful activity and greatly simplified the processes by applying the JIT techniques described in Chapters 3 and 11, you'll usually find that your views about what systems you need will have changed significantly. This doesn't mean that you will need to throw away your existing systems and start again – far from it. Few businesses today can operate successfully without the support of comprehensive computer systems, and you are still likely to need all the key elements with which you are probably quite familiar. What will be different is the way in which you will want to make use of the information; the emphasis will change from a system which effectively tells you what to do to one which provides you with key information to enable you to continually improve performance. In most cases you will find that although some changes to existing systems may well be required, much of what you need will already be there: all you have to do is to decide what you need and then work out how best to 'unlock' it from the system's database. Most modern systems provide query or report-generating facilities to enable you to do this without too much difficulty.

Ideally, then, you should *not* start out by considering how you want to change or develop your systems. The best approach is to launch your improvement projects in the way already explained: wait until these throw up problems, or lack of important information, which lead you to recognize the need for doing something to your systems. In this way, you concentrate your efforts on system developments or changes which will make a direct contribution to those key improvement objectives that have been identified by management as important for the company's future success. Your computer experts will probably be able to satisfy many of your requirements without too much difficulty, but you may well find that they get asked to do more than they can cope with in a reasonable time-scale. In this event you may need to set up a project group to coordinate the requirements of the various improvement teams and to decide priorities or even assist with the preparation of a justification for further investment in computer facilities. If you do this, make sure that this computer group includes members from each of the teams involved, so that their needs are properly assessed when priorities are allocated. A word of warning: don't allow improvement teams to report that they are unable to achieve their objectives because they are 'waiting for the Computer Department'. Their improvement tasks are usually so important that, if they can't get their preferred computer-based solution within a time-scale acceptable to them, they must find an alternative temporary solution, even if this means relying on a makeshift manual method.

Unfortunately, the ideal approach I've described above won't always be feasible. Your current systems may be so unreliable and so inflexible that you just can't afford to delay replacing them. If this really is the case, and you have to go ahead with developing new systems as a matter of urgency, try to make sure that you choose systems that are as flexible as possible so that you can adapt how you use them as your needs change. And, above all, don't use this as an excuse for delaying the start of your other world-class initiatives: these will start delivering benefits of much greater value, and much sooner, than you can ever hope to achieve from systems alone; more than enough, in most cases, to pay for the new systems and computer hardware.

To sum up: a world-class manufacturer needs world-class information systems. You will probably find that much of what you require can be obtained from your existing systems, but you may need to use the information in a different way from at present and you will probably need to change or develop parts of your systems to enable you to extract additional information about your operations and performance, or to overcome problems due to inaccurate data. These topics are considered in general terms in the remainder of this chapter and in more depth in Chapter 14. You will find out what *you* need to do when you start working on strategic improvement projects, and discover what shortcomings there might be in your existing systems.

6.2 INFORMATION FOR PLANNING AND CONTROL

This includes the parts of the systems concerned with capturing customer order details, maintaining parts lists and product structures, sources of components (supplier information for bought-out materials and process details for made-in), details of current stocks and outstanding supply orders, consolidation of orders for planning purposes (e.g. MRP details), and so on.

As you increasingly adopt world-class practices, how will your need for systems change? You'll probably find that you continue to use computer systems for planning your longer term material requirements from suppliers (although the number of these suppliers will be much reduced). Shorter term planning and control needs will be simplified through the introduction of techniques such as Kanban, and some of the more detailed planning and reordering procedures will be taken over by those suppliers to whom you entrust responsibility for keeping specified racks and bins topped up in your stores or alongside your assembly lines. Within your factory, simplified manufacturing paths (following the introduction of improved flow lines, cells and 'focused' factories) will not require complex planning and scheduling systems.

In general, the main parts of your present systems are unlikely to need much in the way of change, other than to improve accuracy (this is covered briefly in Sec. 6.5, and in more detail in Sec. 14.7). However, you will need to alter some of the control parameters to reflect the new operational methods, particularly those concerned with the various JIT aspects covered in Chapter 3 (as you may remember, MRP is essentially a 'push' system, whereas JIT is a 'pull' system). For example, although the same explosion of top-level assemblies into component parts will be needed, you will almost certainly want to change the batching rules in the MRP module to reflect the new JIT requirements: many companies get round this simply by altering the standard batch quantity to 1 for all items, so that the decision on batching-up is left to the planner. Standard set-off times, used in the MRP module, will also need to be changed to reflect the reduction in production cycle time, and you may need to make much wider use of call-off schedules, as a result of introducing Kanbans or 'supermarket' supply methods (see Secs. 3.7 and 3.8 respectively).

If one of your key strategic objectives is to reduce lead time, you will probably need to modify your order processing procedures to ensure that new orders are entered into the computer system more quickly, and that special materials, particularly those with long lead times, are identified and supply orders placed at the earliest possible point. Similarly, if your systems include a module for preparing despatch notes and/or delivery schedules, changes will probably be needed to replace existing weekly delivery cycles with new '24 hours' despatch arrangements.

There may well be other aspects of your existing systems that need to be reviewed and perhaps changed; these will depend on your improvement objectives and on the problems that you identify as needing to be overcome if you are to achieve those objectives.

6.3 INFORMATION FOR MONITORING

Most people would accept that if you want to control and improve performance, you first need to measure it so that you can find out what is actually happening at present. Unfortunately, the emphasis in most monitoring systems is on obtaining financial control information, such as quantity and value of stocks, net cost of sales, fixed assets and liabilities, all of which are required for the compilation of the financial reports, i.e. the Profit and Loss Statement and Balance Sheet required by law. If your company is part of a larger group, it will probably have to produce a number of additional management reports, giving details of various aspects of operating performance such as labour and machine utilization and sales per employee. If your company isn't part of a group, you may well produce similar reports for your own management at present, but in this case your own directors will have the authority to change the reporting requirements if they see good reason for this.

The world-class manufacturing concept requires a fundamental change in the way in which manufacturing activities are managed. As a result, these traditional measures of performance will frequently prove inadequate, irrelevant, or even counter-productive.

For example, suppose a company decides to reduce batch sizes, in order to improve flexibility, shorten lead times and reduce stock levels; its efforts may well fail if no change is made to existing performance measures which, because they are based on the 'number of standard hours produced', encourage large batches to be produced, regardless of whether these match actual customers' requirements. And improvement efforts are particularly likely to fail if the company's payment-by-results scheme is based on these measures of standard hours produced. Can you really expect shop floor workers to cooperate in a campaign to reduce batch sizes if this causes them to earn less bonus?

In any case, the whole point of reporting on manufacturing performance should be to enable management to see that progress is being made towards achieving the goals they have set, and to identify where improvements are feasible or necessary. This means that you need to introduce new methods of performance measurement which satisfy these management requirements, and at the same time you need to review existing performance measures to ensure that those that are irrelevant or counter-productive are as far as possible either modified or removed. I say 'as far as possible' because some of the present measures may be essential elements of producing the financial information required by law, or part of your Group Headquarters' reporting requirements which local management lack the authority to change: where this is the case, remember that even if you have to *provide* the information (for someone else's benefit), you don't have to *use* it for monitoring your manufacturing operations if you can develop more appropriate measures for use within the business.

One aspect of your present accounting systems that you may well need to reconsider is the way in which overhead costs are recovered. In most manufacturing companies this is done by adjusting direct labour rates: years ago this was fine, because direct labour was usually the most significant cost element, but in most manufacturing companies today this is no longer the case and, as a result, factors as high as 500 per cent or more have to be added to direct labour rates in order to recover the overhead charges. Unfortunately, this can have a serious effect on decision-making.

For example, suppose you run a machine shop employing 50 people. You have a ten-year-old CNC machine tool in this shop which isn't very flexible because it takes so long to change the tooling between successive batches; as a result, economic batch quantity considerations typically require batch sizes equivalent to three months' demand. As part of a JIT initiative you want to cut batch sizes to average no more than two weeks' demand. You therefore decide to buy a new CNC machine tool which incorporates quick-change tooling so that set-up time is dramatically reduced; this makes it economic to produce the small batches you require. You decide to retain the old machine since it is still able to produce good quality work and will provide additional capacity during periods of peak demand. It's a sensible decision from the world-class manufacturing point of view, but how will it affect the costs reported in your management accounts and, even more important, how are the relative costs of the two processes reflected in the estimates you will prepare in future when responding to customers' enquiries? You are likely to get different answers depending on the cost accounting convention you use! Compare these three commonly used methods:

- *Method A*
  Depreciation costs are included in shop overheads, which are recovered as a standard percentage uplift on direct labour rates across the shop; set-up time is considered as direct labour (because the set-up is done by the machine's setter/operator) and included in the batch cost on the basis of estimated time required. Result: since the total time required for a batch (including set-up) is less on the new machine, the new machine gives a lower cost.
- *Method B*
  As method A, but set-up time is considered as indirect labour and therefore included in the shop overheads, which are recovered as in method A. Result: the shorter set-up time is no longer a factor, but the new machine will still be slightly cheaper because it incorporates the latest technology, enabling a small saving to be made in the machining time per piece.
- *Method C*
  Depreciation cost is allocated to individual machines according to their current book value; set-up time is considered as direct labour, as in method A. Result: product cost appears cheaper on the old machine because its depreciation cost is minimal; eventually the depreciation cost of the new machine may reduce to the point where its greater efficiency makes it the cheaper, but that's a long way off.

Thus we have three different methods, each affecting the perceived product cost, and yet there is no difference in the *true* cost to the company! Worse than that, with the third method the 'right' decision would be to use the old machine in preference to the more efficient new one. Toyota, the pioneers of world-class manufacturing, use a 'sunk cost' concept when comparing the relative cost of alternative machines. They argue that once a machine has been purchased, its cost is 'sunk' and irrecoverable, so that the depreciation cost is irrelevant; what counts is which machine will have the least total batch cost (including set-up), regardless of its initial cost. That doesn't necessarily mean that the new machine will always win; you will sometimes find that the older machine will give a lower batch cost, for example if it's less complex and so has an operator with a lower hourly rate.

The lesson that we can draw from this is that managers need better information than they can get from traditional cost accounting methods if they are to make decisions that are up to world-class standards. The accounting profession has given a great deal of thought in recent years as to how the quality of costing information can be improved. The most favoured approach is generally referred to as 'Activity Based Costing' (ABC), and this is increasingly being adopted by leading manufacturers; further information on ABC can be found in Sec. 14.1.

Since the new performance measures that are required should reflect the current improvement goals set by management, it follows that there cannot be a standard set of performance measures that can be used in all factories. Indeed, even within one factory, it will be necessary to review the performance measures used whenever management modifies the improvement goals as a result of changes in the market-place, or because previous goals have been achieved. In any case, there are far too many potential areas for measurement for them all to be included in weekly or even monthly reporting. To produce statistics and measures of performance that don't make a direct contribution to your improvement efforts would be to introduce another form of waste. For these reasons, all that I can do here is to suggest some of the measures of performance that I have found useful in quite a number of different situations; these are summarized later in this section and described in more detail in Chapter 14.

When developing your own monitoring systems, remember that people tend to take more care when they know that what they are doing is going to be measured and reported on: you will find that simply introducing a new performance measure will often solve a problem without further action being needed. A typical example of this often happens when you want to reduce set-up time. The first stage of the SMED set-up time reduction technique is to observe what happens at present, so that you can analyse the process into what is called 'external' or 'internal' time. Virtually every time I've introduced this initial measurement process, set-up times have immediately reduced, in some cases by as much as 25 per cent. The reason is that those concerned become conscious of delays that will be marked down to them, and so they make sure that they respond promptly when needed. Another example I've come across repeatedly is the sudden improvement you can achieve in the time it takes to check goods received from suppliers and get them into stores and on to the stock records so that they are available for Production to use: if *you* have problems with delays in Goods Inwards, take it from me that all you have to do is to ask those concerned to produce a weekly report showing the percentage of deliveries cleared within 24 hours and the percentages taking more than (each of) two, three and four days. You will see an immediate improvement!

Finally, here is the selection of performance measures I promised earlier: some of them may well be appropriate to your particular circumstances, or they may stimulate you to develop others.

6.3.1 Lead Times

I put this first on my list because beating your competitors in lead time and delivery performance is one of the most effective ways of achieving a competitive edge and convincing potential customers to order from *you* rather than from your competitors. And yet, how many companies (other than those that have already embarked on a world-class campaign) routinely monitor their lead time performance? Even if customers are happy with your current lead time, they may well become more demanding in the future; in any case, actions taken to reduce lead times are always well worthwhile because, in my experience at least, they *always* result in reductions to both overheads and direct manufacturing costs.

As a start, you should monitor overall lead time performance, i.e. from receipt of order through to delivery to customer. This can be a simple report, stating what percentage of orders (by both number *and* value – the results may be quite different) are delivered within the target time set by management. However, I prefer to produce a cumulative frequency diagram (again, for both number and value) because you can easily read off from this answers to questions such as 'What percentage of orders would have been delivered on time if we had quoted 10 weeks instead of 8 weeks?', or 'What delivery would we have to quote to be confident of achieving a success rate of 95 per cent?'. Figure 6.1 shows an example of a cumulative frequency diagram; the bar chart in Fig. 6.2 is an alternative presentation which shows comparative results for the past three months. The cumulative frequency diagram is an essential monitoring tool for any company for which lead time performance is important; computers aren't likely to be of much help and you may have difficulty in finding guidance elsewhere on how to prepare a diagram manually; details of the procedure are therefore included in Sec. 11.2 and in Appendix One.

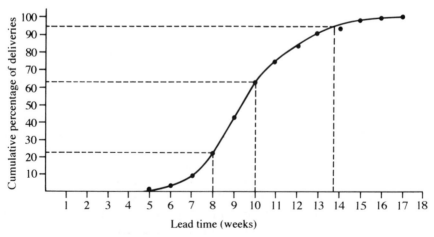

Figure 6.1 Current lead time performance (by value).

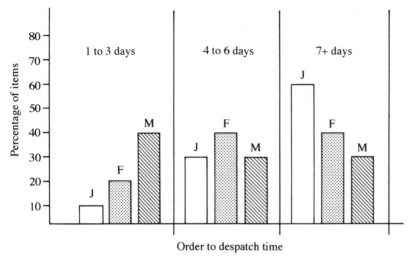

Figure 6.2 Lead time performance (by number of orders): latest three months.

Figures 6.1 and 6.2 only show the overall time it takes you at present to satisfy customers' orders. If you want to do something to improve performance you will need to produce separate information about each of the main elements of the lead time. The first step is to decide what the various stages involved are and how long each of these stages takes, from which you can decide which are significant and should therefore be monitored. The stages are likely to include order processing and specification; planning and ordering of materials; goods inwards inspection; component manufacturing; assembly; and despatch. Further guidance on lead time analysis can be found in Sec. 14.2.

6.3.2 Stock Levels

I put the monitoring of stocks as second on my list because this will usually provide a prime source of information about what is going wrong in your present procedures and practices. Excessive inventory levels are nearly always a symptom of operational problems that people have learned to live with by holding additional inventory as an insurance policy; some of the excess may even be a direct result of those problems. Methods for tackling excessive inventory were described in Chapters 3 and 11, but it's likely to be a never-ending task, and that means that progress needs to be monitored regularly in the same way that sales and profit performance, for example, are regularly monitored. Most companies do this by looking at the overall stock value, but I don't think that's sufficient. Three brief examples will illustrate why.

Example A Inventory has been reducing steadily as a result of the work of a world-class project team; after four successive monthly reductions the inventory value suddenly increases in the next month by over 20 per cent; it gets back on track the following month, but two months later there's another jump in inventory and no one seems to know why.

The reason is, in fact, quite straightforward: on both occasions the jump in inventory was due to a large export shipment which had been delayed at the last minute because one or two minor items on the shipping documents weren't quite ready. If the inventory report given to management had shown a breakdown to raw material, work-in-progress and finished goods, and by product group, someone would immediately have realized the cause of the sudden jump in inventory. They would then have realized that action was needed to make sure that all parts of an export order, however small an individual part might be, were in future all completed by the same date.

Example B A stock reduction team has succeeded in reducing inventory for the past four months, but there are an increasing number of complaints from Sales about shortages and late deliveries. It turns out that the lower inventory was achieved by placing an embargo on all orders to suppliers over a certain value.

The lesson here is that anyone can reduce stock, just by imposing a blanket cut-back on order placing. You need to make sure that your team are doing something more intelligent than that, which means getting them to show you an analysis of the present inventory so that you can agree which categories are to be attacked, and what sort of measures will be taken; having agreed a stock reduction policy, you then need to see regular reports which provide a sufficient breakdown to enable you to monitor progress against the agreed plan.

Example C The world-class project team has introduced call-off schedules for all the high-cost material supplies, installed a Kanban procedure for internal components and cut set-up times extensively, but inventory remains stubbornly high.

The reason could be a build-up of stocks (at all stages) for a range of new products, which would be revealed if the inventory was broken down by product family; or it could be due to a drop in sales which had not been properly compensated for at the production planning stage, which would be revealed if the inventory was broken down into its raw materials, work-in-progress and finished stock categories with an accompanying graph showing both inventory and sales trends.

The message from these three examples is that management need more than just the overall inventory figures in order to identify whether all is well, or whether some corrective action is needed. When you approve an action plan for reducing inventory, you should also agree what regular reports will be needed to enable you to monitor progress and see for yourself the link between actions taken and the resultant inventory level.

You probably won't find the sort of information you need in traditional stock reports because these aren't detailed enough, but it will most likely be there, locked up in your computer database (although it may not be as accurate as you would like until you have taken steps to put that aspect right – see Sec. 14.7).

Section 14.3 includes a summary of the sort of reports that a stock reduction improvement team might need for the routine monitoring of inventory performance, from which they can prepare their monthly summary for management with appropriate supporting detail.

6.3.3 Productivity Improvement

Measures of different aspects of productivity have been in use in most manufacturing companies for many years. For a world-class company, however, greater emphasis needs to be placed on obtaining information on those problems that have to be overcome if the strategic improvement objectives are to be achieved, and on monitoring how successful you are in moving towards your goals. There are two types of measurement in particular that are likely to be useful:

- *Analysis of production delays*: this is similar to the type of 'down-time' analysis which is used in many companies, but instead of concentrating on either labour or machine productive time lost, the emphasis is on delays which interrupt the smooth flow of production in accordance with the production plan. You'll usually find this report a very effective way of picking up problems which affect delivery performance, because the source documents, each of which gives details of a specific delay occurrence, are prepared by the operators themselves and can't be swept under the carpet by local supervision. The source document and summary form are illustrated in Figs. 11.10 and 11.11 respectively; further details on how they should be used can be found in Sec. 11.2.
- *Set-up times*: if one of your objectives is to reduce the productive time lost due to set-up changes (as will often be the case), a weekly summary should be produced showing, for example, average set-up time and number of set-ups taking more than 30 minutes (both are important). If you start a record like this you will find that the number of set-ups taking longer than 30 minutes (or whatever other cut-off figure you have chosen) will drop dramatically, because everyone knows that there will be an inquest if this time is exceeded. Since you will thus have eliminated most of the extreme times, the overall average will also drop noticeably – and all this before you've even started to introduce quick changeover techniques!

6.3.4 Quality Improvement

Improving quality performance is at the heart of world-class manufacturing and this means that you should be monitoring closely whether you are improving fast enough and in the areas where it matters most. You may well be producing most of the key quality performance measurements already; if not, ask yourself whether you should be. Typical reports should include:

- *Scrap and reject analyses*: these should be broken down to show the type of quality problem, its source, the cost of re-work and/or cost of scrapped materials etc. An additional world-class requirement that is unlikely to be on your existing reports is 'lead time impact'.
- *Customer returns*: a summary report analysing the reasons for return. Customer returns due to unsatisfactory quality should always provoke an inquest: since world-class companies normally operate a zero defects policy (at least, as far as their external customers are concerned) you need to find out what failure in your control procedures allowed the faulty product to reach your customer.
- *Concession notes*: a world-class company should always produce a summary report giving details of any concession notes raised, since these imply that waste in one form

or another has occurred. Possibly the materials concerned were in fact perfectly good enough, even if they didn't quite meet your specification (in which case you may be paying for a tighter specification material than is really necessary); or the material could be used, but some additional work was required by your employees (even if you arrange to recharge this to the supplier a delay is likely to result); or you have agreed to accept material that you know is not up to the standard you really require. More often than not concession notes are raised because you are so desperate for the material (the supplier has probably delivered late) that you would rather let it slip through than suffer further delay. Whichever is the reason, it shouldn't be acceptable to a world-class company, which is why you should examine reports of concessions made with considerable suspicion.

6.3.5 Supplier Performance

Suppliers are an important resource of any world-class company, and their performance therefore needs to be managed as effectively as you manage other resources such as your own production facilities. Most of this should normally be left to the Purchasing Department; Sec. 14.4 includes a summary of the key aspects of current supplier performance that they should be monitoring, such as price, quality and delivery, from which they will be able to produce summary reports for management. They should also report on their world-class improvement actions, such as introducing partnership sourcing, joint action with suppliers to improve value for money, and the progressive weeding out of unreliable suppliers; Sec. 3.8 describes what your Purchasing Department should be doing to improve supplier performance and Sec. 11.6 explains how management can assess how effectively they are doing it.

6.4 OTHER INFORMATION NEEDS

The information systems referred to so far deal with the regular reports you need in order to run the business on a day-to-day basis. When you are undertaking improvement projects your improvement teams will often need additional information to help them pinpoint problem areas and gain a better understanding of why problems are occurring or to quantify the extent of a problem and identify the scope for improvement. World-class systems, therefore, need to provide you with a sort of 'intelligence service', a library of information which you can tap into as and when the need arises. You should remember this when setting up an improvement team – try to ensure that at least one member of the team is familiar with your computer's query system, so that they don't have to keep calling on the Computer Department for help (and possibly having to wait their turn in the queue).

Improvement teams should be warned not to get too carried away with enthusiasm – computer time can be expensive, and if they're not careful you could find that the 'simple' report they asked for takes hours to produce and results in a massive computer printout (I've seen it happen!). For example, a team given the task of reducing lead time and improving delivery performance decided that the best way of getting some quick improvement would be to have a blitz on overdue orders. In order to find out where to start, they asked for a computer listing of all overdue orders in the system.

Unfortunately, the backlog situation was so bad that they ended up with virtually the whole of the order book being included and, since they hadn't specified otherwise, the listing was in order number sequence, which made it difficult for them to extract the information they needed. Since the database included the week number of the due date for delivery, and the computer system knew what the current week number was, it would have been quite simple to use the query language to calculate how many weeks each outstanding order was overdue and then generate a report showing, in descending order of lateness, the 50 most overdue orders, which was what they really wanted.

A common requirement when working on strategic improvement tasks is to identify which items currently held in stock should be classed as obsolete. This is partly because you want to get rid of them, but also, most importantly, because you want to try to find out *why* they became obsolete so that you can take action to avoid similar waste recurring in the future. The way in which stock is defined as obsolete for accounting purposes isn't always suitable when you are looking at it from the materials management point of view. Further guidance on how to allow for this is included in Sec. 14.6.

I have said that much of the information that a world-class company requires is likely to be already available within their computer system: 'all' that you have to do is to decide *what* information you want, and then find out how to extract it from your database. However, there are two types of information needed by any company that is striving to be world-class that will not normally be available in *any* computer system: information about how your customers view your performance, and information about your current cost of quality. Both require snapshot studies to be carried out periodically: further information on these topics can be found in Chapters 2 and 4 respectively, and Sec. 12.2 provides more detailed guidance on how to carry out a cost of quality analysis in your own company.

Finally, it's worth remembering that improvement teams often introduce new management reports during the course of their project, and they will often arrange for these to be produced on a regular basis for a time, so that progress towards achieving their improvement objectives can be monitored. Some of these reports could well be worth continuing indefinitely (for example, a report showing lead time achievement); however, others may not really be necessary once the project has been completed. In the latter case, remember that if instructions are given to produce a report on a regular basis 'until further notice', that report will probably go on being produced indefinitely – so make sure that a log is kept of all the special reports that have been requested on an 'until further notice' basis and at the end of the project get the team to go through the log, item by item, and decide whether the report should now be discontinued or, if not, who should in future be the report's 'owner'.

6.5 IMPROVING ACCURACY

Many of the things that go wrong in manufacturing are caused by inaccuracies in the company's information and control systems. A world-class company must have information it can depend on, particularly since it will no longer have much of the protection previously provided by long lead times and high stock levels. It follows that, as an essential part of your improvement strategy, you will need to do something about improving the accuracy of your systems. An effective way of improving accuracy is described in Sec. 14.7.

During the period when a team is working on improving the accuracy of your systems they should, of course, monitor and report progress made, for example through a monthly report showing the number and value of stock errors identified. This shouldn't just show the net change in stock value, as this may well conceal the true extent of all the individual negative and positive adjustments: separate figures should be given both for items reduced and for items increased as a result of stock checks during the month, and the total value and number of items actually checked should be included to indicate what proportion of the detailed stock records are currently inaccurate.

I have said that 'a world-class company must have information it can depend on'. Unfortunately, it is likely to take you some time to purge your systems and procedures of all the things that currently cause inaccuracies to creep into your computer database. In contrast, some of the other changes that you will be working on may quite quickly increase your dependency on accurate information about stock and outstanding orders. To overcome this transitional problem, therefore, you may well need to introduce some additional manual checks and procedures as a protective measure: if you don't, quite apart from losing all credibility for the world-class initiatives, your changes could have a disastrous impact on both manufacturing performance and customer service – the opposite of what you are trying to achieve!

MANAGING THE CHANGE

Although you should start to reap the benefits of your world-class initiatives within a few months, it will usually take several years to develop a lasting change in employees' attitudes and to institutionalize a 'quality creation' culture across the company. Throughout this time management will need to watch out for signs of old habits returning, and they will need to keep reiterating their commitment to the world-class principles. This chapter provides guidance on how the path of change can be smoothed.

7.1 THE GOAL

A world-class manufacturer needs to have:

- An obsession with eliminating waste
- A profound belief that improving manufacturing efficiency is the job of the whole workforce, and not just the job of managers and specialists
- A commitment to providing such a high quality of service to customers that it will stimulate a corresponding commitment from customers to buying the company's products and services
- An understanding that *becoming* a world-class manufacturer is only the first step. To *remain* world-class, there must be a company-wide commitment to a programme of ongoing and continuous improvement that will never end

It's a major undertaking for any company, but the rewards can be immense. Indeed, in an increasingly competitive world, it may well be the only way for a company to survive and prosper in the longer term.

Although sufficient benefits should be achieved within the space of a few months, perhaps even weeks, to encourage you to persevere, it will usually take years to complete the task – if, indeed, the task can ever be truly complete, since 'continuous improvement that will never end' is the final goal. To become a world-class manufacturer involves a fundamental change in how your whole business operates; that inevitably takes time and the change process needs to be managed very carefully in order to ensure success.

This book will, I trust, help you decide what you have to do to achieve the world-class goals in your particular circumstances, and it should provide sufficient technical guidance for you to get started. But how well you succeed will depend not just on how effectively you apply the various techniques: it will, above all, depend on your determination to persevere with your world-class plans at times when progress seems to be wilting, and resistance to change appears so entrenched that you begin to despair of ever overcoming it. Don't be surprised if that happens – it normally does! It helps if you can recognize it for what it is: the dying struggles of the old order. Be prepared: handle the situation with determination, and you'll usually find the breakthrough follows with surprisingly little bloodshed; even some of those who were the most persistent resistors will often become the most zealous converts. Being prepared means: progressing by stages, so that people can get used to the world-class ways and gradually come to see for themselves the benefits that can be achieved; expecting that set-backs will happen, and responding by reinforcing the message and restating management's commitment; and, above all, being patient, recognizing that it takes time for people to change the habits of a lifetime. Some tips on each of these follow.

7.2 PROGRESS BY STAGES

Every company will differ in what it has to do, and in how long it will take it to achieve its world-class goals. When you've finished reading this book you may decide that the techniques described in the chapters on JIT are the most appropriate for you to start with, or you may feel that the total quality approach or developing new products or new markets are the priority in your particular circumstances. But whatever you decide to concentrate on first, don't jump in with both feet! Take it a stage at a time to give people a chance to adjust in the way they think about their jobs.

I can't give you a hard and fast 'world-class action programme', simply because, as I've said, every company will differ in what it has to do. However, the stages described below illustrate what is likely to be involved for the 'average' company, together with an indication of the sort of time-scales to expect.

7.2.1 Stage 1 (1 to 2 Months)

Before launching your world-class campaign, make sure you've reviewed your business strategy thoroughly so that your priorities for action reflect what your customers will respond to quickly. You might think that cutting costs is the greatest priority, but it's a lot easier to manage the change if you can stimulate additional sales at an early stage, to mop up any surplus capacity released by your improvement activities. And, while the final responsibility for deciding on future strategy must be down to the Chief Executive, you'll find it much easier to steer the company towards achieving that strategy if the top management team have been properly involved in the review process, as explained in Chapter 2.

7.2.2 Stage 2 (1 Month)

Once you've got your strategy sorted out, the next step is to tell people what you are planning to do, and why it's important for the future success of the company and for their personal long-term job security. When you're talking about the changes ahead, take particular care over explaining *how it will affect them*. If you just talk about 'improving efficiency' they'll interpret this as 'job losses' unless, at the same time, you explain how the labour released through productivity improvements will be absorbed. Section 13.4 suggests what should be included in this initial awareness training.

7.2.3 Stage 3 (12 Months and Ongoing)

Start your world-class campaign with key strategic projects aimed at achieving step change improvements, partly to get a quick return on your investment, but mainly to demonstrate to the whole workforce what can be achieved when the 'experts' really work as a team and are empowered to apply their experience without the traditional organizational constraints. Consider carefully whether one of these initial projects should be targeted specifically at ways of increasing sales in the short term, for the reasons explained earlier. Section 2.6 gives guidance on the selection of priorities for the initial projects.

7.2.4 Stage 4 (Ongoing, Starting Towards the End of Stage 3)

Once you start to get results from the key strategic projects, it will be time to spread the net wider by getting the whole workforce involved in continuous improvement groups. You'll need to keep them on track by getting them to concentrate on customer/supplier links, so that all their efforts are directed towards improving the quality of service they provide to their own personal customers; if you neglect to give them this guidance you may well find that all their efforts are directed, instead, at environmental and personal welfare matters. With any luck, you'll find that your desire to widen the net will be anticipated in those areas affected by the initial projects, with the shop floor workers concerned wanting to get more directly involved before you even raise the subject of continuous improvement groups; but this is only likely to happen if you've stimulated their interest, and their desire to get involved, by publicizing the achievements that have been gained so far through the initial projects.

When publicizing achievements, make sure that you give credit to those who have achieved success; get rid of any lingering thoughts among the diehards that 'you shouldn't tell anyone they've done well, they'll only ask for more money'. Success, recognized, encourages them to feel pride in what they have achieved, and getting people to feel pride in what they do is at the heart of the world-class philosophy. It will also encourage enthusiasm for improvement, and enthusiasm can be quite infectious: the more infectious it becomes, the more chance you have of turning it into an epidemic, spreading the world-class message to all parts of the company.

You should also remind everyone of management's commitment to the world-class programme at every opportunity, demonstrating through your actions that this is more than mere lip service; in particular, this means making sure that you aren't sending out the wrong signals (see Sec. 4.8). Getting senior managers to undertake a 'personal commitment task', and publicizing what these are, will provide positive evidence of their commitment to the world-class programme, and this will carry particular weight if the Chief Executive is prepared to talk about his or her own personal contribution.

7.2.5 Stage 5 (Ongoing)

Finally, remember that both market priorities and competitive pressures are changing all the time, and that means that you need to review your own priorities regularly. Make sure that you explain this point in the initial awareness training, so that you can remind your people of it if, at a later date, you have to change priorities; if you don't take this precaution, you'll run the risk of losing management credibility when you do change priorities or, at the very least, of getting your people thoroughly confused.

7.3 BE PREPARED FOR SET-BACKS

Introducing change as fundamental as the world-class manufacturing philosophy demands won't always go smoothly. As Dr Kanter, the guru of *change management*, says: 'Every success is a failure in the middle' (details of Dr Kanter's book and video are included in the Bibliography). Take it from me, the time will come when you start wondering whether it's worth all the effort; that's the time when some of your senior colleagues will start withdrawing their support, just when you most need it. And, ironically, the more enthusiastic you were at the start, the more likely it is to happen.

The root cause of the problem is that there's nearly always at least one member of the top management team who, when first hearing the world-class message, is against it either because of a conviction that it won't work, or because of worry about being able to cope with the change personally. At that stage, though, anyone with such views will usually be prepared to go along with the wishes of the majority of the top management team, and the more enthusiastic the Chief Executive appears, the less likely the person is to oppose the proposals openly. After all, the reasoning goes, they'll drop the idea soon enough when they find it doesn't work and, to quote Dr Kanter again, 'Why waste a good negative'. Typically, these doubts won't surface as long as things are going well; but as soon as there's a hitch, that's when such a person will come out of hiding and there'll probably be others who'll join in at that stage:

- 'I never really thought it would work.'
- 'It's all rather pie in the sky, isn't it? We really ought to get back to today's priorities.'
- 'Is it really worth all this effort? After three months of hard graft, what have we really got out of it.'
- 'My people are always sloping off to world-class meetings; they're neglecting their real jobs.'

That's when the Chief Executive needs to be firm, reminding them of the 'vision' they've agreed and why they all felt at the start that 'do nothing' was no longer a feasible option.

Tell people at the beginning about the 'every success is a failure in the middle' syndrome; then, when it happens, simply reminding them of the saying will often be enough to kill any risk of rebellion. If that doesn't do the trick, remind everyone that they had all agreed at the strategy review that 'do nothing' wasn't a feasible option: if they now feel that 'world-class' isn't, after all, the answer, another new approach will have to be tried instead – which should that be? That argument is usually enough to bring even the most reluctant back on board!

7.4 BE PATIENT

To quote Dr Kanter again: 'Instant success takes time'. You can select initial projects that will start to yield benefits within a few months, and everyone will be talking about what the world-class approach has enabled you to achieve, but the underlying culture, how your people think and operate, won't have changed – or at least, not permanently. Attitudes can't be changed overnight and, unfortunately, the process can't be hastened. Don't be fooled by the enthusiastic noises you might hear in the first few months: a lot of it will simply be a reaction to all the attention management is paying to activities that carry the world-class label; take your eye off the ball, switch your attention to some other subject, and you'll find interest in world-class waning.

World-class ways of thinking and working won't stick until your people really believe (because they've seen and experienced it for themselves) that:

- Their own job is easier because they have a clearer idea of what they have to do and because less goes wrong with their material and equipment
- There's less cause for frustration, because if they see something that's not right, *they* can do something about it themselves or they have the means to get someone else to
- Whatever their job, they have a better idea of how they contribute personally to the company's products or services: they are no longer just a cog
- They can take pride in their work because they know what their customers rely on them for, and they know that they satisfy their needs professionally
- They can take pride in their team (and therefore don't want to let their mates down); and they can take pride in their company and its products, because they have confidence in their fellow workers

You'll know that you're there when you hear someone, asked where he or she works, reply 'I'm in Jack's team', rather than 'I work in the widget assembly shop'.

That will take time to achieve, usually between two and five years, depending on the size and complexity of your business and on where you are starting from. Once the world-class way of working has been institutionalized into the company's culture it would be extremely difficult to break down, even if management's commitment appears to slacken. But until that happens, the full, continuous and highly visible support of top management in general, and the Chief Executive in particular, will be vital.

THREE

METHODS AND PROCEDURES

Each chapter in Part Two is linked to a corresponding chapter in Part Three, which provides additional information and guidance, together with illustrative case studies. These linking chapters are preceded in Part Three by a chapter describing a greatly improved version of the traditional brainstorming technique that will be needed at both the initial planning and subsequent implementation stages, and by a chapter consisting of a series of check-lists to help readers assess how their company currently measures up against world-class standards.

IMPROVED BRAINSTORMING METHODS

Effective teamwork is essential to a world-class manufacturer, and brainstorming is such a key teamwork tool that it needs to be exploited to the full. Most managers will be familiar with the basic technique, but few know how to use it to its maximum potential. This chapter describes how to do this, illustrating the process through an example in which the objective is to produce an action list for attacking an acute material shortages problem.

8.1 THE NEED FOR IMPROVED BRAINSTORMING

Most managers are familiar with the brainstorming technique and its close relative the fishbone diagram, and will have used one or the other for developing ideas in all sorts of situations. Few, however, have had any formal training in how to get the best out of the technique and, since it seems so simple, most would feel that they already know as much as they need to.

In a way, it's rather like a game of football: go and watch your local club match, then go home, switch on the television, and watch a Premier League or International match; they're in a different class from your local team, they're *'world-class'* and it shows in the way in which they play, both as individuals and as a team. The sort of brainstorming you may have been used to in the past may have been perfectly adequate when you were competing at the local club level, but if you want to play in the Premier League your technique needs to be up to their standard. That's what this chapter is about.

I'll start with a brief description of the basic brainstorming and fishbone diagram process, in case any readers are not familiar with them; I'll then describe in general terms how this basic process can be improved significantly; and, finally, I'll illustrate this improved process with an example taken from an actual project, in which the team's objective was to find ways of overcoming a serious problem of material shortages.

8.2 THE BASIC PROCESSES

8.2.1 Brainstorming

The brainstorming technique can be used for a wide variety of applications, such as considering how lead time can be reduced; thinking up ways of increasing sales; developing ideas for new products; preparing an action list for reducing inventory; and identifying possible causes of a problem. Essentially, it's a method of generating a list of ideas from a group of people in a brainstorming session, typically lasting no more than 20–30 minutes. It works best with groups of 6 to 12 people; they should try to avoid sitting round a table as this tends to act as a barrier; arranging a group of chairs in a horseshoe, with a flip chart standing at the open end, is much better. One member of the group acts as facilitator to control the brainstorming session, making sure that everyone has a chance to participate and that the group keeps on track. Ideally the facilitator should be one of the 'outside' members of the group, i.e. one who does not own part of the problem that's being brainstormed.

A brainstorming session should usually be preceded by a brief introductory discussion, in which the facilitator makes sure that everyone understands the subject to be brainstormed and what the objective is (for example, 'Produce a list of ideas for reducing lead time'). It may be necessary for the group to go and have a look at any processes involved if they are not already familiar with them, although this should normally have been done prior to the session.

The brainstorming session starts with the facilitator inviting group members to contribute ideas. There are two ways of doing this: by going round the group, asking each person in turn; or by allowing anyone to speak (generally referred to as the 'free for all' method). The free for all method is usually best to get the session going.

It's essential that ideas are recorded as they are generated in a form that everyone can see. The best way of doing this is to write the ideas on a flip chart; that way, everyone can see the ideas offered so far, and this helps to generate further ideas. You should get more ideas than there is room for on one flip chart sheet, and it therefore helps to have two flip chart stands available, with two members of the group acting as writers, each taking alternate ideas as they are offered – this speeds up the writing and keeps the flow of ideas going. Whether you use one flip chart or two, when the sheet is full, tear it off and fasten it up on the wall: if it's kept on display, you'll find that the participants will keep referring back to it and this will help stimulate new ideas; *never* turn the completed sheet over so that it's no longer visible.

If the flow of ideas slows down, the facilitator should stop the 'free for all' session and switch to going round the horseshoe, inviting each participant in turn to contribute an idea; anyone who can't think of an idea reasonably quickly should say 'pass'. Even when ideas are still flowing well, the facilitator should switch to the 'round the horseshoe' method if it appears that some members are dominating the session or if one or more members are not contributing at all. It often happens that a junior member of the group hesitates to speak even though they have some good ideas to offer. The 'round the horseshoe' method puts pressure on them to say something and at the same time puts a rein on the dominant members of the group.

No idea should be rejected, however stupid; the facilitator should jump on anyone who ridicules an idea, or says that it won't work, because it will inhibit people from coming up with innovative ideas for fear of being made to look foolish. I find the most effective way of stopping objections like this, particularly from the more senior members of the group, is to encourage everybody to shout 'Humphrey' whenever it happens (the origin of 'Humphrey' is explained in Sec. 13.1.3 on page 321). The facilitator should also make sure that the flow of ideas doesn't get interrupted by discussion: this should be left to the end, when reviewing the ideas listed. The emphasis throughout should be on the quantity of ideas, rather than the quality, since even a poorly expressed or inappropriate idea might well stimulate someone else to come up with something really valuable.

When all members of the group pass in succession the brainstorming session is over, although the facilitator should first ask if anyone has any last-minute ideas – this some-time results in a further tail-end 'free for all'. You'll probably find that you have around 20 or 30 ideas listed, though this will depend on the subject and the scope it offers for ideas. The final step is for the group to go through the list, clarifying any ideas that they don't understand, and then to agree a short list of five or six of the best ideas for further action. At the end of the session the facilitator will normally transfer all the ideas to paper and send a copy to all participants for future reference: those not selected initially may well prove worth further consideration at a later date.

8.2.2 Fishbone Diagrams

This technique is a development of the basic brainstorming procedure; it gets its name from the appearance of the diagram produced, although some people prefer to call it a 'cause and effect' diagram, for reasons that will become clear in a moment. You may also hear it referred to as an 'Ishikawa diagram', after Professor Ishikawa of Tokyo University, who developed the method.

The purpose of the diagram is to show, in a structured way, possible causes of the problem being studied. It is particularly useful for looking at the possible causes of a persistent and complex quality problem.

An example of a fishbone diagram is shown in Fig. 8.1, which is taken from an actual application. The problem being studied was an unacceptably high level of defects in a moulded rubber component, the defects taking the form of surface blisters. The group studying the problem realized that the blisters were probably caused by a com-bination of factors, and there were many factors that could be contributing. They could have started straight off with the brainstorming method described above, but they decided they would have more success if they first broke the problem down into a number of subsections. The fishbone diagram was the technique they used for this.

To start the diagram, they first wrote down, on the right-hand side of a large sheet of paper, the 'effect' they wanted to look at, i.e. 'blisters'. They then drew a horizontal line (representing the backbone of the 'fish'). From this they drew a number of branch-ing 'bones', each being a major subgroup of the possible 'causes' or contributing factors. In this case, they decided that the main subgroups should be: MATERIAL; MEN; MOULD; PROCESS; and PRESS. A brief brainstorming session followed, in which they were aiming to identify the most likely causes under each of the headings in turn,

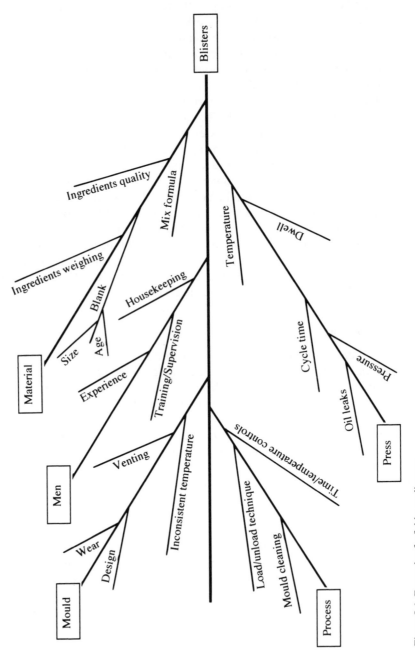

Figure 8.1 Example of a fishbone diagram.

from which they could then select a short list of areas for more detailed investigation. Two possible causes were selected from each of the headings and arrangements were made for these to be studied in more depth through a series of experiments. Although some of the possible causes on this short list turned out not to be significant, the experiments enabled the team to identify which were the significant factors, and so solve the problem.

A disadvantage of the fishbone diagram technique is that it is difficult to draw it on a standard size flip chart. You can overcome this limitation to some extent by drawing the chart vertically instead of horizontally, i.e. with the effect at the bottom of the chart and the central backbone drawn as a vertical line down the centre of the chart. However, because the lines branch out at different angles, the more branches you have, the more difficult it becomes to write without standing on your head! An alternative method is to spread a large sheet of drawing paper (A2 or A1) on a table and get the team to stand (not sit) round the table; then use marker or felt tip pens to draw the diagram, writing all words in capital letters to make it easier for those who are looking at the diagram upside down.

One final point: resist the temptation to have more than four or five main branches in your diagram or it will become so complicated you'll have difficulty in marking up all the sub-branches, let alone interpreting them when the diagram's finished. As you'll see in a moment, a much better way is to use the fishbone diagram to get your ideas organized, but then to use the brainstorming technique to develop them further.

8.3 THE IMPROVED PROCESS

The objective of the improved brainstorming process is to generate many more ideas than can normally be achieved with the basic method. The reason why you need to do this is that if you keep on generating more and more ideas they tend to become more innovative, and at the same time the risk of missing the 'best' idea is minimized. This is particularly important when you are brainstorming ways of improving a manufacturing process, or exploring new sales or product development opportunities.

In the 'shortages' example below, if your list only contains 20 ideas you may well overlook one that's important; if your list contains 70 or more ideas the risk of this happening is virtually eliminated. You can be sure that all the most important causes of your shortages problem are somewhere in your list: all that you need to do then is to use the skill and experience of the team members in a methodical way to select a short list of, say, 8 or 10 of the ideas; you can be confident that this short list will include the three or four most important causes, even though, at this stage, you can't be sure which they are.

The shortages example in the next section illustrates how a list of ideas can be greatly expanded through an iterative process using a combination of the brainstorming and fishbone diagram techniques, followed by a two stage short-listing process. But first I'll describe briefly the eight stages of the process, and then explain in more detail two methods of producing a short list. Don't be put off if at first it appears to be too long and drawn out a process: it only seems like that when it's described in writing! In practice the whole process shouldn't take much more than an hour at the most, even for a fairly complex problem, and you can, if you wish, complete the process in two stages with a break after Stage 5; if you schedule the second session a few days after the first, that will have the added advantage of giving the participants time to think up some additional ideas, to extend your category lists still further.

8.3.1 Process Stages

- *Stage 1: Advance preparation*
  The objective is to get the initial brainstorming process off to a good start, with a quick flow of ideas and with everyone contributing. Ideally, give those involved advance warning of the topic to be brainstormed and ask them to make a note of ideas before the meeting. If that's not feasible, allow five minutes before starting the brainstorming for participants to jot down a few ideas. When you're ready to start, remember that it's best to arrange the seating in the form of a horseshoe, rather than round a table, with a flip chart stand (or, better, two) at the open end.
- *Stage 2: Initial brainstorming*
  The objective of this stage is to pool the ideas which individuals have prepared in advance, and then to extend the combined list with further brainstorming. The ideas should be numbered consecutively as they are recorded on the flip chart, and as each sheet is completed it should be fastened to the wall where it can be seen by all. Use the 'round the horseshoe' method initially, to make sure that everyone participates; no one may repeat an idea that's already been included on the flip chart list, but they can keep extending their personal list at this stage by adding any ideas that occur to them while it's someone else's turn to speak; that way you keep them involved throughout and, at the same time, you're using the initial list of ideas to stimulate new ones. When several participants in succession say 'pass', keep the brainstorming moving by switching quickly to the 'free for all' method until the flow dries up completely.
- *Stage 3: Fishbone diagram*
  Now that the group have had a chance to think about the subject and have generated probably 30 or more ideas, switch to drawing a fishbone diagram in order to classify the ideas into a number of categories. Don't, however, take the fishbone diagram any further than the first level; the objective is to discuss possible headings and then to whittle these down to no more than four or five categories which between them cover the bulk of the ideas generated so far – include an additional category called 'others' to take care of any ideas that don't fit readily under the four or five main headings selected. Label the headings, for example A, B, C etc., and put the finished fishbone skeleton on the wall where it can be seen by everyone.
- *Stage 4: Categorizing the ideas*
  The next step is to go through the list of ideas, item by item, marking the category label against each. You'll probably find that some of the ideas can be categorized under more then one heading, in which case they'll end up on more than one list; that doesn't matter at this stage (except for the 'others' category since, by definition, this should consist only of ideas that don't fit readily under any of the other headings).
- *Stage 5: Brainstorming by categories*
  Now return to the flip chart and copy out all the ideas for the first category on to a new list, renumbering them as you go. While the facilitator is copying out the new list, the rest of the group should be jotting down any other ideas they can think of for that category. When the re-listing of the first category has been completed, recommence brainstorming as in Stage 2, starting with the ideas that participants have just jotted

down and continuing from there as before; you should find that you can extend the original list considerably now, because everyone's attention is concentrated on a specific part of the problem and they have an initial list to get them started. The facilitator should occasionally remind the group of the category currently being brainstormed, to make sure that they continue to concentrate on that category and don't drift back into a general, unstructured, session.

Repeat the process for each of the categories in turn, ending with the 'others'; for each category list start the renumbering from '1'. You'll probably find that participants will occasionally think of another idea for one of the categories previously completed (this happens particularly when you are trying to extend the 'others' list); in this event, the idea should be added to the appropriate list.

- *Stage 6: Short-listing by categories*

Take the completed brainstorming list for the first category and select a short list of the best ideas, using one of the techniques described below. Before starting the selection process, the facilitator should go through the list, item by item, making sure that everyone understands each of them and eliminating any duplications.

When you've finished selecting the short list it's most important to ask if any member of the group is unhappy that a particular item has been eliminated through the voting process: if so, at this stage you should seriously consider adding it to your list. There are two reasons for this, both a consequence of the voting procedure used for short-listing: the first is that the person objecting might be the only one who really understands the subject of the idea (for example, it might be a technical point that only an experienced process engineer would fully appreciate), and the second is the need to retain the support and commitment of every member of the group, which could be put at risk if an idea that one of them considers to be very important is overruled by the other participants.

When your short list is completed for the first category, repeat the process for each of the others, so that you end up with a set of five or six sheets, each consisting of the 'best' ideas for a particular category.

- *Stage 7: The final short list*

Prepare a final short list, combining all the categories, by selecting the 'best' 10–12 ideas, the only constraint being that there should be at least one idea included from each category. As before, the facilitator should check if anyone is unhappy that a particular idea has been omitted and, if the objector insists, add it to the list. You will usually find at this point that it makes sense to combine some of the ideas, or to change them slightly (by consensus) to make it easier to define an action task.

- *Stage 8: Selecting priorities for action*

The final step is to sort the list by ranking them in what the group considers to be their relative order of importance, and then to decide which will be actioned first, what the next step will be, and who will be responsible for carrying it out. At this stage you can no longer put off consideration of ideas that only one member of the group considers to be very important. In practice, you will often find that any previously stated objection is withdrawn at this stage; if it isn't, it's inadvisable to overrule the objection for the reasons explained earlier – the best solution is usually for the group to agree to a limited study to explore the feasibility of the idea, and to set a date when they will review whether or not to proceed with it any further.

8.3.2 Short-Listing Techniques

I'll briefly describe two commonly used short-listing techniques; you are likely to need both, depending on the stage at which they are used.

The A, B, C method This method is most useful when there are more than, say, a dozen items on the list you are selecting from. It's easy to use and doesn't take long to complete, even with a lengthy list of ideas. All that's required is for the facilitator to take the group through the list, item by item, asking for a show of hands first for A and then for C (the B classification is reserved for the facilitator to apply). The definition of the three classifications is as follows:

> A means 'Possible for short list'
> C means 'Not on short list'
> B means 'Not sure, keep as reserve'

If the show of hands indicates a clear majority (around two thirds, or more) in favour of either A or C, then the appropriate letter is written on the flip chart alongside the item; if there's no clear majority then, by default, it's marked as a B. The whole process should be completed as quickly as possible and discussion should be avoided, since if there's any doubt the item should be classified as B: you will nearly always find that you end up with more As than you really need, so that any that the group are doubtful about can be safely relegated to the B and C reserve lists.

The final step is to write your selected short list on the flip chart by extracting just the A items. Don't discard the Bs and Cs: they should be kept as reserves and reconsidered by the group two or three months later; their understanding of the problem will be much greater by then, and they may wish to reconsider some of the ideas previously rejected.

The preference voting method In Europe this is often called the *'Eurovision Song Contest'* method, after the annual television programme of that name.

Each participant is asked to select the five items which he or she considers to be the 'best', allocating points to each in accordance with their assessment of their relative importance, as follows: 5 points to the first choice, 4 points to the second choice, and so on, ending with 1 point for the fifth choice. The participants are allowed a maximum of five minutes to make their selection; the facilitator should then ask each in turn for their votes, marking the points on the flip chart alongside the selected items; when all the votes have been recorded they are added up and the top five or six are listed in descending order of their score, to form the required short list.

This short-listing method has the great advantage that it gives you a list ranked in order of importance and, since in practice the Pareto Principle will nearly always apply, you can usually identify a clear cut-off point which will help the group decide which items on the final list should be included in their immediate action plan. However, it's really only suitable if the original list contains no more than about a dozen items: with a longer list it becomes difficult for the participants to select just five as 'best', and their votes are likely to be spread over too many items for there to be the four or five clear winners you are looking for. A good compromise is to use the A, B, C method to whittle the original list down, and then apply the preference voting method to just the A items, which should be a more manageable list.

Whichever method of short-listing you use, remember that some participants will be a lot less familiar with the topic than the others who are in the group as 'owners' of the problem. In some ways that's a good thing, since it will encourage lateral thinking and innovation, but there is a slight risk that it might affect the outcome of the voting. However, you can protect against this risk quite easily by asking if anyone is unhappy that a particular idea has been eliminated in the short-listing process; as you will have noticed, this has been allowed for in the description of the improved brainstorming process given above.

8.4 BRAINSTORMING: THE MATERIAL SHORTAGES EXAMPLE

This example is taken from a project in which the team's briefing reads as follows:

> As all members of the team will be aware, for some time now we have been suffering from a persistent shortages problem, which is preventing us from providing the quality of service to our customers demanded by our 'world-class' objectives. These shortages lead to continual interruptions to production and affect raw materials, components for assembly, and the availability of some finished products which are nominally sold on an 'ex-stock' basis. Even in the case of products made to order, shipment is often delayed because some items are missing when the bulk of the customer's order is ready for despatch. Your task is to analyse why so many shortages are occurring, and prepare an action plan for dealing urgently with the most significant causes.

Figure 8.2 (page 154) shows the list produced during the initial brainstorming stage; at this point the right-hand column would have been blank, the space being left for Stage 4. The team members had been asked to prepare a list of ideas in advance and bring this with them to the meeting; with the help of this advance preparation the initial brainstorming session produced over 40 ideas. The facilitator stopped the brainstorming at this point because the flow of ideas was slowing down, and the team then spent five or ten minutes discussing possible ways of categorizing the ideas listed so far; their conclusions were shown in the form of a fishbone diagram, reproduced in Fig. 8.3 (page 155).

Their next step was to go through the original list, marking the appropriate category against each idea; the results are shown in Fig. 8.2, on the right-hand side of each sheet. As you can see, they decided to include some of the ideas in more than one category, which is quite normal in this Stage 4 process.

The remainder of this example is limited to just one of these categories: 'External Suppliers', indicated in the right-hand column of Fig. 8.2 by X.

The Stage 5 re-listing of the 'External Suppliers' category is shown in the first 21 items of Fig. 8.4 (page 156); at this point the right-hand column would have been blank, the space being left for the subsequent A, B, C short-listing. As you can see, when the team concentrated their brainstorming on one category at a time they were able to double the number of ideas they'd originally produced for this category.

For the initial short-listing process the facilitator then took them through the list of 43 ideas, with a show of hands determining for each whether it should be classed as A, as C or, where there was no clear majority for either of these, as B, the appropriate letter being entered in the right-hand column of the flip chart. The 11 ideas classed as A were

SHORTAGES (1)	
1. Incomplete supplier delivery	X
2. Inadequate training	P
3. Supplier delivers late	X
4. Large order wipes out stock	C
5. Slow runner problems	M
6. Better checking systems required at Goods Inwards	X, S
7. Incorrect computer data	X, S, m
8. Trade counter sales take committed stock	C
9. Purchase order not made (human error)	P
10. Staff shortages	P
11. Breakdown in factory	m
12. Wrong labour available	m

SHORTAGES (2)	
13. Lost paperwork	X, P
14. Antiquated machinery	M
15. Transport (incoming)	X
16. Parts ordered late	X, S
17. Parts ordered incorrectly	X, S
18. Holidays of suppliers	X
19. Ancillary components not available	X
20. Bad weather	O
21. Bad employee morale	P
22. Customer incorrectly flagged as on stop list	C
23. Employee absenteeism	X, P
24. Employee holidays	P

SHORTAGES (3)	
25. Production inefficiencies	X, m
26. Unforeseen scrap	X, m
27. Lack of employee flexibility	P
28. Poor forecast of demand	C
29. Badly placed stock (or 'lost')	P
30. Machine bottleneck	m
31. Factory lead time	m
32. Not paying suppliers (stop list)	X
33. Poor relationship with suppliers	X
34. Design specialists not coming forward	X

SHORTAGES (4)	
35. Lack of focus on 'A' runners	m
36. Errors in processing	m
37. Action not taken when told of problem	X
38. Poor communication	X, C, S
39. Jobs held up in office	C
40. Insufficient data on drawings	X, C
41. Rework takes up time	X, m
42. Duplicate orders	C, S
43. Bad quality from suppliers	X
44. Our poor knowledge of what customers want	C
45. Customers poor knowledge of what they want.	C

Figure 8.2 Shortages: initial brainstorming results.

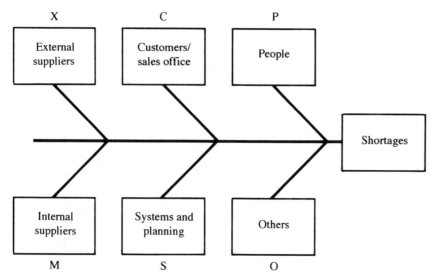

X   C   P

External suppliers

Customers/ sales office

People

Shortages

Internal suppliers

Systems and planning

Others

M   S   O

Figure 8.3 Shortages: fishbone diagram.

then transferred to a new flip chart illustrated in Fig. 8.5 (page 157). As I explained in the previous section, the facilitator should always check whether any participant is unhappy that a particular idea has been eliminated in the short-listing process; in the example, the Buyer felt strongly that shortages were often caused by suppliers refusing to deliver because of overdue invoices, and this was therefore added to the A list.

The final step was for the team to select the two or three 'best' ideas from this list for inclusion in the final short list combining all the categories. They used the 'preference voting' method for this, the results of the voting process being recorded on a flip chart, reproduced in Fig. 8.6 (page 158). As is usually the case, only a few of the ideas (in this instance four) were assessed by the team as being particularly significant, the rest being transferred to a 'reserves' list for review at a later date. Of the four ideas selected, numbers 32 and 33 were effectively a subdivision of number 21: after discussion the team agreed that most of the problems arose with the supply of castings from two specific suppliers, and involved either faults in the casting process itself, or imperfections in the subsequent zinc coating process (also the responsibility of the castings suppliers). The three ideas relating to suppliers' quality problems were therefore combined as one 'action item' on the final list covering all categories (the combining of ideas for one reason or another is quite common at this point). At the request of the Buyer, idea number 14 (suppliers refusing to deliver because of overdue invoice payments) was also provisionally included in the final list. However, the Buyer was asked to collect details of specific orders delayed for this reason; the team would then review whether or not to include this in their action list when this information was available.

SHORTAGES (SUPPLIERS ①)	
1. Incomplete supplier delivery	A
2. Supplier delivers late	A
3. Better checking systems required at Goods Inwards	B
4. Incorrect computer data	B
5. Lost paperwork	C
6. Transport (incoming)	C
7. Parts ordered late	B
8. Parts ordered incorrectly	C
9. Holiday of suppliers	C
10. Ancillary components not available	A
11. Employee absenteeism	C
12. Production inefficiencies	C

SHORTAGES (SUPPLIERS ②)	
13. Unforeseen scrap	A
14. Not paying suppliers (stop list)	C
15. Poor relationship with suppliers	A
16. Design specialists not coming forward	C
17. Action not taken when told of problem	B
18. Poor communication	(see 27, 28 & 29)
19. Insufficient data on drawings	C
20. Re-work takes up time	B
21. Bad quality from supplier	A
22. Suppliers' suppliers	C
23. Undesirable batch size	B

SHORTAGES (SUPPLIERS ③)	
24. Prioritize other people's work	B
25. Suppliers' transport	B
26. Personality clashes	C
27. Poor communication (telephone)	A
28. Poor communication (fax)	C
29. Poor communication (telex)	C
30. Supplier changes spec'n	C
31. Weighing error at Goods Inwards	A
32. Substandard material	A
33. Substandard finish (i.e., coating)	A

SHORTAGES (SUPPLIERS ④)	
34. Lost tooling on slow runners (e.g., pattern equipment	B
35. Tooling found damaged	B
36. Lost specifications	C
37. Lost experience of people (following retirement or redundancy)	C
38. Strikes	C
39. Our transport loses part, or all, of delivery	C
40. World Cup football affects attendance	C
41. Ditto, World Cup rugby	C
42. Inadequate cover when key personnel absent on training courses	C
43. Can't get hold of key supplier staff when in management meeting	A

Figure 8.4 Shortages: brainstorming 'External suppliers' category.

The process described here for the 'External Suppliers' category was repeated for each of the categories and a final list was then compiled, consisting of the top two or three ideas from each of the categories. *All* of the ideas on this list would have to be tackled to be sure that the most important causes of the shortages problem were indeed included. However, not all the 10 or 12 ideas listed could be dealt with at the same time, so the team's final task was to decide, through the 'preference voting' method, the preferred order of priority for their final action list.

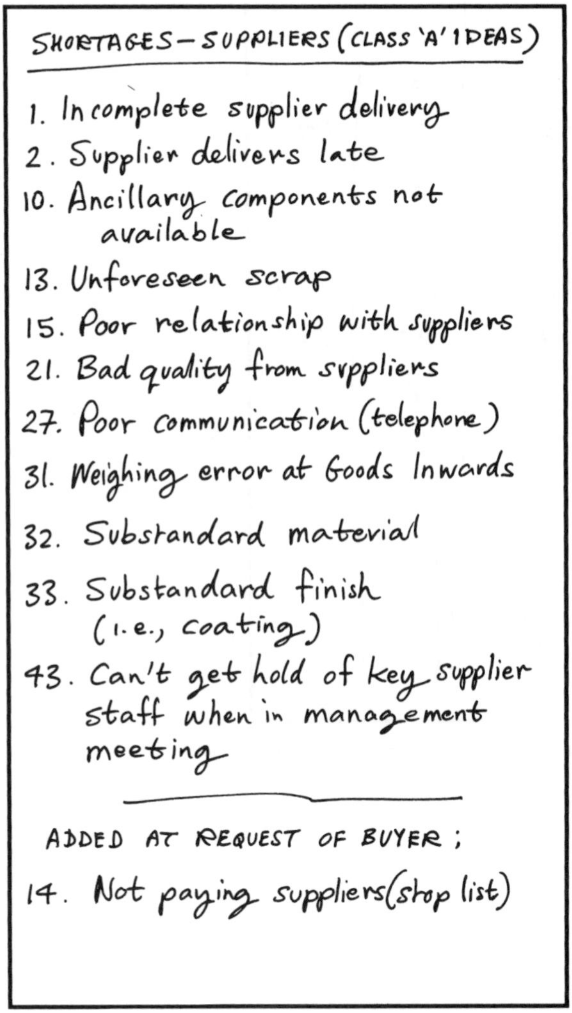

SHORTAGES – SUPPLIERS (CLASS 'A' IDEAS)

1. Incomplete supplier delivery
2. Supplier delivers late
10. Ancillary components not available
13. Unforeseen scrap
15. Poor relationship with suppliers
21. Bad quality from suppliers
27. Poor communication (telephone)
31. Weighing error at Goods Inwards
32. Substandard material
33. Substandard finish (i.e., coating)
43. Can't get hold of key supplier staff when in management meeting

---

ADDED AT REQUEST OF BUYER;

14. Not paying suppliers (stop list)

Figure 8.5 Shortages: initial 'A' short list for 'Suppliers' category.

SHORTAGES ('SUPPLIERS'—FINAL SHORT LIST)

IDEA No.	SCORES	TOTAL	RANK
1	3+4+2+4+5	18	4th
2	2+1+5	8	
10	1+1	2	
13	1	1	
15	1+2+3	6	
21	4+5+5+5+4+3+4+5+2	37	1st
27	2+1	3	
31	2+1+3	6	
32	3+4+3+2+5+5+3+4+4	33	2nd
33	1+3+4+4+5+3+2	22	3rd
43	1+2+3	6	
14	5+2+1	8	

NOTE

Buyer asks that No.14 is included in final short list

Figure 8.6 Shortages: results of final short-listing process for 'Suppliers' category.

THE WORLD-CLASS CHALLENGE – WHERE ARE YOU NOW?

This chapter provides a series of check-lists to help readers assess how their company currently measures up against world-class standards. It will also assist them in preparing a case for convincing colleagues in their top management team that there is an urgent need for action, and for explaining to them how feasible it will be for their company to achieve significant improvements in manufacturing effectiveness by applying the world-class approach described in this book.

9.1 USING THE CHECK-LISTS

Reading the preceding chapters of this book should have convinced you that your company needs to make some dramatic improvements in effectiveness if it is to achieve its full potential and survive and prosper in the longer term. Unfortunately, some of your senior colleagues are likely to be less enthusiastic than you. They will want to see some concrete evidence of the need, before committing themselves to what is inevitably going to involve a major change in the way in which the company operates. You will have to explain to them why something needs to be done, how urgent the need is, and how feasible it will be for the company to achieve the degree of improvement you think necessary. This chapter is intended to help you prepare your case.

At this stage we are only concerned with 'taking the pulse' of your business; a more detailed analysis can be left until later, once you have identified through the strategy review process which areas should be given the greatest priority. You shouldn't need more than a day or two to get sufficient evidence together to confirm your own assessment, and to enable you to present a convincing case to your colleagues. You should then aim to involve them in deciding *what* needs to be done and *how*, questions which are dealt with in more detail in the remaining chapters of Part Three.

The check-lists which follow are subdivided into sections corresponding to the subjects covered in separate chapters of this book, with each subdivision preceded by a brief comment on key points. For each item on the check-lists a cross-reference is provided to the appropriate section in the relative chapters, in case you require further details on the points referred to. Some items could logically be included in more than one list: to avoid repetition they are included in the check-list for the first relevant chapter only.

As you go through the check-lists you will probably find it useful to compile a summary of what you assess your current performance to be for each item; I suggest you rate this on a six-point scale, with 0 meaning 'we don't do this at all at present', and 5 meaning 'I believe we're already up to world-class standard for this item'. I can't give you a 'standard' score assessment for the total points you might score because some of the items don't apply to every company, and because some items are of much greater significance than others. However, it *will* help you to see where there is scope for considerable improvement, and if your average score is less than 3 you can be quite sure that your company is still a long way from achieving its full potential, and that you still have a lot to do before you can rate your performance as world-class.

9.2 CHECK-LIST: STRATEGY AND MARKETING

'Taking the pulse' doesn't just mean looking at your factory, i.e. the supply side. You also need to look at the demand side, assessing how your customers react to both you and your competitors. The objective is to ensure that whenever you are planning any improvement activities, the emphasis is always on improving your competitive strength, so that your efforts will be rewarded by customers being willing to give you more business. Remember the acid test: if your salesforce hear that another major manufacturer is selling similar products to yours in a particular market, would it frighten them off, or would they say 'If they can sell there, so can we'?

When using the check-list below, your assessment of current performance should be based on what you are doing formally, as opposed to relying solely on the judgement of your Sales and Marketing people. However, to complete the picture you should also ask your Sales and Marketing Director questions such as: 'How have you been doing recently compared to your main competitors?', 'Is competition getting fiercer?', 'Have you achieved any significant improvements in the last year or two?', 'Or are you beginning to fall behind?,' 'Have any of your traditional competitors made a world-class type breakthrough yet?', and 'Have any new competitors arrived on the scene, who have moved the goalposts?'

Check-list: Chapters 2 and 10

1. Does the whole Board of Directors understand your strategy and are they committed to it? (Sec. 2.1)

2. Have you carried out a formal 'strengths, weaknesses, opportunities, threats' analysis within the last 12–18 months? If so, have you also set a date by which you intend to update this? (2.2)

3. Have you carried out a formal review of strategy, *involving the top management team*? (10.1) If so, have you also set a date by which you intend to update this?

4. Is your competitive strategy (cost leadership, differentiation, niche) determined instinctively, or is it the result of a conscious decision following careful analysis of competitor activities, and recognizing that a different strategy may be needed for different product family/market combinations? (2.2)

5. Do you periodically undertake market research, such as competitive benchmarking or PRP, specifically aimed at establishing what potential customers think of your products and services compared with those of your competitors? Do you use competitive benchmarking, in particular, when drawing up specifications for new products? (2.2)

6. Do you periodically review the current life-cycle position of your main products? (2.2)

7. Have you conducted an employee attitude survey within the last 12 months to determine current attitudes to quality and customer service? (2.3)

8. Does your business strategy incorporate the 'planning for downturn' concept? (2.4)

9. Do you have any improvement projects currently in progress aimed specifically at achieving a major step change improvement in performance *that you believe to be important to customers*, such as improving differentiation of your products rather than just reducing price through lower manufacturing costs? (2.6)

10. Developing new products is time-consuming and costly: there is a limit to how much can be done in any one year. Do you make decisions on what needs to be done now and what can be left until later on the basis of what is essential to enable you to achieve your strategic objectives and protect the company's future, or is your decision based simply on how much you think your current resources can cope with? (10.1, Worksheet 8)

11. Do you give targets to your sales force which are linked to those product families and markets identified in your strategy as the ones on which you wish sales efforts to be concentrated? (10.1, Worksheet 9)

12. Have you checked that your sales plan and current action plans are compatible with the *long-term* plan and 'mission' you have agreed for the future development of your company? (10.1, Worksheet 9)

13. Do you have regular strategy update meetings to review whether changing circumstances mean that the strategy may need to be revised? (10.1.7)

9.3 CHECK-LIST: JUST-IN-TIME

The aim of the just-in-time approach is to provide a fast, reliable and flexible response to customer's requirements at least cost and with minimum dependence on inventory. In assessing your performance under this heading the key indicators will be lead time; delivery performance; the proportion of people's time that doesn't add value; and the ratio of inventory value to current sales. You should be looking for hard evidence of a steady and continuous improvement in all these areas, coupled with step change improvements in a number of specific aspects. The check-list below suggests how you can obtain most of the evidence you need on lead time, delivery performance and inventory.

Assessing how much unnecessary cost is being incurred through not making the best use of people's time will be more difficult; however, you should be able to make a reasonable judgement on this through a simple 'activity sampling'-type exercise that can be carried out quite unobtrusively. Just walk round your factory using your fingers as a sort of abacus: if the first person you see is doing a task that is adding value, stick out a finger of your right hand; if the task doesn't add value, use a finger of your left hand instead. For subsequent observations, continue to add a finger from the appropriate hand or (to avoid running out of fingers!) take back a finger from the other hand. Until you've started applying the world-class approach you're unlikely to run out of fingers; in other words, you'll probably find that only about half the activities are actually adding value. If you're nearer to achieving world-class standards you may need to carry a notepad to record your observations. You'll never be able to eliminate non-value-adding activities completely, but you can at least see how much scope for improvement there still is, compared with a target of, say, 80 per cent value-adding that you will need before you can really claim to have achieved world-class performance.

Check-list: Chapters 3 and 11

1. Do you have a culture in which people are encouraged to expose any problems that are encountered so that they can be put right once and for all, or is the normal practice to go for a 'quick fix'? (Sec. 3.1)
2. Do your people, generally, think that 'waste' means process scrap, or do they understand the wider concept and continually strive to reduce all types of waste? (3.2)
3. Are process flow charts used as a means of identifying those process steps that cause the main elements of lead times? And is there an ongoing programme to reduce lead time by concentrating specifically on these key areas? (3.3)
4. Do you have a 'production delay' reporting procedure in which *operators* can draw attention to quality or productivity problems which cause delays to planned work? (3.3 and 11.2)
5. Do you continually monitor lead time and delivery performance? If so, do the graphs show a significant improvement compared with, say, 12 months previously? (3.3, 11.2 and 14.2)
6. Are you monitoring and routinely reporting both average *and* excessive set-up times and, if so, do these records show a significant improvement over the last 6–12 months? (11.3)
7. Have you used the SMED technique to systematically reduce set-up times, and have *operators* (as well as managers and technical staff) been encouraged to participate? And are your buyers familiar with the techniques so that they can encourage key suppliers to apply them also? (3.4)
8. Have you, within the last 12–18 months increased the frequency with which you review material requirements and update schedules, reduced batch sizes ordered

from outside suppliers, and challenged the level of finished stocks demanded by Sales and Marketing? (3.5)

9. Do you provide a 'next day despatch' service from your factory or warehouse for products offered as 'ex stock'? (3.5)

10. Have your inventory controllers identified the 'Top 100' or so purchased items and taken action to eliminate all instances of long lead time for these items? (11.4)

11. Is a 'resource/skills matrix' used in every department of the company to plan skills development and improve labour flexibility? (3.6)

12. Are Kanbans used (a) to minimize replacement time for frequently used materials and components, and (b) to simplify re-ordering paperwork? (3.7)

13. How well are you managing your suppliers? (see Sec. 11.6 for the seven levels of purchasing development)

14. Do you receive 'certificated deliveries' from your key suppliers (i.e 'zero defect deliveries')? (3.8)

15. Do you use the 'Simultaneous Engineering' approach to reduce the time needed to develop new products and to minimize the need subsequently for modifications? If so, can you demonstrate the success of this approach through what has actually happened with recent new product developments? (3.9)

16. Do you consciously and systematically endeavour to make new product designs (a) *flexible*, so that they can readily be adapted to suit differing customer requirements, and (b) *manufacturing friendly*, for example by making them more suitable for manufacturing in cells, minimizing the need for lengthy set-up changes, reducing the use of long lead time materials, re-designing to avoid potential quality problems, and making greater use of standard materials and components? (3.9)

17. Have you also used the value analysis or value engineering techniques to systematically review the design of all your main *existing* products, with a view to reducing cost and making them more manufacturing-friendly? (3.9)

18. If your manufacturing process is very dependent on machinery or process plant, have you taken steps to (a) get greater effectiveness and better value for money from your maintenance activities through the reliability-centred maintenance (RCM) approach, and (b) reduce the waste associated with equipment either breaking down or performing below par, through the application of total productive maintenance (TPM), involving operators? (3.10)

19. Do you have a 'traffic light' system in your manufacturing area, so that operators can signal to Supervision and Maintenance when they first notice a problem affecting quality or productivity, so that corrective action can be taken *before* it becomes serious? (3.11)

20. Have you appointed 'crisis avoidance teams' to anticipate potentially serious problems arising in your manufacturing equipment and processes, both to minimize the risk of such problems actually occurring and to ensure that, if they do, contingency plans have been prepared to ensure a prompt and organized reaction? (3.11 and 11.10)

21. Do you use simulation techniques *before* introducing major changes in process equipment or layout to anticipate (and avoid) potentially serious problems that might otherwise have been overlooked? (3.11)

22. Have you introduced the cell manufacturing concept to improve work flow, reduce set-up delays and minimize work-in-progress stocks? (11.9)

9.4 CHECK-LIST: TOTAL QUALITY

The total quality philosophy is based on *defect prevention* in place of the traditional *defect detection and correction*, the concept being that customers will only get full value for money if this hidden cost of quality is eliminated. Achieving world-class standards, therefore, means developing a 'quality creation' culture, in which every member of the workforce takes personal responsibility for the quality of his or her own work, and where it's accepted by all that the goal of 'right first time, every time' applies to every employee and to every aspect of the company's operations, not just to the manufacturing process.

The key indicators to look for, therefore, are evidence that 'quality' is widely recognized as being everyone's responsibility, and not just that of the inspectors and the Quality Control Department; evidence that the concept of everyone being both a customer and a supplier has been understood and that efforts are continually being made to improve the quality of service provided at each customer/supplier link; and evidence that efforts are being made in all parts of the company's operations to improve the achievement of 'first time' quality.

The check-list which follows should be sufficient for the 'taking the pulse' stage. More detailed guidance, should you require this subsequently, can be found in the *Guidelines for Identifying and Addressing Total Quality Issues*: this is a self-appraisal model published by The European Foundation for Quality Management (EFQM); contact details for EFQM are included in the Bibliography.

Check-list: Chapters 4 and 12

1. Where are you now? Have you reached the 'fourth era of quality' yet, where *everyone*, throughout the company, understands the total quality philosophy and accepts personal responsibility for the quality of his or her work? Or are you still in the second era, where people rely on others to inspect what they have done? Or are you part-way there, in the third era, with a framework of formal quality assurance systems and procedures in place, independently assessed by a recognized certification authority? (Secs.4.1 and 4.2)
2. Have your people formally analysed who their customers and suppliers are, and agreed standards for all their inputs and outputs (the DPA process)? If so, are you using this as a basis for planning and agreeing what should be given priority for the continuous improvement process? (4.3)
3. Have you completed a 'cost of quality analysis' within the last 12 months? If so, have you used this as a basis for deciding where action is most needed to reduce the costs of 'not getting it right first time, every time'? (4.4)
4. Who do your people think is responsible for quality in your company? (the right answer is 'everyone', with the Chief Executive as the overall 'Quality Boss') (4.8)
5. Do you use market research techniques such as 'competitive benchmarking' or the 'problem ranking process' (PRP) to find out what your customers really think about the quality of your products and the service you provide? (12.1)
6. Do you use SPC control charts as a means of anticipating processes going out of control *before* this happens and in time for corrective action to be taken? (12.5)

9.5 CHECK-LIST: TOTAL EMPLOYEE INVOLVEMENT

I said in Chapter 5 that 'the best opportunity for achieving a major breakthrough in manufacturing performance will come not so much from investing in new equipment or computers, nor from improving incentive payment schemes, but from making better use than ever before of the skills and experience of your whole workforce'. Some key indicators of successful total employee involvement are:

- There are always one or more multi-disciplinary teams of 'experts' working on major projects, in which: the project objectives are linked to achievement of the company's corporate plan; the team's work is coordinated by a facilitator and is *not* under the direction of a Project Manager or Team Leader; and the team members are 'empowered' to reach decisions and then act upon them with the minimum of second guessing by senior management.
- Shop floor workers are routinely involved in some organized form of continuous improvement activity (such as continuous improvement groups or quality circles), and the results of their efforts are monitored and regularly reviewed by senior management.
- Positive action is taken, on a continuous basis, to develop the skills and experience of each member of the workforce and, in particular, to improve labour flexibility.
- Managers and supervisors are clearly committed to spending part of their time on bringing about longer term improvements in performance, either through their individual 'personal commitment' tasks or through sponsoring and encouraging multi-disciplinary improvement teams.

As you will no doubt realize, what people tell you they are doing should be treated with some degree of scepticism: you also need to consider what sort of track record they have in recent years in improving manufacturing performance.

The check-list below should enable you to assess where you are now; more detailed guidance, should you require it, can be found in the check-lists included in the *Investors in People* documentation (see Bibliography).

Check-List: Chapters 5 and 13

1. Are you using the teamwork approach really effectively and involving the shop floor (a) on major projects, for which you set truly 'step change' targets and (b) on continuous improvement activities within each department? Can you *prove* that you are using teamwork effectively, by drawing up a list of what has actually been achieved as a result of specific team projects? (Secs. 5.1 and 13.1)
2. Are all these improvement initiatives structured with a view to achieving the objectives set out in your business plans? Do all your people, not just the managers, understand why it is important for these objectives to be achieved, and the effects this might have on them personally? If you are at an early stage of introducing the world-class concepts, have you done anything positive to reassure those who fear that 'increased productivity' will mean 'fewer jobs'? (5.2 and 13.1)
3. Do team members always participate willingly, or do some continue to resist due to 'pressure of other work'? (5.2 and 13.1)

4. Are your improvement projects structured in the 'world-class' way, with a facilitator to coordinate their work in place of the traditional project manager? (13.1)
5. Do you empower teams to take responsibility for decisions and implementation? Are they allowed or, better still, encouraged, to challenge 'sacred cows' (if so, which sacred cows have been challenged successfully, i.e. which have actually been changed, within the last 12 months)? (13.1)
6. Do you review progress on world-class improvement activities regularly and routinely at company and departmental management meetings, quantifying what has actually been achieved and comparing this with targets set? (5.2)
7. Do you set targets for the proportion of their time managers should spend on world-class initiatives and, if so, do you make sure that they are achieving their targets? (5.2)
8. Do your managers have 'personal commitment tasks' and, if so, are they all required to report progress regularly in front of their colleagues? (5.6)
9. Have you prepared a 'People Plan' that details the proposed development of your human resources, placing greater emphasis than in the past on training? Are these perceived training needs formally linked to the strategy review, to ensure that the workforce as a whole will have the necessary skills to achieve the company's corporate objectives? (5.7)
10. Have you restructured the way in which your management is organized, to reflect the 'empowering people' concept and to place greater emphasis on team leaders instead of the traditional multi-level management structure? (5.8)
11. Have you ensured that your whole workforce understands the world-class concepts, in particular the need for both step change *and* continuous improvement, through a company-wide briefing programme? (13.4)

9.6 CHECK-LIST: WORLD-CLASS INFORMATION SYSTEMS

I said in Chapter 1 that 'Systems should not be thought of in their own right as the means of achieving world-class performance, but rather as an enabling tool. There is really only one test or key indicator that matters: do your current systems *help* or *hinder* you in your efforts to improve performance and achieve world-class standards?'. The following check-list should help you answer this question.

Check-List: Chapters 6 and 14

1. Are your manufacturing systems (particularly the inventory parts) sufficiently accurate and reliable to support the control and decision-making processes, or are users continually complaining about them? (Sec. 14.7)
2. Do the 'owners' of the systems meet at least once a year to consider any changes that may be necessary to further improve their reliability? (14.7)
3. Do your current computer systems provide sufficient flexibility to enable you to adapt them to your world-class needs, as these develop? In particular, is there a query language that will enable you to 'unlock' the information in your database without the need for additional programming? (6.4)

4. Do you routinely monitor and report lead time, delivery performance and set-up time information? If so, do these reports demonstrate that a steady improvement in performance is being achieved? (6.3, 14.2 and 14.5)
5. Does your costing system provide inaccurate or misleading information on the true cost of individual components and products, because of the way in which overheads are recovered? Or have you introduced procedures such as 'activity-based costing' to enable decisions to be made on a sound basis? (6.3 and 14.1)
6. Do your systems readily provide all the information you need to monitor the progress you are making towards achieving your business objectives? (6.3 and 14.5)

9.7 CHECK-LIST: MANAGING THE CHANGE

When you raise the suggestion with you senior colleagues that you should apply the sort of world-class approach described in this book, you will probably get the answer that they've tried some of the techniques already. If this is the case, and yet your answers to the check-list questions above have convinced you that you still have a long way to go in order to reach world-class standard, the reason will probably be the way in which the change programme was managed in the past (perhaps I should have said *'failed* to be managed'!).

If you have indeed tried any of the 'new' techniques, such as just-in-time or total quality, key indicators of how well the intended change was managed might be:

- Did they achieve all that was expected? If not, why not?
- Were the changes 'shop floor' driven? And did they recognize the need to react specifically to customers' 'hot buttons'?
- Was the emphasis on the technique (i.e. 'we're putting in just-in-time'), or on the customer benefit ('we're cutting lead time and improving delivery performance')?
- To what extent do those involved believe their effectiveness was hindered by 'brick walls' between departments? Has anything been done recently to break down these barriers and, if so, with what success?

You should also consider whether people talked too glibly beforehand about the benefits which they hoped to achieve or, after the event, claim to have achieved. You can test how valid these claims are by asking them to show you which specific figures on the management accounts will show the benefits; and if they claim 'this has saved ten people', ask for the names of the people whose jobs have been eliminated, and what happened to them – were they made redundant or were they simply moved to another job and, if so, how will their output in their new job be reflected in the accounts? These sorts of questions help you assess how effectively your people have managed change in the past, because the whole point of change is to achieve benefits: as far as possible, those benefits need to be forecast beforehand in order to justify the changes proposed, and they need to be measured after the change programme is completed to demonstrate that the changes were successful.

Some specific aspects of managing a programme of change aimed at achieving world-class performance are summarized in the check-list below.

Check-List: Chapter 7

1. Do you have a successful record of introducing change in recent years, encompassing any of the world-class philosophies, for example elements of just-in-time or total quality? If so, are you still experiencing resistance to change? (Sec. 7.1)
2. If you have launched a project aimed at achieving a step change improvement in productivity, did you at the same time launch a project aimed at increasing sales sufficiently to at least absorb the resources freed, in order to counter the assumption that 'improving efficiency means that some people will lose their jobs'? (7.2)
3. Have your efforts to involve the whole workforce in the 'continuous improvement' process been preceded by step change projects, to provide a high-profile demonstration of what can be achieved through effective teamwork? (7.2)
4. Are your continuous improvement efforts directed towards improving the quality of service provided at each customer/supplier link? (7.2)
5. Do you make sure that everyone is regularly informed about your world-class activities and the successes achieved, for example through a *World-Class Newsletter*? (7.2)
6. Do all members of the top management team (particularly the Chief Executive) keep reaffirming publicly their whole-hearted commitment to the company's world-class objectives? (7.3)

REVIEWING STRATEGY

Linked to Chapter 2, this chapter provides more detail on the process of reviewing strategy. Sample worksheets are included to illustrate the process and useful analysis techniques are summarized. The chapter concludes with two case studies: the first shows how conflicting views on future strategy at Intertronic Business Systems were resolved through the review process, and the second how Cincinnati Milacron developed a new strategy, involving competitive benchmarking, which enabled them to regain their position as a world leader in their field.

10.1 THE REVIEW PROCESS

10.1.1 Introduction

The process of developing a world-class strategy was described in Chapter 2. In this section I'll explain it in more detail, using a set of worksheets to illustrate the sort of information that needs to be analysed. These worksheets are taken from a real-life strategy review; although some details have been amended in order to protect the company's identity, the changes are not significant in respect of the business analysis or action plans agreed.

The company in this example designs and manufactures a wide variety of paint-spraying equipment, ranging from simple spray guns at one end of the scale to sophisticated computer-controlled painting installations at the other extreme; the latter typically includes an environment-controlled booth equipped with work holding and rotating devices and robots for applying the surface-finishing media. In addition, the company has a Contract Services Division which acts as a subcontractor to other manufacturers, providing a surface-preparation and surface-finishing service. There is also a wholly owned subsidiary company in 'Southern Europe' which had been acquired a few years previously, and which has a similar and overlapping range of products of its own design. The combined annual turnover is in the region of Ffr150 million. The review of future strategy at the Headquarters site, from which the example worksheets have been adapted, was instigated by the Chief Executive, who had joined the company a few months earlier.

Although the general principles of the review process will usually be the same regardless of the type of business, the information that *you* will need in order to make sensible decisions about *your* future strategy may well differ in some respects from that shown in the example. For some companies the worksheets provided in the *Competitive Manufacturing* workbook (see Bibliography) may be more appropriate; or you may prefer to do as I do, and use the set shown in Figs. 10.1–10.11 (or those from another source) as a basis, *modifying them to suit your particular circumstances*. It's well worthwhile doing this modification if some of those who will be participating in the strategy review don't have previous experience of the process: they are likely to be confused or put off if they feel that some of the worksheets they are asked to complete are not really appropriate to their situation.

10.1.2 The Review Process Structure

There are four stages to the review process described below:

- *Stage 1*: Understanding your market position (Worksheets 1–5)
- *Stage 2*: Assessing your current manufacturing performance (see below)
- *Stage 3*: Assessing the future market; threats and opportunities (Worksheets 6–9)
- *Stage 4*: Developing your new strategy (Worksheets 10 and 11).

You will usually find that you don't have enough information readily available to enable you to complete all the worksheets in the detail suggested. You should therefore plan to complete the review in two stages: the objective in the first workshop should be to get everyone familiar with the review process and to identify what additional information is required; the objective in the second workshop should be to complete the review and develop your new strategy, with the period between the two workshops being used to collect the additional information required. Sometimes this additional information will take some time to obtain, for example if extensive market research is necessary. In this case you will need to decide if you can really afford to wait that long; it may be necessary to go ahead with the second workshop without waiting for the results of the external market research, in order to avoid any delay in launching urgent improvement projects; you can then revise your strategy when the additional information is available, should this prove necessary.

10.1.3 Stage 1: Understanding Your Market Position

To start with you need to summarize where you get your business at the moment. Worksheets 1, 2 and 3 are used to record the main products and services you sell, to what categories of customers and in which geographical markets. Worksheets 4 and 5 are concerned with what the key market requirements are, how well you currently satisfy these requirements compared with your competitors, and hence what your competitive strengths and weaknesses are.

Worksheet 1: Existing products and services Start by listing your current products and services in the first column. Only show the main groups of 'product families' (as shown in Fig. 10.1), or you will find yourselves getting bogged down in too much detail in the later stages of the analysis, when separate worksheets have to be prepared for each product family. Most businesses have some product types which are insignificant in terms of the company's total business and these only need to be included if you expect them to grow in importance in the future.

At this point you will need to discuss whether you need to break the analysis down further by market type. For example, if the bulk of your sales are mainly to one type of customer, you may be able to ignore Worksheets 2 and 3, completing the analysis of existing products and services by filling in the remaining columns of Worksheet 1. Suppose, however, that half your sales are to the home market where you are the market leader, and the other half of your sales are to export markets, where competition is much tougher; in such circumstances you may well have to adopt a different strategy for the two types of market and you will then need to use Worksheets 2 and 3 to identify the most important combinations of product family and market type.

Ideally, even if you are going on to use Worksheets 2 and 3, you should complete the remaining columns of Worksheet 1 since this will help the participants to get a better understanding of where business is being won (and, equally important, where it isn't, because that can provide a pointer to where additional opportunities might be found.

The 'Sales %' column is simply, for each product family, the value of sales expressed as a percentage of total sales value for all products.

The 'Contribution %' column is normally the contribution or margin for each product family, expressed as a percentage of the total contribution for *all* products. The main purpose of this and the preceding column is to identify clearly which product families are currently responsible for the bulk of your sales revenue and profit. However, there *are* circumstances in which it is preferable to show instead the margin of each product family relative to its *own* sales value, for example to highlight significant variations in margin between different product families.

The 'Market share' column entry doesn't need to be precise. If you do know what it is, then enter the appropriate percentage figure, together with those of your main competitors; if you don't know the actual percentage shares, state the ranking of your company and the top three or four competitors or, if the market is fragmented with no one company having a significant share of the market, enter 'fragmented'. If you have difficulty in deciding what to enter, consider whether you need to commission some market research to get a better understanding of your position relative to that of your competitors. Remember that the main purpose at this stage is to make sure that all members of the review team understand the extent to which any action you might take to increase sales might provoke a reaction from your competitors. For example, if the market is very fragmented with no main market leader you could probably double your sales without your competitors noticing, whereas if you are the market leader with, say, over half the current market, your future strategy might need to concentrate on protecting your share of existing markets while looking to other markets for growth.

Worksheet 1: Existing products and services

Product family	Sales (%)	Contribution (%)	Market share	Growth	Remarks
1. Standard Booths					
2. Special Booths		See Worksheet 3 for breakdown of key product/market families			
3. Sprayers					
4. Contract Services – Surface Preparation					
5. Contract Services – Surface Finishing					
6. Spares					
7. Service					

Figure 10.1 Worksheet 1: Existing products and services

The 'Growth' column is probably the most important from the point of view of deciding your future strategy. I suggest you use a five-point scale, as follows:

- Declining rapidly   enter -2
- Declining   enter -1
- Static   enter 0
- Growing   enter $+1$
- Growing rapidly   enter $+2$

In the example illustrated in Fig. 10.1 there were a number of very different types of products and markets with differing customer requirements, so that the detailed analysis was left until the most important combinations had been identified through the next two worksheets.

Worksheet 2: Existing markets Figure 10.2 illustrates two different ways in which current sales can be broken down by market type.

Some companies will find it best to concentrate on *customer* types, as shown in the upper part of Fig. 10.2. In other cases it may be preferable to break sales down by *core products*, subdividing each into types of market, as shown in the lower part of Fig. 10.2. The choice will depend on what information is appropriate in your particular circumstances to enable you to select (for Worksheet 3) what your key product/market families are at present, and (for Worksheet 7) what additional combinations of products and markets, not currently exploited, offer the best opportunities for expanding sales by building on your existing specialist skills and reputation. If in doubt, try both, but do think first about whether the information you are asking for is readily available from existing records, or whether it will involve a lot of manual analysis of past orders (in which case you should only ask for the analysis to be done if you are really sure that you need it).

Entries in the 'Sales', 'Contribution', 'Market share' and 'Growth' columns should be as explained for Worksheet 1.

Worksheet 3: Existing key product/market families Worksheet 3, illustrated in Fig. 10.3, is prepared by combining the most significant products and markets identified in Worksheets 1 and 2. Ideally, you should aim to include the 20 per cent or so of product/market families which account for 80 per cent of your sales turnover and profit. Unfortunately, most companies find that their business is too fragmented for them to be able to achieve this, and you'll probably end up with a lot more than 20 per cent of product families in order to include a minimum of around 70 per cent of sales and profit.

When you're deciding which combinations to include, don't stick too rigidly to the subdivisions of markets which you used in Worksheet 2. As you can see in the example illustrated, sales of 'Special Booths' to all types and locations of markets have been combined in Worksheet 3: this was because further analysis of a sample of past orders showed that there was in practice little difference in market characteristics or competition between the various subdivisions of potential sales outlets originally considered.

In the example, the analysis, which shows contribution in terms of each product's *own* sales, revealed that two product groups, Special Booths and Service, made a loss at the time. These two product groups were related, since on investigation most of the Service activity was found to be concerned with correcting problems with the Special

Worksheet 2: Existing markets

Customer type	Location	Sales (%)	Contribution (%)	Market share	Growth	Remarks
A1-DEFENCE INDUSTRY	HOME (≤100 km)					
A2- " "	" (>100 km)					
A3- " "	EXPORT					
B1-MOTOR INDUSTRY	HOME (≤100 km)		See Worksheet 3 for breakdown of key product/market families			
B2- " "	" (>100 km)					
B3- "	EXPORT					
C1-OTHER PRIVATE SECTOR	HOME (≤100 km)					
C2- " "	" (>100 km)					
C3- " "	EXPORT					
C4 " PUBLIC SECTOR	HOME					
A. STANDARD BOOTHS						
A1-Motor Industry	Home					
A2- Others	Home					
A3- All	Export					
B. SPECIAL BOOTHS			See Worksheet 3 for breakdown of key product/market families			
B1-Defence Industry	Home & Export					
B2-Motor Industry	Home					
B3- " "	Export					
B4- Others	Home					
B5. "	Export					

Figure 10.2 Worksheet 2: Existing markets.

174

Worksheet 3: Existing *key* product/market families

Product/market family	Sales (%)	Contribution (%)	Market share %	Growth	Remarks
1a. Standard Booths (Home)	4.8	5	70	+1	– STRATEGY = 'COST LEADER'
2a.Special Booths (All Markets)	9.6	(3.3)	45	+1	– STRATEGY = 'DIFFERENTIATION'
3a. Sprayers (Home)	6.3	21	80	–1	–STRATEGY = 'COST LEADER'
3b. " (Export)	5.2	21	30	–1	– STRATEGY = 'NICHE / DIFF'N'
4a. Contract Services– Surface Preparation	5.0	8	50	+1	3 main competitors : STRATEGY = 'NICHE/COST + SERVICE'
5a Contract Services – Surface Finishing (DEFENCE)	6.2	5	16	+1	–Only 1 competitor (US Parent) but he is World Market Leader : STRATEGY = 'NICHE/DIFF'N'
5b. " (OTHER)	3.7	6	80	+1	–STRATEGY = 'NICHE/DIFF'N (SERVICE)
6a Spares (All Markets)	13.9	71	45	+1	–Future growth dependent on sales of special booths and (to a lesser extent) Sprayers. STRATEGY = 'DIFFERENTIATION'
7 Service (All Markets)	2.8	(13)	80	+1	– Much of the current Service activity is warranty work on special booths within first 3 months after installation. But scope for profitable growth of annual overhaul and maintenance business. STRATEGY = 'DIFFERENTIATION'

Figure 10.3 Worksheet 3: Existing *key* product/market families.

Booths during the warranty period. The fact that these two parts of the business were making a loss had not been recognized earlier because operating costs for individual product families had not been accounted for separately; it was only when costs were separated for the purposes of the strategy review that it was realized that the bulk of the company's technical and design overheads were incurred by the Special Booths product, and the full extent of the problem was thus revealed. You will see later how this information was picked up at a subsequent stage of the strategy review, when preparing the action plans.

It's also a good idea at this stage to decide what your current marketing strategy is (cost-leadership, differentiation or niche), and record this in the 'Remarks' column. You'll probably find that you don't actually have a clearly defined policy on this at present, which is precisely why I suggest you record it on this worksheet: doing so forces your team to consider what marketing stance they want to adopt, which needs to be settled before you go on to assess your current performance against a number of competitive criteria.

Worksheet 4: Market requirements vs. current performance Having decided which your key product/market families are, the next step is to look at how good you are at satisfying customers' requirements in these at present. This involves looking at a number of factors, such as product performance, price, lead time and delivery reliability. What matters here is not what *you* think is a good selling point (perhaps because it's an aspect you're good at); what really matters is what *customers* think is important enough to *affect their choice of supplier*.

Worksheet 4 (Fig. 10.4) is used to show graphically how well (or how badly) you are currently performing compared with what the market wants. It will often be the case that your competitiveness varies depending on which product family and which market you are looking at; you therefore need to complete a separate Worksheet 4 for each combination of product and market that you've identified (through Worksheets 1 to 3) as being a key product/market family.

Worksheet 4, when completed, will take the form of a bar chart containing a number of paired lines drawn with a felt pen, one pair for each of a number of performance criteria. The upper line of each pair shows the *customers' view* of that factor's importance on a scale of 0 (not significant) to 5 (highly significant); the lower line of the pair shows your *current achievement* on a scale of 0 (poor) to 5 (good).

The worksheet is pre-printed with the six performance criteria that nearly always need to be considered, and there are a further five lines provided for you to add additional criteria as appropriate. These might, for example, include factors such as 'after-sales service', or the 'comfort factor' afforded by sticking to a long-established or leading brand name supplier. You may well need to commission some external market research in order to decide which factors are most important to *your* potential customers, and also to rank them in order of importance. If you are forced to rely on feedback from your sales force or distributors, treat what they say with caution; research shows that they usually don't know as much as they think they do about what really is important to customers! You should also take the precaution of splitting the strategy review team into two sub-teams, getting one team to draw the upper line (the customers' view) and the other sub-team to draw the lower line (the actual performance).

Worksheet 4: Market requirements vs. current performance
(use a separate sheet for each key product/market family)

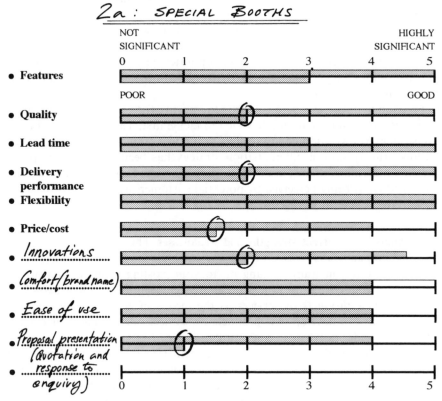

Key: – The upper part of each line should be used to indicate how
significant CUSTOMERS consider that factor to be.
– The lower part of each line should be used to indicate the
company's ACTUAL performance currently.

Figure 10.4 Worksheet 4: Market requirements vs. current performance.

In the example illustrated in Fig. 10.4, there are five performance criteria where actual performance is currently worse than customers' requirements by more than two points. If *your* analysis comes out as badly as this you will at least know that you've now identified plenty of opportunities for improvement, and ones that potential customers are likely to respond to! However, before deciding which to challenge first, do make sure that the results of the analysis look reasonable: remember what I said in the previous paragraph: 'If you are forced to rely on feedback from your sales force or distributors, treat what they say with caution; research shows that they usually don't know as much as they think they do about what really is important to customers!' The worksheet shown in Fig. 10.4 is, in fact, the first version submitted: it was challenged by some members of the team on the grounds that no fewer than five factors had been marked as being the most significant in customers' eyes (level 5 grading), a further three factors were given a level 4 grading, and not a single factor was given less than a level 3. True, customers would probably agree that all these factors are important, but they are sure to rate one or two of them as the most significant of all, and *that's* what you want to know. In the strategy review illustrated, a sample of customers were subsequently invited to rank the 10 factors included in the original version of Worksheet 4 in order of importance to *them*. The results were then incorporated in a revised version of the worksheet, which showed that 'Quality' and 'Delivery performance' were considered by customers to be the most important.

If there are too many areas where you need to improve for you to be able to tackle them all together, you will have to decide which to tackle first. This will depend on the competitive strategy you've adopted; in the illustration, for example, 'price/cost' would be given a low priority since a differentiation strategy has been adopted for Special Booths; 'quality' and 'innovations', in contrast, should be given a higher priority to re-establish the product as being perceived by potential customers as so much better than competitors' products that price ceases to be a deciding factor.

Worksheet 5: Analysis of current strengths and weaknesses This worksheet is used to summarize your company's *strengths*, on which you can build, and its *weaknesses*, which need to be overcome if you want to hang on to your existing business. If you can improve on those of your current weaknesses that are significant to customers, you'll be less dependent on new products or services as the means of achieving your growth targets. If you *do* have to develop new products or services, identifying your current strengths will help you decide where to concentrate.

Getting a thorough understanding of your current strengths and weaknesses *as perceived by potential customers* is so important that it's worth going to some trouble to find out what customers really think. Consider using market research techniques such as 'competitive benchmarking' and the 'problem ranking process', described in Sec. 2.2: the first will help you to assess your strengths and weaknesses compared to competitors, and the second will help you to decide which of these are the most important to potential customers.

An extract from a completed Worksheet 5 is shown in Fig. 10.5; note that several pages will normally be required for this worksheet, with each of the selected key product/market families being considered in turn, first for strengths and then for weaknesses.

10.1.4 Stage 2: Assessing Your Current Manufacturing Performance

Some aspects of current manufacturing performance, such as quality, lead time and delivery performance, have already been referred to briefly in Worksheet 4. The review team may well include members who have a sufficiently detailed knowledge of the current situation to enable the team to decide the priorities for action, and to draw up terms of reference for any improvement projects which need to be included in the action plan (covered later, in Worksheet 11). However, you may decide that additional information is needed before terms of reference can be prepared. For example, in the case of the 'quality' factor:

Worksheet 5: Analysis of current strengths and weaknesses

Product/market family	Strengths	Weaknesses	Contributory factors
2a SPECIAL BOOTHS (all markets)	- Ease of use		- Understanding and correct interpretation of customers' requirements - Technical expertise
	- Comfort		- Brand name - Image in market place, particularly Europe - Prudence in not over-reaching ourselves when agreeing technical and performance specifications - Strong support from HQ
	- Features		- Strong sales/technical understanding of the <u>need</u> for innovation, and a willingness to go for steady, continuous product improvement
	- Innovation from Development	(See also 'weaknesses' on page 3 'Innovation from Research')	- Our ability to provide 'bolt-on' innovation

(Continued on page 3)

Figure 10.5 Worksheet 5: Analysis of current strengths and weaknesses. *(Continued overleaf.)*

Worksheet 5: Analysis of current strengths and weaknesses

Product/market family	Strengths	Weaknesses	Contributory factors
2a SPECIAL BOOTHS (all Markets) (Continued from Page 2)		– Quality	– Lack of understanding in some departments of need for quality – Lack of management commitment in past – policy was 'OUTPUT is FIRST PRIORITY, QUALITY SECOND'
		– Delivery Performance	– Too much emphasis placed on meeting monthly budgeted output, instead of on customers' needs – Insufficient resources to cope with highly fluctuating workload in all departments i.e., Technical, planning, Purchasing and Production.
		– Innovation from Research	– Lack of investment in original research – Insufficient attention paid to competitors' developments
		– Proposal Production	– We take too long to respond to enquiries due to lack of resources – Proposals are technically good, but presentation is poor

Figure 10.5 Worksheet 5: Analysis of current strengths and weaknesses. (*Concluded.*)

- Where are quality problems occurring? Why are they getting through to customers? Is the problem recent or long-standing? Does it affect all products in the family or only some? Are all customers affected equally, or only some? Is the problem caused by faulty materials or in our own manufacturing process? (And so on . . . .)

Similar sorts of questions may also need to be asked about the other manufacturing-related factors that were included in your Worksheet 4.

One way of finding the answers to questions such as these would be to carry out a full audit of your manufacturing function, encompassing equipment, people and systems. Indeed, many consultants who specialize in strategy work recommend that you should routinely carry out a detailed audit of the manufacturing function as part of the strategy review process. While accepting that there are times when this is advisable, as a general rule I prefer to concentrate only on those aspects of manufacturing performance which have been identified in Worksheet 4 as currently performing *significantly below the standard required by potential customers*. This will save a great deal of time, so that you can get on with the key task of developing your future strategy, and it will also ensure that attention is directed at putting right the things that *matter to customers*. In my view, the best time to carry out a detailed audit of the manufacturing function is *after* the new strategy has been agreed: you can then look at your *existing* manufacturing function in terms of what is required of it in the *future*, the objective being to identify any changes that might be necessary to bring the manufacturing function in line with what is required to meet the new strategy.

10.1.5 Stage Three: Assessing The Future Market (Threats and Opportunities)

The worksheets completed so far have been concerned primarily with what is happening now and in the recent past; they're effectively a snapshot in time. If you base your new strategy just on these (as many companies do), then you are really assuming that nothing will change other than the way in which you and your competitors fight for a share of the market. That was fine in the days when the markets for our products were pretty stable, but, unfortunately, the world has changed. The pace of innovation today, coupled with the instability of markets in some parts of the world, make it increasingly important to ask the question: 'Can we rely on current levels of demand for our products continuing'. In other words, looking backwards isn't enough; we also need to look at the future, to try to anticipate things that might go wrong, and also to look for opportunities that can help us achieve our longer term objectives.

Worksheets 6 (Threats) and 7 (Opportunities) These are illustrated in Figs. 10.6 and 10.7 respectively, and should be completed for each of the key product/market families identified in the previous worksheets. You should also consider where each of these key families is at present in its life cycle, so that you can identify the extent to which you need to plan the launch of new products to compensate for those with declining demand. An explanation of the life cycle concept can be found in Sec. 2.2. You need to be particularly careful not to interpret a growth in sales (as recorded in Worksheets 1, 2 and 3) as meaning that there's no problem: sales will sometimes increase towards the end of a product's life cycle because of price discounting or competitors withdrawing from the market. Nor should you assume that a product is past its 'sell by' date just

Worksheet 6: Assessing the future market: threats

Product/market family	Threat	Possible actions/responses
2a SPECIAL BOOTHS (all markets) *(Life cycle = B/C)*	- Virtual domination of world defence applications by our US competitor	- Try for a foothold in US markets by improving our profile in US Defence manufacturers' minds and by lobbying - Improve Support at enquiry stage to our distributors in each European country and ask them what we can do to help them get their country's Defence Industry to give preference to us as a European Supplier
	- Reduction in need for CNC-controlled Surface finishing due to development of new materials	- Consult our contacts in industry to identify new application areas
	- Competitors build on our slow response time to capture orders and so demonstrate their ability, so that we lose subsequent orders too	- Take whatever action is needed to achieve 'World-class' performance * (possible key strategic project?) *

Figure 10.6 Worksheet 6: Assessing the future market: threats.

Worksheet 7: Assessing the future market: opportunities

Product/market family	Opportunities	Possible actions
2a. SPECIAL BOOTHS (all markets) Life cycle = B/C	– Improve design, technical and production co-operation between HQ and Southern Europe associate company (At present, the only inter-company contact is in Finance; other departments jealously protect their technical skills, even though the two companies do not compete as they keep strictly to their own geographical markets. We can each improve our competitive edge by pooling our design, technical and production expertise, and by eliminating some areas of duplication.)	1. Improve communication – Exchange product information (existing sales literature and technical data sheets) – Exchange visits between 'experts' from Design, Technical and Production departments 2. Technical Audit of both companies, to identify product overlaps and centres of excellence 3. (Following 1 and 2) Develop plans for exploiting the combined resources more effectively

Figure 10.7 Worksheet 7: Assessing the future market: opportunities.

because it's reaching the end of its life cycle in a particular market: there are numerous examples of motor cars which have reached the end of their life in some markets, but which still continue to be manufactured in large quantities in other parts of the world.

As you can see from the illustrations, your estimate of where each product/market family is in its life cycle should be entered in the first column of Worksheets 6 and 7. The actual diagrams, as illustrated in Figs. 2.1 and 2.2, don't really need to be drawn for the purposes of the strategy review. However, they can be very useful later, when you want to explain to others why management have decided that new products or markets need to be developed in order to compensate for product/market families that are nearing the end of their life cycle.

Worksheet 8: Improving performance of existing product/market families If you can improve on your current weaknesses that are perceived by potential customers as being significant, then you'll be less dependant on having to introduce new products and services, or opening up new markets, to achieve your sales and profit targets – and it will probably cost a lot less and get results sooner.

You have already recorded on Worksheet 4 the competitive criteria that potential customers consider to be the most important, and you've also shown how your present performance measures up to customers' expectations. Worksheet 8 should now be used to list the performance criteria in which you need to improve most. List these in order of priority, starting with those rated highest by customers, and then in order of your greatest shortfall in performance. You will probably need to use the brainstorming technique to identify the main causes of your poor performance, followed by one of the short-listing techniques to select the most important (this process is described in detail in Chapter 8). Figure 10.8 illustrates the sort of information you should enter on the worksheet.

Worksheet 9: Summary of future products and markets You should now be ready to draw up a sales plan for existing product/market families, taking into account the increased sales you can expect to achieve from improving on your current weaknesses, and the reduction in sales that has to be allowed for as a result of the threats you've identified. Most companies will have an existing annual budgeting procedure that can be used for this; if not, you can use Worksheet 9 (Fig. 10.9), entering in the columns provided the sales volumes, revenue and profit you are looking for from each product in each market. What you are effectively doing here is to *target* your markets, so that your sales force knows what products, and which potential customers and markets, management wants them to concentrate on. In other words *you* are in the driving seat, *you* influence how and where the company grows, and *you* are ensuring that your sales force doesn't just react to events. To achieve this, you need to make sure that your list shows clearly:

- What new products need to be added
- Which existing products should be dropped, or progressively phased out, and whether this would affect sales of other products
- Which existing markets should be closed down, or treated on a reactive basis only
- Which new markets need to be opened up

Worksheet 8: Improving performance of existing *key* product/market families

Product/market family: _2a. SPECIAL BOOTHS. (all Markets)_ _ _ _ _ _

Performance factor	Contributory factor	Proposed action	Remarks
QUALITY (Target = 5; Actual = 2)	– Poor definition of 'quality' requirements	– Clarify quality requirements better at Tech. Spec'n and Detailed Design Stage	– As already required by ISO 9000.
	– Lack of understanding of 'quality' requirements in Production and at subcontractors	– Establish 'quality improvement team' – Consider introducing quality circles in all departments	– A multi-disciplinary interdepartmental team is needed; use Pareto analysis to identify key problem areas – Key subcontractors need to be involved – can we talk to some of them about 'Zero Defects' and 'Certificated Deliveries'?
	– Lack of commitment by management (at end of month, achieving budgeted output often takes precedence over quality)	– Quality awareness seminar for senior management led by Chief Executive	
DELIVERY PERFORMANCE (Target = 5; Actual = 2)	– Quality problems	(see above)	– We'll continue to suffer production delays until we get the quality problem sorted
	– Late deliveries from subcontractors	– Discuss problem areas with subcontractors to get their viewpoint – Identify long lead time materials and specify earlier in design stage	– Subcontractor delays may be their fault, but in many cases it's because we haven't allowed them enough time

Figure 10.8 Worksheet 8: Improving performance of existing *key* product/market families.

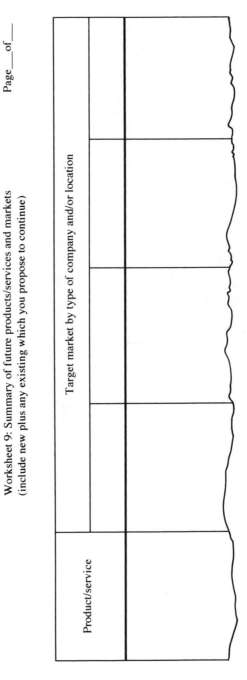

Figure 10.9 Worksheet 9: Summary of future products/services and markets.

Worksheet 9: Summary of future products/services and markets
(include new plus any existing which you propose to continue)

Page____of____

Product/service	Target market by type of company and/or location			

In the example, Worksheet 3 showed that the Special Booths product group made a loss equivalent to 3.3 per cent of sales turnover (you may remember that product groups had not been separately costed until required for this review). The Service product group made an even greater percentage loss as a direct result of problems arising in the Special Booths products shortly after they were delivered to customers. An obvious option to consider was to cease production of Special Booths; however, answering the second of the above questions revealed that the highly profitable spares business was almost entirely dependent for its longer term future on continuing sales of Special Booths, making action to improve that product's performance a high priority. With most of the other product groups the company's current market share was already so high that any significant growth in sales of these products would require the opening up of new markets. These conclusions may seem to you to be so obvious that you may be wondering why the company went to all the trouble of carrying out a formal review of strategy. I can only say that neither point had been realized by top management until they undertook the review featured in these worksheets; perhaps their past business success had made them too complacent, so that they had not appreciated the extent of the problems which their recent technological advances had introduced. I suspect that they are far from unique in that!

Before going ahead with the development of new products and markets you should first consider the extent to which you want to and should do this now, rather than next year, for example. The sort of questions you should consider are:

- Can you achieve your sales and profit objectives *without doing anything*? (If you are tempted to answer 'Yes' to this question, ask yourselves if you really want your company to be world-class: if you do, then, at the very least, you need to commit yourselves to a policy of continuous improvement, which should enable you to increase your sales and profit targets).
- Can you achieve your sales and profit targets simply by improving performance in your current product/market families?
- If so, what action must be taken? (record this on Worksheet 8).
- If not, as well as identifying the necessary performance improvement actions, decide which new products and/or markets must be added to your list.
- If you follow a differentiation strategy, do you need to develop new products simply to maintain your reputation as an innovator and to ensure that you are not overtaken by a competitor?

Developing new products is time-consuming and costly: there is a limit to how much can be done in any one year. The objective at this stage of the strategy review is to decide what needs to be done now and what can be left until later, and to make this decision on the basis of what is essential to enable you to achieve your strategic objectives and protect the company's future, rather than from how much you think your current resources can cope with. If you decide that certain developments are essential, then you either have to find a way of doing them, or you have to change your strategic objectives.

10.1.6 Developing Your New Strategy

Having decided what products you expect to sell and what markets you intend to target, the final stage is to decide what changes you must make to the way in which you operate at present in order to make this possible. In particular, you need to consider what obstacles you will have to overcome, both internal and external. To some extent you can identify likely obstacles by looking at your current performance shortfalls (Worksheet 8) and the possible threats you've identified (Worksheet 6); reverse brainstorming (explained in Sec. 3.11) is a useful technique for extending these lists. The comments on 'planning for downturn' in Sec. 2.4, and on 'reducing the risks of change' in Sec. 3.11, should also be considered before finalizing your strategy.

You should also check whether your current operations and resources are adequate, bearing in mind any new products or change in mix you are planning and the means by which you will achieve performance improvement. The sort of questions to ask are:

- Are your production facilities appropriate and do you have sufficient capacity?
- Do you have the right processes and technical support?
- Do you need to change your organizational structure, or introduce new concepts such as just-in-time or total quality?
- Does your workforce have the right skills and flexibility, or do you need to plan additional recruitment and training programmes?
- Are your systems and control procedures adequate?
- Do you need to do anything to improve your suppliers' performance, for example by introducing 'partnership sourcing'?
- If you intend to introduce new products, do you have sufficient (and appropriate) design and development resources, and are there adequate procedures to control their work?
- If your new strategy results in a different level of sales, or a change in product mix, what effect will this have on your overhead allocations? Does your costing system accurately reflect the actual costs incurred at varying demand levels and provide the information needed by management for decision-making purposes, or do you need to introduce 'activity-based costing'?
- Are there any significant implications for cash flow in the proposed strategy, resulting either from a change in product mix, or from the need to fund product and marketing development costs? If so, is it a temporary problem during the period of change, or is there a longer term corporate financing problem that needs to be addressed?

All these points are considered in more detail elsewhere in the book.

Worksheet 10: Problems and obstacles This should be used to record the most important potential problems and obstacles you've identified, and the action that you need to plan in order to overcome them (Fig. 10.10).

Before going any further you should make sure that your sales plan and the actions you are proposing are compatible with the long-term plan and Mission you have agreed for the future development of your company. For example, the sales targets shown on Worksheet 9 may satisfy the growth in revenue and profit you require, but if most of this is targeted to come from the home market, and your longer term goal is to achieve 'a third of sales revenue from Pacific Rim countries', then you need to reconsider whether your longer term goal is realistic; if you think it is, you will need to revise your sales/ markets targets. And if you've not already decided what you need to do to bring about a change of culture across the whole company, getting everyone involved in the process of

Product/market family	Obstacle	Likely effects	Action required
2a SPECIAL BOOTHS (all markets)	– Excessive overhead rate (60% of 'cost of sales') – Analysis shows that Technical and Design costs account for half of this overhead rate	– Our 'normal' margins are unsustainable with such high overheads – Future sales of spares (71% contribution) are dependent on previous sales of Special Booths – If we want to maintain future profit from sales of spares we have to keep on selling Special Booths	– Reduce time spent by Technical and Design staff on processing enquiries by: (a) qualifying leads better (b) using database of past quotes to produce 'short-cut' estimate via 'comparative estimating' technique *(c) Standardizing options commonly required, to minimize new design work *(d) Installing CAD system
	– Virtually every job is currently 'designed' specially	– Warranty problems common in first 2 to 3 months after delivery; results in high service costs and poor customer service – Excessive use of skilled Tech and Design staff on replicating work done on previous jobs – Special materials ordered too late results in delivery problems	* Develop 'modular' design approach wherever possible to minimize proportion of untried elements in finished equipment and to ease material supply problems – Only accept enquiries for non-modular equipment if a higher margin is believed to be achievable.

Figure 10.10 Worksheet 10: Summary of potential obstacles to achievement of improved performance and/or new products/markets.

continual improvement and encouraging them to accept personal responsibility for the quality of their own work, then think again: it won't happen unless you take active steps to bring it about, and if it *doesn't* happen you're most unlikely to achieve success as a world-class company. Your plans should therefore include consideration of how you are going to communicate your strategy proposals to your workforce in sufficient detail for everyone to understand what are the key tasks that need to be undertaken, and why they are necessary. You may also have to arrange a company-wide education and training programme, to make sure that the people who will have to bring about the changes which will help your company to become world-class have the necessary skills and understanding to equip them for the tasks ahead.

Worksheet 11: Action plan briefing sheet When you're satisfied that you've completed the strategy review process, you should have a list of a dozen or more key tasks that need to be undertaken in order to achieve the strategic objectives you've agreed. The final step is to prepare an 'Action Plan Briefing Sheet' for each of these tasks, as illustrated in Fig. 10.11. If you don't formalize the implementation of your strategy in this way, there's a serious risk that it will just turn out to be yet another 'wish list' that no one ever manages to find the time to do anything about.

There is, of course, a limit to the amount of change that a company can accept at any one time. You may, therefore, have to select those with the highest priority for immediate action, holding the remainder back for the time being. In making your selection, don't go solely on commercial considerations; you also need to consider which will most encourage company-wide cooperation. Two factors in particular should be recognized:

- A project which achieves *significant and highly visible improvements* will help to overcome resistance to change because everyone will then realize that it's not just 'management's latest fad', but that the company really is changing.
- Improvements in productivity are usually interpreted at 'shop floor' level as leading to job losses; if you want people to cooperate you must convince them that they won't be doing themselves out of a job, and the best way of doing this is to include in your 'key actions' list a project specifically aimed at increasing sales: the objective of your productivity improvement projects is then to make it possible for you to satisfy the *additional* orders generated by the sales project.

10.1.7 Reviewing Progress

Naturally you will expect to review progress in implementing your plans at your regular management meetings. However, you need to do more than this: markets and products are changing all the time, so that you need to review your action plans periodically in case these must change too. It's better to plan a special meeting of your review team for this purpose, rather than to try and include it in your routine management meetings, when pressure of other business may get in the way. At the end of your strategy workshop, make a point of setting a date for a Strategy Update Meeting in two or three months' time.

Worksheet 11: Action plan – Item No. ...**3**...

Product/service: _____ 2a. SPECIAL BOOTHS _____

Target market(s): _____ ALL _____

Reason for required action: *We currently treat each enquiry for a special booth as a 'new requirement' and design equipment specially, which is very costly and frequently makes our prices uncompetitive. Consideration of past quotations indicates that many of the component parts are so similar that we could perhaps design a number of core modules to cover the range of sizes and operating features most commonly required. Only minor 'customizing' would then be required to satisfy an individual customer's order, the majority of components being existing, field-proven designs.*

Objectives of required action:
(1) *Identify a possible range of core modules, based on past enquiry files*
(2) *Review a representative sample of past enquiries and identify which could have been satisfied by these proposed core modules: estimates should be given of (a) the proportion of all enquiries that could have been satisfied through these core modules;*
   (b) for those which could, the proportion of estimating time that would have been saved

Target date(s):
 – Progress reports to Jean Pajot on 30 September and 15th November
 – Final report to Board by 31 December
Manager responsible:
 Jean Pajot

Others involved:
 Roger Wilson, Pierre Laval, Claudette Morell, Mario Taverna

Figure 10.11 Worksheet 11: Action plan.

10.2 USEFUL ANALYSIS TECHNIQUES

This section provides a brief summary of some of the techniques that might be useful when carrying out a review of strategy. Its purpose is to make sure that you are aware of them *before* you start your workshop, so that you are ready to use them should the need arise.

Brainstorming Most people who take part in a strategy workshop will be familiar with the brainstorming technique. However, it's rare to find it really used effectively. I suggest that anyone who is going to lead the strategy review should ensure that they are thoroughly familiar with Chapter 8 prior to the first workshop.

Short-listing The brainstorming technique, when used to its full potential, will result in a long list of ideas. You then need to whittle this list down to a short list, sorted in order of priority. Since this process will often result in someone's cherished ideas being eliminated, it's important that everyone feels that the short-listing process is fair and unbiased, so that the whole team is committed to and accepts ownership of the final list. Suitable short-listing techniques are described in Chapter 8.

The Pareto Principle Most participants will be aware of the Pareto Principle and understand, for example, that a relatively small proportion of the company's products or customers account for a significant proportion of total sales. A brief explanation of the Pareto Principle is included in the Glossary (Appendix Two) at the end of this book.

Market research Two market research techniques that are likely to be particularly relevant are 'competitive benchmarking' and the 'problem ranking process'. Both are described in Sec. 2.2. A case study illustrating the application of competitive benchmarking is included below.

The Delphi approach If you are in a 'leading edge' type of business, involving, for example, biotechnology or the latest electronics applications, you may find the 'Delphi approach' useful. This is a technique for assessing the most likely time-scale in which the latest theoretical applications of technology will become commercially viable. The Delphi approach is beyond the scope of this book: if you think it might be useful, I suggest you contact a university with a strong Business Marketing Department who are the most likely people to know of the technique and to be able to help you organize a project.

10.3 CASE STUDIES

Intertronic Business Systems Limited

Background

The present day Intertronic company has developed from a privately owned business founded in 1963 to supply and service office equipment, primarily typewriters, dictating machines and calculators. From its early days the company placed great emphasis on high-quality after-sales service and this was a significant factor in its success over the years. As a result, it was able to win a number of long-running contracts with blue-chip organizations, such as the leading clearing banks, supplying and maintaining equipment for them at their Head Offices and branches, particularly in the London area. Although Intertronic's product range and customer base have developed significantly in recent years, the provision of a very high standard of customer service continues to be the cornerstone of its business.

By the time of this case study the company had moved to prestigious premises at Alperton in the Greater London conurbation, some eight miles to the west of the City. Although the traditional typewriter, dictating machine and calculator type of business still provided a sizeable part of the company's revenue, the Managing Director (and principal shareholder) Mr Bond had recognized some years earlier that the business would have to become increasingly computer-oriented. He had therefore taken steps to build up the necessary expertise, partly through recruitment and partly through an extensive programme of training for the company's technical staff; this had enabled Intertronic to become an approved supplier for a number of leading hardware products including, for example, IBM personal computers and a range of associated equipment. Subsequently, additional skills in software applications had been either acquired or developed internally and 'Accredited Systems Centre' status had been achieved with a number of leading systems suppliers; as a consequence Intertronic was now able to provide approved training and consultancy support for the majority of office systems applications, to complement the sale and after-sales service of hardware products. The company's growth strategy was increasingly being directed towards the provision of complete software solutions based on the concept of 'one-stop' shopping, offering the very best equipment, the very best advice and the very best after-sales service, the longer term objective being to achieve recognition as a quality 'Systems House'.

The Need for a Strategy Review

The strategy described above was already proving successful; it had led to the opening of many new accounts and the prospects for continued growth in the new areas of business were encouraging. However, Mr Bond had recently become increasingly concerned at how some of Intertronic's fundamental business characteristics were changing as the emphasis shifted from traditional office equipment to computer-oriented products:

1. There were significant cash flow implications: with traditional equipment such as typewriters, dictating machines and calculators, much of the revenue was generated through annual maintenance contracts so that the business tended to have a positive cash flow. The revenue from computer-related products, in contrast, tended to be generated through sales of hardware and software, for which suppliers had to be paid before payment was received from customers; even the revenue generated through the training support service was received after wages costs had been paid for the staff providing those services.

2. Sales and marketing costs were greater with the new product range since business tended to involve a large number of comparatively small value accounts, there was less opportunity for repeat sales, and more promotional efforts were necessary to keep potential customers informed about the ever-changing product range in a highly competitive market. With the traditional products much of the revenue was generated through the renewal of a comparatively small number of large annual maintenance contracts, and a steady income from sales of new equipment could be maintained through the replacement of equipment covered by these contracts.
3. The new types of equipment generally needed less routine servicing and repair than equipment such as typewriters, dictating machines and calculators which had many more mechanical parts; because of this, however good the services offered by Intertronic, the concept of an annual maintenance contract was harder to sell.
4. Because of the shorter life cycles of both hardware and software products, staff needed continual re-training to ensure that they were kept fully up to date with all the latest releases. This involved not only the direct cost of paying for staff to attend external courses, but also the loss of revenue that those staff would otherwise have been able to earn had they not been away.

The implications were not as bad as they might seem from the above, because the costs of supporting the sales of the new range of equipment were also incurred by Intertronic's competitors, so that they could be reflected in the pricing strategy adopted. However, there were clearly important differences compared with the traditional type of business, and these differences needed to be properly taken into account when planning Intertronic's future strategy, particularly the increase in working capital that would be needed if the positive cash flow part of the business were to decline further to the point where it eventually ceased to be a significant part of the product mix. Even so, with the problem recognized, Mr Bond did not anticipate any particular difficulty in adapting to the new situation. What concerned him more was that Intertronic would find it increasingly difficult to maintain its unique character, with great emphasis placed on the quality and reliability of its after-sales service, which had enabled the company to prosper and grow in the past. What Intertronic really needed, he felt, was a new product type which had similar after-sales service requirements to the products that had served them so well in the past.

Photocopying equipment could, Mr Bond felt, provide the answer; but unfortunately the photocopier industry had a poor reputation in the UK, and at first sight didn't fit readily with the 'high-quality and reliability' image that Intertronic had taken years to develop. His management team were divided on the issue, with one or two of his longest and closest associates strongly opposed to the proposal because of the damage that they felt entering this field would have on the Intertronic name. Others favoured the idea because they saw the opportunity for expanding the one-stop shopping concept, with sales of one type of product opening up prospects for selling other products in the Intertronic portfolio. While recognizing that he must himself be responsible for taking the final decision on whether or not to go ahead with the idea, he was loath to do this over the heads of some of the more senior members of the management team, whose opinions he respected. He therefore decided to organize a strategy planning workshop at which senior management would consider the options and reach a consensus on what they felt should be the company's future direction. To ensure that each member of the management team had an equal opportunity to contribute to the discussion, he arranged for an outside consultant to act as facilitator, and he confined his own involvement to proceedings at the beginning and end of the workshop to ensure that no one was unduly influenced by any contribution he personally might make to the discussion.

Developing the New Strategy

The objectives of the workshop were defined as:

1. To review the company's current business activities, assessing strengths and weaknesses and identifying opportunities and threats.
2. In the light of these strengths, weaknesses, opportunities and threats, to discuss and agree the business's strategic objectives (i.e. the 'vision' of where management wanted and expected Intertronic to be in three to five years' time).
3. To prepare an outline plan for change, encompassing proposals for tackling identified constraints and opportunities, and proposals for a programme of training to equip staff (at all levels in the company) to undertake the change tasks effectively, so that the business strategy can be achieved.

The workshop consisted of two sessions. In the first, the primary task was to ensure that everyone involved understood the review process, and to take the analysis far enough to identify some of the key questions that would have to be resolved. The second workshop session was held two weeks later, to allow those involved time to collect any further information needed for completing the worksheets; this intervening period also gave everyone time to think over the key questions that had been identified in the first session.

A series of worksheets were used, similar to those illustrated earlier in this chapter. The main points arising from this process were, in summary:

- *Review of existing products, services and markets* showed that the traditional typewriter, calculator and dictating machine business still accounted for more than half of sales revenue; life cycle analysis of this product family revealed that although revenue earned from maintenance contracts was still holding up (just), sales of new equipment were declining, which would inevitably lead in time to a reduction in maintenance work. Sales of new computer-related equipment were growing steadily and already exceeded 25 per cent of total turnover; however, the associated maintenance revenue was low (mainly because of customer resistance to the concept of maintenance contracts for computer hardware), competitive pressures were high and, as a result, margins were tight.
- *Assessing strengths and weaknesses from the customers' point of view* showed that Intertronic had a clear competitive advantage in the case of traditional equipment because of the perceived importance of after-sales service, for which the company had developed an outstanding reputation. With computer-related equipment, in contrast, after-sales service was considered by most customers to be a lower priority; the quality of the products (mainly seen in terms of recognized brand

names) and the ability of the salesperson to understand the customer's problem and formulate the 'right' business solution were considered to be of the greatest significance to customers, followed closely by price. The team rated Intertronic's strengths, in terms of product quality and understanding of customers' problems, to be as good as any of their competitors in the computer-related business and better than most; however, they accepted that they weren't seen as being *significantly better* than some of their main competitors, and this often led to price being the determining factor in buying decisions (Intertronic were rarely the lowest price supplier, nor did they want to be).

- *Future threats* were considered next. Of all those identified, the threat which stood out concerned the maintenance business for traditional products such as typewriters, dictating machines and calculators: contracts with a small number of large organizations accounted for a sizeable part of the business and, with the product clearly past the peak of its life cycle, failure of even one of these major customers to renew the contract at the next annual review point could have a serious impact.

At this point the formal analysis was temporarily abandoned to allow a lengthy (and sometimes heated) discussion to take place on what should be done to counter this threat. Although the subject had been discussed on numerous occasions in the past it had never been resolved, if only because views on alternatives, such as going into the photocopying business, were so polarized. It often happens in business that if 'what to do' can't be agreed, then 'do nothing' is the solution adopted. Now, probably for the first time, everyone involved understood the significance of the problem and why 'no decision' wasn't acceptable. Even though at that point they disagreed on *what* to do, as a result of the review process they were all united in their belief that they *had* to find a solution.

After a period of free-ranging discussion, the facilitator guided the review team into a brainstorming session to identify feasible options, following which a short list was agreed. The remaining worksheets were then considered briefly in order to identify what additional information was needed to enable the review to be completed at the second workshop, two weeks later. Two of the questions raised earlier in this chapter, in Sec. 10.1.6, were recognized as having particular significance:

- Does your workforce have the right skills and flexibility, or do you need to plan additional recruitment and training programmes?
- Are there any significant implications for cash flow in the proposed strategy, resulting either from a change in product mix, or from the need to fund product and marketing development costs? If so, is it a temporary problem during the period of change, or is there a longer term corporate financing problem that needs to be addressed?

The two weeks allowed between the two workshop sessions were used to collect the additional information needed to complete the worksheets, and it also provided time for reflection and for the team members to discuss the options with their colleagues. When the review team re-convened, they quickly agreed to go ahead with several of the ideas which had been included in the short list, all of which fitted comfortably with the range of products and services already included in

Intertronic's portfolio and therefore helped to develop the 'one-stop shopping' concept. However, it was clear to all members of the review team that this action was not sufficient. Of all the ideas considered, only the photocopying business satisfied all the criteria they had defined in the previous workshop: annual maintenance contracts with 'up-front' payment terms were well established as the norm in the photocopier business; the technology involved was not as sophisticated as computer-based products, so that even the older and less adaptable maintenance staff could be readily re-trained; photocopying equipment complemented the existing product range and could be used as a 'door opener' for selling other products and services; and it would introduce a range of associated products such as paper and toners that could be added to Intertronic's new consumables catalogue. Above all, the expected level of sales would be more than enough to compensate for the decline anticipated in the other types of maintenance business.

By now, the logical process of reviewing strategy had brought everyone to the point where there was no longer any argument about *what* had to be done: all were agreed that Intertronic should move into the photocopier business, and that this should be a high priority. The argument that still had to be settled was *how*: should the new business be started under another name, in case the poor image of the photocopying business world tainted Intertronic's reputation; or should they operate the new business openly as an integral part of Intertronic? Re-examining the Strengths worksheet reminded them that the past success of Intertronic over many years had been the emphasis they had always placed on providing 'The very best equipment, the very best advice and the very best after-sales service'. The fact that their future competitors weren't renowned for providing this level of customer care, the team decided, simply meant that Intertronic would have a clear competitive advantage that they were confident would appeal to the traditional Intertronic type of customers.

All were in agreement that a new General Business Division should be formed, which would continue to market the existing range of traditional business equipment and, in addition, would launch a new venture to sell and maintain photocopying and facsimile equipment. The remaining reservations of those who had originally been opposed to the idea were finally settled during the subsequent discussions with the Managing Director, Mr Bond; it was agreed that if an acquisition was to be considered as a quick way of entering the photocopier market, particular care would be taken to ensure that the business acquired could be absorbed readily into the existing Intertronic organization, and not have to operate separately, so that Intertronic's corporate values and standards of customer care would influence the way in which the new business operated. In addition, they decided that the company should do whatever was necessary to achieve certification to the BS 5750/ ISO 9000 quality standard; this would not only stress the importance that Intertronic placed on the quality of every aspect of their operations and distance them further from less reputable operators, it would also provide a strong sales advantage when dealing with large public sector customers who were increasingly giving preference to suppliers with such a qualification.

The strategy review process had achieved its purpose: all concerned now *understood* what needed to be done and *why* it was necessary; they had all been *involved* in the process of deciding what was the best strategy to follow; and, above all, they had reached a consensus on what to do, to which every member of the team felt *personally committed.*

The Results

Formation of the General Business Division started with the introduction of new copier/fax products; the main supplier chosen for these was Panasonic, who already supplied some of the computer-related products in Intertronic's portfolio, and with whom a good working relationship already existed. With suitable staff either recruited or specially trained, the company soon received recognition from Panasonic as an Authorized Dealer, able to sell and maintain the full range of Panasonic copiers and facsimile machines.

Within a few months of start-up Intertronic was able to acquire an existing well-established photocopier business, which provided a useful customer base and enabled the new division to reach a profitable size quickly; the small core of trained and experienced maintenance staff were moved into Intertronic's Alperton head-quarters to supplement their existing resources and provide the strength needed to support the increasing level of sales. Steps were also taken to obtain certification to the BS 5750/ISO 900 quality standards: Intertronic achieved this on 11 July 1991 – one of the first businesses in its field to do so.

During the three years that have elapsed since the strategy review described in this case study, the software support side of the business has grown significantly. Following a major investment in staff training, Intertronic has achieved the coveted status of Accredited Training Centre for *WordPerfect* and is also an approved Training Centre for a comprehensive range of leading office systems, including *Lotus 1-2-3, Seachange Database, Tetra Accounts, Microsoft Word* and *Ami Pro.* As expected, sales of typewriters have dropped dramatically (from around 3000 to only 200 units a year), and sales of calculators have virtually disappeared: although the number of units under maintenance contract hasn't been seriously affected yet, inevitably it won't be long before these too decline, reflecting the fall off in sales of new equipment. However, this will no longer present a problem for Intertronic, since the photocopying side has already grown to the point where it is now an important part of the business and, as intended, is providing a new outlet for the type of long-term maintenance contracts which have been at the heart of Intertronic's past success.

Cincinnati Milacron UK Limited

How a long-established machine tool manufacturer regained its position as a world leader in its field.

Background

Cincinnati Milacron is one of the oldest machine tool manufacturers in the world. First incorporated as the Cincinnati Milling Machine Company in Ohio, USA, as long ago as 1884, by the late 1920s it had become the largest machine tool builder in the world. In 1934, in order to meet growing demand for its products, the company opened a factory in Birmingham, UK (the subject of this case study). In addition to the range of milling machines for which Cincinnati were by then world-famous, this factory also manufactured on a smaller scale a range of grinding machines, power presses, coin minting presses and broaching machines.

In 1970 the name of the parent corporation was changed to Cincinnati Milacron Inc., reflecting that its interests were now much wider than the milling machines which once formed the main core of the business. By 1993 worldwide sales were expected to be in excess of $1 billion.

For some years, however, faced with growing competition throughout world markets, corporate management had become increasingly concerned about Cincinnati's longer term prospects for survival as a leading machine tool manufacturer. They realized that more attention needed to be paid to keeping product designs up to date, as they were finding it increasingly difficult to compete with some of the advanced machine tools offered by other manufacturers. Although the loss of market share in traditional products had to some extent been compensated for by diversification into other types of product, this had caused a loss of focus, so that the Cincinnati name was no longer the dominant force in any particular field, as it had been for so many years in its past history. Major changes were needed if the company was to survive in the longer term and re-establish itself, as the leader it had once been, in world markets.

Creating the Climate For Change

Since the original formation of the corporation, it has been restructured into three operating divisions:

- **Machine Tools** (which includes Cincinnati Milacron UK Limited)
- **Plastic Processing Machinery**, principally extruders, blow moulding and injection moulding machinery
- **Industrial Products**, a speciality products group comprising three separate businesses: cutting fluids, grinding wheels and cutting tools

To create a climate for change, each division was given the responsibility for developing its own world-class strategy. They were allowed considerable freedom in *what* they did, provided that they incorporated two important world-class principles in their approach:

- They were to place particular emphasis on *customers*
- They were to use *a multi-disciplinary team* to develop their strategy and, if the proposed strategy was approved by corporate management, in the subsequent implementation process (the team approach was referred to within Cincinnati Milacron as 'Wolfpack').

This approach was very different from past practice, but it was adopted enthusiastically by all concerned and is widely recognized as having been fundamental to the outstanding success of all the divisions in achieving the required objectives.

Developing a New Strategy for the UK Business

Prior to the strategy review the UK business had concentrated primarily on the manufacture of customized vertical and horizontal CNC machining centres and conventional machine tools. Essentially they sold solutions to customers' problems: special designs were developed for many applications by adapting 'standard' modules to suit each requirement. While this was a high value-adding business, unfortunately the market for such products had been steadily declining for a number of years. The increasing flexibility offered by new technology meant that competitors could often satisfy customers' requirements with standard machine tools. Not only were these cheaper, they could also be readily adapted to produce different parts when the customer introduced new product designs. This adaptation process was much more difficult with the type of machines offered by Cincinnati Milacron at that time.

Faced with a declining market for their current products, the UK management team decided that the future survival of their business depended on re-positioning the company in the market-place. To succeed in this they would first have to define a standard product range with the potential for selling in volume in world markets, and they would then have to develop designs which would meet the technical requirements they had defined and which at the same time could be manufactured at a cost that would provide a satisfactory level of profit. Quite a challenge! But, as you will see in a moment, they succeeded.

The first step was to find out what customers wanted. Extensive market research was undertaken, initially in the UK and USA; at a later stage this was extended to other parts of the world, such as the Far East. The team decided not to use professional market research consultants because all the information they needed could be obtained through their worldwide network of sales outlets and through the machine tool trade associations in the USA and UK, of which they were members, and their European and Japanese equivalents. This initial research revealed that there was a strong and growing market worldwide for low-cost, economical vertical machining centres.

The next task was to carry out a competitive benchmarking study, to identify the best that was currently available from other manufacturers in this field. This would enable the team to prepare a design specification for a range of products which would be sufficiently attractive to potential customers to enable Cincinnati Milacron to capture a sizeable share of the market they had identified.

Competitive Benchmarking

The team first prepared a detailed list of technical and performance features, drawing on the technical expertise of Cincinnati Milacron's own staff, advice from their sales outlets and a study of competitors' technical literature. The list included criteria such as:

- Overall range of X, Y and Z axes
- Axis performance (speed)
- Accuracy
- Spindle performance (speeds, kW, torque)

- Floor space required
- Tool weights, sizes and dimensions
- Speed of tool change
- Pallet criteria
- Standard tooling capacities and options

and there were many more, including, of course, information on prices and delivery times.

A detailed analysis of all the main competitors' machines was then made, with the results presented in a table which enabled the best performer to be identified for each of the criteria. Marketing Manager Mike Colvin, who was responsible for much of this analysis, comments: 'We went to a lot of trouble to research the market thoroughly. We wanted to make sure that we ended up with a product that was really world-class, and not one that was best in just a limited range of countries. Our objective was to be the world's best on three or four of the features we'd listed, and between 70 and 80 per cent competitive on all the rest'.

Once the analysis was completed, a full business plan (referred to internally as 'Recommendation of Specific Objectives') was submitted to corporate management for approval. Formal approval was obtained, with the UK factory given responsibility for developing the new 'Sabre' product (initially as one machine but subsequently extended to a full range) and for becoming the sole manufacturing source for worldwide sales. Once the new products had been launched, the design and manufacture of the existing range of CNC machining centres previously carried out by the UK factory would be progressively phased out.

The 'fast track' development approach that was used to design the new products is described in Sec. 11.7. However, the team recognized from the outset that although product design was an essential part of re-establishing the company as a world-class manufacturer, there were many other changes that would need to be made in order to support the design with a truly world-class service to customers. The rest of this case study describes some of these other changes.

Making Manufacturing World-Class

One of the key performance criteria identified in the benchmarking study was the need to provide rapid delivery. Although the distributor network could normally be relied on to satisfy the end customer's requirement ex stock, the distributors' stock needed to be replenished quickly to ensure that other sales opportunities could be satisfied without delay.

This was a very different scenario from the sort of lead times that were acceptable for the special-purpose machines that had been manufactured in the factory in recent years. The whole production process would need to be speeded up and this would have to include the procurement of materials. Special teams were set up to plan and implement the changes, working in parallel with the development of the new designs:

- SMED techniques were used to reduce set-up times, so that small batches of components could be manufactured economically.

- Layout of component manufacturing and machine build areas was improved in order to simplify material flows and reduce queuing between processes.
- Where necessary, new machinery was introduced to relieve potential bottlenecks, to achieve the first-time quality requirements, or to meet manufacturing cost targets (this investment in new machinery included the installation of some of the new range of machines: this had the additional benefit of enabling the company to get rapid feedback on the equipment from the operational point of view through its own skilled operators).
- New quality assurance systems were introduced as a means of encouraging the whole workforce to place particular emphasis on 'first time quality' (this has enabled the company to achieve certification to quality standards ISO 9001/ BS 5750 Part 1, a useful additional marketing benefit).
- 'Partnership sourcing' techniques were used to improve the supply of raw materials and bought out components (80 per cent of components for the new product range are obtained from a small number of carefully selected outside suppliers, many of them on a sole source basis).
- Long component lead times are no longer accepted: if a reliable supplier cannot be found, the component is either manufactured in-house or the design of the component is modified to overcome the problem.
- New business systems were developed to improve material procurement and control of production.

As a result of the changes made, internal manufacturing times have been reduced to less than 30 days, compared with a worst case of 110 days previously. The company is now able to quote confidently an ex-works delivery of 8 weeks for the Sabre 750, and usually expects in practice to achieve 4–6 weeks, or even less. The actual build process is completed in a maximum of 2 weeks. The current Sabre range consists of four vertical and one horizontal CNC machining centres and further models are being developed; because of the high degree of commonality incorporated in the designs, the factory is able to achieve a high degree of flexibility in manufacturing, altering the mix of machine types at short notice to suit the requirements of customers.

The improvements to the manufacturing processes, summarized above, enabled Cincinnati Milacron to achieve a successful launch of its new product range and subsequently to increase production to match the very significant growth in sales that followed. However, the company still sees the need to keep on improving in order to make sure that it retains its position as a world leader in its field. Two initiatives have been launched recently with this in mind:

- A 'process auditing' team has been established in the Birmingham factory, with a brief to continually review all manufacturing processes, identifying and eliminating 'waste' progressively in order to ensure that the cost-effectiveness and quality of manufacturing is continuously improved.
- A 'total quality leadership' (TQL) campaign has been introduced throughout the Cincinnati Milacron Corporation worldwide, aimed at involving the whole workforce in the commitment to world-class leadership, concentrating in the first instance on customer focus and satisfaction, innovation and continuous improvement.

Marketing and Sales

The story would not be complete without mention of the marketing and sales aspects. Potential customers needed to be told about the company's new focus, and changes had to be made to the sales organization to reflect the switch from selling customized products, with the emphasis on 'solutions to problems', to selling a standard range of CNC machining centres where the emphasis would be on 'value for money' in comparison with competitive products.

Professional marketing consultants were retained to assist in preparing the product launch. The 'Sabre' name was selected for the new range and a sales brochure for the range was produced. A separate Technical Data Sheet is provided for each machine in the range, which fits into a pocket at the back of the main brochure: this allows for maximum flexibility, since only a loose data sheet needs to be produced when a new model in the Sabre range is introduced or when the specification is modified to incorporate the latest developments. This is important since the products are being continually improved to ensure that the Sabre range maintains its position as market leader.

With the launch of the Sabre range the role of the sales organization had to change. Instead of selling direct to end users, working out the best way to satisfy their manufacturing problems, the sales force now concentrates on providing support through the extensive distributor network, and in contributing to the design process by providing feedback from the field on the performance of Cincinnati Milacron's products relative to competitors' products and by identifying what further improvements or new features are likely to be important to customers.

Finally, it is worth noting that having once had to respond to the extreme competitive pressures which led to this project, Cincinnati Milacron are determined not to allow such a position to develop again. The analysis carried out in the competitive benchmarking process is therefore updated at frequent intervals. The latest comparisons are taken into account when the next product in the range is being developed, and any improvements introduced are also incorporated in the rest of the range (taking advantage of the high degree of commonality of parts that is a feature of the new designs).

The Results

The first machine in the range, the Sabre 750, was launched in May 1989, just twelve months after the project started. The second machine was launched nine months later, and the third only six months after that. Six months from start of design to launch is now the norm for the simpler products, and no more than twelve months for the most complex; in the past this would typically have taken three years. The machines have proved very reliable in use and enabled up-times as high as 98 per cent to be achieved consistently over a protracted period.

The company's success in re-establishing itself in world markets is summarized by John Bloxham, Managing Director of Cincinnati Milacron UK: 'In 1988 survival was paramount: the fact that we have significantly improved performance, despite the recession, in the past five years is testament to the success of the new product development team. We are exporting to the Far East: we're an established global player with a standard range of machines; and our market position has changed from being just one of many suppliers to being one of the leading performers in our field. Our order book is growing steadily and we can now look to the future with renewed confidence.'

ELEVEN

IMPLEMENTING JUST-IN-TIME

Linked to Chapter 3, this chapter has two purposes: (a) to help managers assess in more detail the scope for improving their own manufacturing processes through the application of the JIT concepts; (b) to describe some methods and procedures which will assist them in the first year of implementation.

11.1 IDENTIFYING WASTE

The problem most people face when attacking waste for the first time is that there's so much of it, it's difficult to know where to start. Remember that 'waste' in world-class terminology doesn't just mean scrapped material, it means *any activity that doesn't add value*. If you carried out the simple activity sampling test described in Sec. 9.3, you probably found that between a third and a half of the activities you observed could be considered as waste. Of course, this doesn't mean that productivity could be doubled just by telling people not to waste their time, since we will never be able to eliminate all such activities. However, it does show that there's tremendous scope for improving performance if we focus our attention on identifying and then reducing waste.

It helps to have an organized approach to attacking waste. The two methods most commonly used can be thought of as:

- **Targeted attack**, in which management sets specific improvement targets (such as 'reduce lead time by 50 per cent'), and everyone is encouraged to identify, and then reduce or eliminate, examples of waste which are directly relevant to achieving management's targets

- **Open warfare**, in which 'waste' is declared Public Enemy Number One; the whole workforce is encouraged to look for examples of waste in their own workplace and to find ways of reducing or eliminating them; *any* type of waste is considered fair game

I explained in Chapter 1 why you will usually need to start with a step change improvement in performance, and then follow this with sustained 'continuous improvement' in order to stay on top. You will usually find the targeted attack method most appropriate when you are trying for a step change, and the open warfare method when you are aiming more generally at improving your rate of continuous improvement.

11.1.1 Targeted Attack

The objective with the targeted approach is to get *noticeable* results *quickly*, partly in order to get a step change level of improvement, but also to stimulate others to want to get involved and so start the process of changing your company culture.

In the first instance, a targeted attack is normally spearheaded by a Task Force or Strategic Improvement Team, although local shop floor teams, or even individuals, may become involved at a later stage (see Chapters 5 and 13 for more details on establishing effective teams).

The improvement targets need to be clearly defined so that people can understand and relate to them. For example, 'reduce lead time from four weeks to ten days' or 'achieve zero defect deliveries to customers', together with target dates for completion, are readily understandable by all; targets such as 'reduce waste' or 'improve quality' are so vague that they might well feel overwhelmed at the immensity of the task and so be at a loss to know where to start.

The team members' first task is to make sure that they all have a good understanding of all the operations and procedures relevant to their project. As part of this task they will need to draw a process flow diagram: this is a key step in identifying waste.

Figure 11.1 shows a typical flow chart. The process describes the steps involved in taking a batch of castings from raw material stores, drilling and tapping a hole, inserting a grub screw and then returning the finished castings to the component stores. This type of process flow chart uses a variety of symbols to indicate different types of waste. As you can see, only two of the activities (numbers 12 and 17) actually add value: all the others are waste. These are the activities that the team need to concentrate on in order to achieve their improvement objectives. Suppose, for example that their key objective is to reduce lead time: all they need to do now is to add a time-scale to the chart and then, applying the Pareto concept, concentrate their efforts on those wastes that take the most time. You might think that this sounds so simple that it must be too good to be true. But it really is that simple. If a team of 'experts', i.e. those closest to the problem, analyse what happens at present systematically in the way described, they will nearly always find ways of doing things better than ever before. All they need is a simple methodology, and encouragement to apply it.

Here's another example, taken from real life.

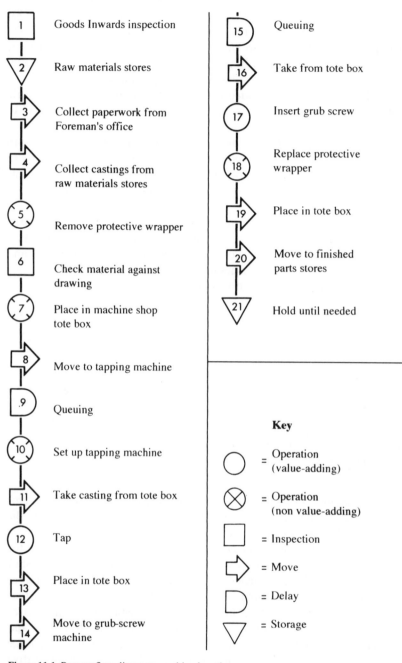

Figure 11.1 Process flow diagram: machined castings.

11.1.2 Example: Reducing Press Down-Time

An industrial rubber products manufacturer had a moulding shop with about 25 presses of various sizes. Some were engaged on continuous production of rubber mouldings for the motor industry, but the majority were used to produce relatively small batches for general industrial applications. Once set up, these presses would typically run for three or four days, with three shifts covering 24 hours. At the end of a batch run the mould would have to be changed ready for the next batch. Before production could start on a new batch, the mould would have to be heated up to the correct operating temperature and the first off would have to be checked by an inspector to see that it conformed to specification.

The company had a growing backlog of orders and customers were complaining to the extent that management became concerned that unless action was taken urgently to improve output and delivery performance, orders would be lost. Initial investigations indicated that the main cause of the problem was the production time lost between successive batches.

A team was therefore set up, comprising members drawn from the production shop concerned, plus representatives of sales, planning and engineering departments. As a first step, the team arranged for someone to observe a mould-changing operation and report on the time taken for the various activities involved.

The results of this observation study were as follows:

Time	Activity
0600	Previous batch complete: mould change fitter requested
1300	Fitter arrives
1500	Mould disassembled: waiting for fork-lift to remove mould
1530	Fork-lift arrives, removes old mould to store, returns with new mould; fitter commences mould assembly
1700	Fitter called away to deal with breakdown in another shop; mould not yet fully assembled
1730	Fitter returns and continues with mould assembly
1830	Mould change complete; heating up of mould commences
2000	Mould up to temperature; inspector approves first off and new batch commences production

This information was presented in the form of the flow chart shown in Fig. 11.2. This is a sort of Gantt chart, i.e. the activities are drawn to a time-scale, which has the advantage of making lengthy activities stand out clearly.

Two members of the team, the Engineering Manager who was responsible for the mould change fitter and the Production Manager to whom the Production Shift Foremen reported, were particularly surprised and embarrassed by the results, and at first insisted that this must be an exceptional case. But further checking revealed that this was typical of what happened when a mould had to be changed at the end of a batch run. You may well think it surprising that the Engineering Manager and the Production Manager didn't know what was happening, but again in my experience this is typical. Both of them had so many production problems and administrative tasks to deal with every day that they'd never before looked in such detail at how the day-to-day routine of changing moulds was tackled: they, like the production operatives, had been accustomed to mould changeovers taking hours to complete and

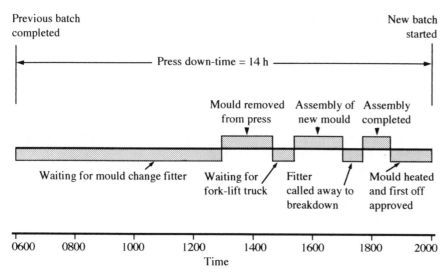

Previous batch completed

New batch started

Press down-time = 14 h

Mould removed from press

Assembly of new mould

Assembly completed

Waiting for mould change fitter

Waiting for fork-lift truck

Fitter called away to breakdown

Mould heated and first off approved

0600   0800   1000   1200   1400   1600   1800   2000

Time

Figure 11.2 Press down-time analysis.

they accepted it as the norm. The diagram forced them to look more critically at what was happening.

The obvious starting point was to find out why it took seven hours for the fitter to arrive. There were a number of contributing factors, but the main reason for the delay was that nobody had ever told the fitter that press down-time was seriously affecting the company's ability to meet customers' requirements, and that future orders could well be lost as a result. The problem was overcome simply by specifying that this was a priority task and ensuring that the Engineering Shift Foreman was given an hour or so's advance warning of when a mould had to be changed. Interestingly, once the new norm had been established, the production operators' attitude to delay changed: if the fitter failed to arrive within twenty minutes or so, one of the operators would make sure that the foreman knew and that he did something about it.

The team subsequently went on to tackle the other delays identified in the diagram (this is the subject of the second case study in Sec. 11.3). The task set for them by management was to reduce the waste of lost production caused by press down-time during the mould changeover operation. The process flow analysis helped them to identify the various elements of the waste; once these had been identified, the task of eliminating, or at least significantly reducing, them was straightforward. Of course, not all improvement tasks are that straightforward; but many certainly are.

To sum up: with a targeted approach, efforts to identify and attack waste are focused on achieving specific improvement targets set by management. These targets need to be clearly defined and relevant to the day-to-day tasks of those involved. People who are primarily operators and not used to problem solving need a simple methodology to get them started: process flow analysis is likely to prove a useful tool for encouraging them to look critically at what happens at present and so identify relevant wastes.

11.1.3 The Open Warfare Approach

Even with the open warfare approach, you might be able to use the process flow analysis method to identify all the various waste activities in a department. However, in most cases it wouldn't be a practical approach because, with there being no constraints on which types of waste to attack, it would usually take too long to prepare process flow diagrams for all the various activities undertaken in the department concerned. The answer is to use brainstorming to generate examples of wastes currently experienced, and then to select which of these to target first using one of the usual short-listing techniques (these, and brainstorming, are explained in Chapter 8).

Remember that the essence of the open warfare approach is that management doesn't set specific targets. This means that you should leave it to the people involved to decide for themselves which wastes to concentrate on first. The idea is that you will be more successful in gaining their commitment, and so achieving the sustained continuous improvement you are looking for, if you allow them to work on things which *they* believe are important. However, there is one proviso that you should make in the early stages: they mustn't pass the buck to another department. Everyone's usual first instinct is to identify someone else's waste; people need to be reminded that 'Charity begins at home', and their first priority should be to get their own house in order. Before producing their short list, they should classify the ideas on their original brainstorming list as either internal or external ('internal' means that the waste occurs entirely within the department and it can be attacked without involving any outsiders; 'external' means that someone else, from outside the department, will have to be asked to do something about that particular waste). In the initial stages you should insist that improvement teams only tackle wastes that are completely internal. Only when they can prove their track record in tackling these should they be allowed to join forces with other departments in tackling external wastes.

The open warfare approach is used extensively in total quality management campaigns which have 'company-wide continuous improvement' as a central theme. It is also used in the just-in-time approach, typically (though not essentially) around a year after step change project teams have been launched. Quality circles, departmental improvement groups, Kaizen groups or world-class teams are typical of the terms used to describe this type of activity. Further guidance on this aspect of teamwork is included in Sec. 12.3 on department purpose analysis.

11.2 REDUCING LEAD TIMES

The main techniques for reducing lead times are dealt with under separate headings in the remaining parts of this chapter. This section is concerned primarily with getting an understanding of what is happening at present, what lead times you are actually achieving and what goes wrong so that you fail to keep your delivery promises.

The first step, preparing a process flow diagram, was covered in Chapter 3 and a sample diagram was shown in Fig. 3.1. Let's now look at how to prepare an analysis of your actual lead time performance. To do this we'll work through an exercise together. The instructions are given in some detail, since you may want to get someone who's not very familiar with drawing graphs to analyse your own lead time performance, following this example.

11.2.1 Exercise: Lead Time Analysis

Your company currently quotes 8 weeks delivery, but the sales force have been complaining that they are losing orders because of poor delivery performance. Management has asked you to investigate whether there really is a problem, or whether the sales force are using just a few instances of late delivery as an excuse for their failure to meet sales targets.

As a first step you decide to collect data covering all deliveries made in a typical week. You find that, in the week selected, 175 deliveries were made. For each of these deliveries you have worked out how many days elapsed from when the customer's order was received until the date when the goods were delivered. The results are shown in Fig. 11.3. You now need to present these results in a diagram that will enable management to see at a glance whether or not there is a problem.

The first step is to analyse the data shown in Fig. 11.3, to show how many orders were satisfied in 5 weeks, how many in 6 weeks, how many in 7 weeks, and so on. In case you are not sure how to do this, the procedure is described in detail in Appendix One.

56	91	59	62	64	50	53	119	55	59	63	59
69	95	68	102	66	46	65	65	36	50	64	92
68	55	45	39	66	67	53	56	62	61	88	91
47	62	33	65	85	70	55	71	65	69	81	59
100	82	63	62	74	45	86	60	61	76	50	61
101	54	77	80	58	44	71	56	82	49	108	61
64	58	76	78	97	66	77	67	60	83	60	63
89	71	107	79	51	87	50	79	90	80	58	81
67	52	59	98	57	46	58	40	69	72	72	70
70	74	84	94	83	99	52	57	57	64	57	49
75	73	74	49	84	68	78	99	63	64	102	67
50	60	79	75	98	83	61	76	58	105	52	73
51	81	37	74	59	62	66	69	67	87	65	42
69	69	48	60	94	59	68	65	90	72	63	56
64	56	69	68	61	54	88					

Figure 11.3 Lead time analysis: data for exercise.

The results of this analysis are shown in columns 1 to 4 of Fig. 11.4. You *could* stop your analysis at this point and present the results as a simple histogram (you can see what this would look like in column 3, by turning the analysis form on its side). Histograms are becoming increasingly popular because most offices these days have access to a computer program which will produce the finished diagram direct from the raw data. But will it be enough to satisfy management's requirements? Remember that your instructions are 'to investigate whether there really is a problem, or whether the sales force are using just a few instances of late delivery as an excuse for their failure to meet sales targets'.

The diagram enables you to draw several conclusions:

- Lead times are typically in the range 8 to 11 weeks.
- Only a small proportion of deliveries are made in less than 8 weeks.
- A significant proportion of deliveries are made more than 11 weeks after the order is received (i.e. 3 or more weeks later than promised).
- Some deliveries can be as much as 9 weeks late.

1	2	3	4	5	6	7
					Cumulative	Percentage
			Total	Cumulative	total	of total
Days	Weeks	Occurrences	occurrences	total	percentage	occurrences
29–35	5	I	1			
36–42	6	ЖТ	5			
43–49	7	ЖТ ЖТ	10			
50–56	8	ЖТ ЖТ ЖТ ЖТ II	22			
57–63	9	ЖТ ЖТ ЖТ ЖТ ЖТ ЖТ ЖТ II	37			
64–70	10	ЖТ ЖТ ЖТ ЖТ ЖТ ЖТ ЖТ I	36			
71–77	11	ЖТ ЖТ ЖТ IIII	19			
78–84	12	ЖТ ЖТ ЖТ II	17			
85–91	13	ЖТ ЖТ I	11			
92–98	14	ЖТ II	7			
99–105	15	ЖТ II	7			
106–112	16	II	2			
113–119	17	I	1			

Figure 11.4 Lead time analysis (1).

These conclusions would probably be sufficient for management to accept that there was, indeed, a problem and they could reach this conclusion quickly and easily just by looking at your diagram. So you have certainly answered the main question. However, the conclusions are not very precise and it won't be easy to answer the supplementary questions that management are likely to ask, such as:

- What percentage of orders are currently delivered within the quoted lead time of 8 weeks?
- What percentage of orders would be delivered within the quoted lead time if this were changed to 10 weeks?
- What lead time would we have to quote in order to be confident that at least 95 per cent of orders were delivered within the quoted lead time (assuming that we don't do anything else to improve the situation)?

Having got this far with your investigation, it would be worth doing just a little more work in order to produce a 'cumulative frequency diagram', which will enable questions such as these to be answered easily. The process is described in detail in Appendix One; the data needed to plot the diagram are shown in columns 5 and 6 of Fig. 11.5, and the diagram itself in Fig. 11.6.

This cumulative frequency diagram, with the help of a few carefully placed dotted lines, should give management all the information they need to reach the decision that there is indeed a problem *and*, at the same time, for them to gain a good understanding of exactly how bad the problem is. For example, they can read off from the diagram that

1 Days	2 Weeks	3 Occurrences	4 Total occurrences	5 Cumulative total	6 Cumulative total percentage	7 Percentage of total occurrences
29–35	5	I	1	1	0.6	0.6
36–42	6	﷢	5	6	3.4	2.9
43–49	7	﷢ ﷢	10	16	9.1	5.7
50–56	8	﷢ ﷢ ﷢ ﷢ II	22	38	21.7	12.6
57–63	9	﷢ ﷢ ﷢ ﷢ ﷢ ﷢ ﷢II	37	75	42.9	21.1
64–70	10	﷢ ﷢ ﷢ ﷢ ﷢﷢ ﷢ I	36	111	63.4	20.6
71–77	11	﷢ ﷢ ﷢ IIII	19	130	74.3	10.9
78–84	12	﷢ ﷢ ﷢ II	17	147	84.0	9.7
85–91	13	﷢ ﷢ I	11	158	90.3	6.3
92–98	14	﷢ II	7	165	94.3	4.0
99–105	15	﷢ II	7	172	98.3	4.0
106–112	16	II	2	174	99.4	1.1
113–119	17	I	1	175	100	0.6

Figure 11.5 Lead time analysis (2).

'only 22 per cent of orders are delivered within the quoted 8 weeks lead time'; and 'on present performance, if the company wanted to be confident of meeting the delivery promise on at least 95 per cent of orders it would have to quote 14 weeks in place of the current 8 weeks'.

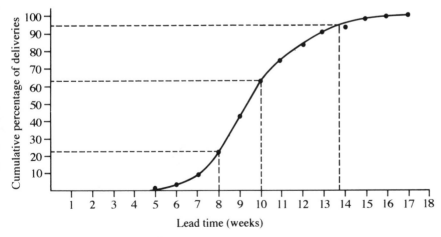

Figure 11.6 Current lead time performance.

11.2.2 Lead Time Frequency Distribution Diagrams

So far we've looked at two different ways of showing lead time performance diagram-matically: as a histogram, and as a cumulative frequency distribution diagram. There is a third way which is sometimes useful. This method, called a frequency distribution diagram (i.e. without the 'cumulative'), is similar to a histogram but has a 'best fit' smooth curve drawn through the plotted points instead of the vertical bars normally used in a histogram, and shows 'percentage of orders' instead of the actual number of orders (column 7 in Fig. 11.5).

An example is shown in the solid line curve in Fig. 11.7. This sort of diagram is useful for illustrating your 'first stage' improvement target (dotted line A), assuming you decide to get delivery performance under control first, together with your 'second stage' target of reducing the quoted lead time (dotted line B). Presenting the data in this way helps everyone concerned to understand what you're trying to do and provides a benchmark diagram with which subsequent analyses of performance can be compared.

This type of diagram can also be useful if your initial analysis of lead time data throws up a strange result, as shown in Fig. 11.8. The team that produced the original analysis from which this example is taken had difficulty in plotting a smooth curve in their cumulative frequency distribution diagram. It was only when they re-plotted the data in the form shown in Fig. 11.8 that they realized they were really looking at a combination of three different distributions, as shown by the vertical dotted lines: section A consisted of deliveries of products nominally available ex stock; section B were products made to order, but from standard designs using materials normally avail-able from stock; and section C were products that had to be specially designed to suit the customers' requirements and often needed special materials to be ordered. As a direct consequence of this analysis, new procedures were established to streamline

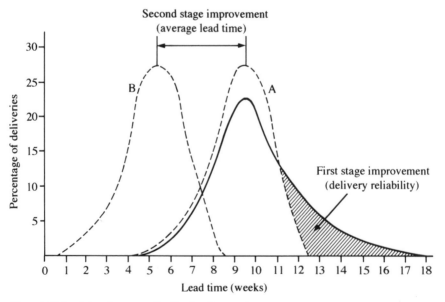

Figure 11.7 Lead time frequency distribution diagrams.

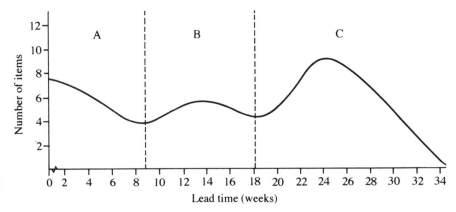

Figure 11.8 Combination of different lead time distributions.

the processing of category A and category B orders, with the result that lead time performance for these improved significantly at virtually no extra cost.

11.2.3 Improving Delivery Performance

Let's start by considering two different situations:

Situation 1: 'It takes us two weeks from receipt of a customer's order to complete the technical specification and drawings, and another four weeks minimum to obtain materials. Manufacturing then need four weeks to make the components and a further week to complete the assembly; delivery normally takes another week. That's a total of at least eleven weeks. However, we always quote eight weeks delivery because that's what the market expects.'

Situation 2: 'We quote eight weeks delivery, which should normally be quite long enough to process a customer's order. However, only two out of three orders actually go out either on or before the due date; the remaining third of orders can be anything up to seven or eight weeks late for no apparent reason.'

A company that's in Situation 1 will usually be forced to tackle the overall lead time problem first (i.e. in Fig. 11.7, moving from dotted line A to dotted line B). Even if current delivery performance is poor (shown in the figure by the solid line having a long 'tail'), this will probably be caused primarily by changing priorities, determined from day to day on the basis of who shouts the loudest. The best approach is to prepare a process flow diagram, pick out one or two areas that account for a significant chunk of current lead time, and do something to reduce the time needed. Once you have cut the time needed to satisfy a customer's order to what is acceptable to the market (in the case illustrated in Situation 1 this would mean cutting the real lead time from eleven weeks to eight) then, and only then, should you turn your attention to the Situation 2 problem: why some orders take longer than others to complete.

If your company is suffering from the type of poor delivery performance described in Situation 2, it's usually a sign that something's going wrong in the processes you go through to satisfy a customer's requirements. If that's the case it follows that you need to find out *what* is going wrong, *why* it is going wrong, and then *how* you can put it right so that it doesn't happen again.

Here's a list of just some of the causes you might find:

- Information or instructions received late
- Wrong information
    - incomplete
    - inaccurate
    - late changes
- Material shortages
    - ordered too late
    - ordered incorrectly
    - supplier fails to meet delivery promises
    - supplier delivers faulty materials
    - supplier refuses to deliver for commercial reasons (credit limit exceeded; overdue accounts)
- Production delays
    - production rejects requiring re-work or replacement of scrapped materials
    - missing or broken tools, jigs or fixtures
    - local bottleneck problems
    - overall capacity problems
    - subcontractor delays (e.g. heat treatment)
    - lack of compliance to schedules (batching-up, 'cherry-picking', changing priorities, split batches, etc.)

You will find many more possible reasons for shortages in the exercise included in Sec. 8.4, and I'm sure you can add other reasons to the list above. However, what's important is not the *possible* reasons, but what is actually causing delays in *your* factory. Three useful ways of finding this out are described below.

Brainstorming Get a group of 'experts' (i.e. those directly involved, who see the problems every day as they happen) to make a list of causes, and then ask them to vote on which they think are the most significant. This process is described in more detail in the shortages exercise in Sec. 8.4.

Late despatch analysis Give someone the task of looking *each day* into any orders despatched the previous day which were more than, say, three days late. If this is done immediately after despatch there's a good chance that people will still remember the reason(s) for delay. You may at first have to take more than the suggested three days late as your cut-off point to avoid the task becoming excessive. If you record the main causes you should soon be able to build up a picture of where corrective action is most urgently needed.

An example is shown in Fig. 11.9. This 'Analysis of Order Despatch Performance' was prepared by the Spares Division of an industrial machinery manufacturer (spares were offered on an ex stock basis). It proved very useful in helping management confirm that urgent improvement was necessary, and where attention needed to be paid. It was interesting to see how the number of 'no apparent reason' latenesses, high in this earlier

ANALYSIS OF ORDER DESPATCH PERFORMANCE

Week ending: ......5/2/93......

Number of despatches: ......153......

On time or early: ......85 (=56%)......

Late: ......68 (=44%)......

Reasons for lateness:

   (a) <u>Commercial reasons, total:</u>   ......27 (=17·6%)......
          Made up of:
              - Customer exceeded credit limit: ......14 (= 9.1%)......
              - Customer on stop list: ......13 (= 8·5%)......

   (b) <u>In-house reasons, total:</u>   ......41 (= 26·8%)......
          Made up of:
              - Shortage: ......19 (= 12·4%)......
              - No apparent reason: ......15 (= 9·8%)......
              - Others: ......7 (= 4·6%)......

Figure 11.9 Analysis of order depatch performance.

report, subsequently reduced once the people involved realized that whenever a despatch was late they should make a note of the cause of the delay. Perhaps not surprisingly, delivery performance actually improved just because it was being recorded and systematically analysed.

Production delay analysis A similar analysis should be prepared of delays that occur during the production process. This is very similar to the 'waiting time' or 'machine down-time' analyses which have been used for many years to monitor manufacturing performance. However, these latter analyses only report occasions when the use of a manufacturing resource is delayed; if the operator, or machine, concerned can be switched to some other job (even if there is no immediate need for this), then the resource is considered to be usefully employed and no lost time is reported. A production delay report, in contrast, is used to identify when *the progress of a production job* is delayed. It is a particularly useful report in a JIT environment, where the objective is to complete the sequence of production operations in the shortest feasible time.

The sample report shown in Fig. 11.10 was filled in by an assembly operative (it's important that operators should be encouraged to complete the report themselves rather than get their foreman to do it, to avoid any risk of subsequent cover-up that might prevent management getting to know what problems exist).

A copy of every production delay form should go to some central point so that the reasons for delay can be analysed. An example of a summary report is shown in Fig. 11.11. You will probably need to wait until you have 30 or 40 completed forms before you can decide which are the most common causes of delay for inclusion in your own summary report.

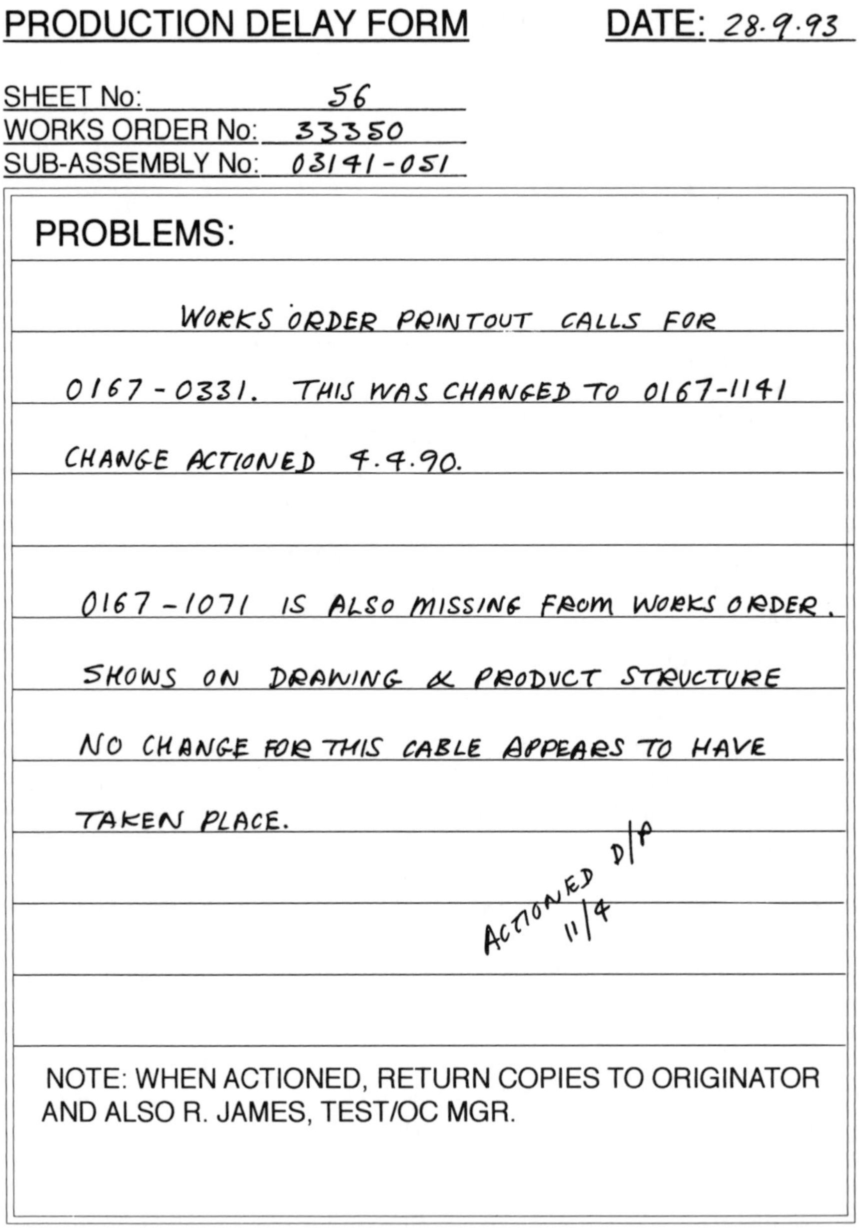

PRODUCTION DELAY FORM   DATE: _28·9·93_

SHEET No: _____ _56_
WORKS ORDER No: _33350_
SUB-ASSEMBLY No: _03141-051_

PROBLEMS:

WORKS ORDER PRINTOUT CALLS FOR

0167-0331. THIS WAS CHANGED TO 0167-1141

CHANGE ACTIONED 4.4.90.

0167-1071 IS ALSO MISSING FROM WORKS ORDER.

SHOWS ON DRAWING & PRODUCT STRUCTURE

NO CHANGE FOR THIS CABLE APPEARS TO HAVE

TAKEN PLACE.

ACTIONED D/P 11/4

NOTE: WHEN ACTIONED, RETURN COPIES TO ORIGINATOR
AND ALSO R. JAMES, TEST/OC MGR.

Figure 11.10 Example of a production delay form.

11.2.4 Improving Lead Time

Your process flow diagram will identify the stages in the process that take the most time. However, this initial process flow diagram will usually only show the time taken at each main stage of the process, and before taking action you may well need to prepare a more

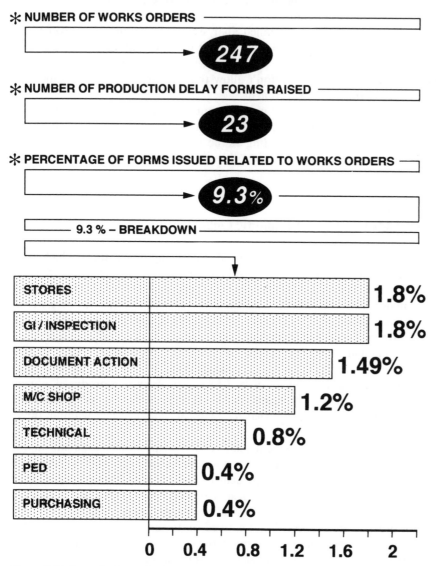

Figure 11.11 Example of a production delay summary report.

detailed breakdown of the time required at those stages that you have selected for improvement.

For example, in Fig. 3.1, 'Technical specification and design' was shown to take an average of 30 days. Further breakdown might involve finding out how long was taken on each of the elements: how long the order had to wait before a designer was available; the time it then took to prepare the design specification; what sort of delays are experienced in getting customer approval (and, possibly, then amending the design and re-submitting to the customer); how long the approved design specification then had to wait for a draughtsman; and how long it then took to complete the detailed drawings and release them to Planning.

When you have completed the detailed analysis, the techniques described in the remainder of this chapter should enable you to find ways of achieving your lead time reduction target. However, if you have previously worked hard on improving delivery performance, do make sure that you don't allow this to deteriorate again while your attention is diverted to the lead time problem!

Finally, don't assume, as so many managements do, that improving lead time is necessarily Manufacturing's problem. It often is, but just as often it will involve other departments. It's no good just concentrating on the manufacturing stages, only to be let down by other parts of the organization, as is illustrated in the following case study.

Case Study: Manufacturer of Domestic Lighting Fittings

This company manufactured a range of domestic lighting fittings which were distributed through independent specialist lighting shops. The range was supported by an illustrated catalogue, and all items were advertised as available on an ex stock basis. For many years the trade had accepted this as meaning two to three weeks, but recently this had changed as a result of increasing competitive pressures so that shops were now demanding delivery within seven to ten days. In order to meet these demands the company installed a new on-line order processing system so that requirements which could not be met from stock could be ordered from Manufacturing within 24 hours of receipt of order (the computer system produced a 'want list' overnight, every night). The manufacturing facilities were also reorganized and new equipment installed, to ensure that requirements could be met within a three-day cycle.

Three months later, management realized that many orders were still taking more than ten days to complete and business was being lost as a result. A consultant was called in with a brief from management to find out why Manufacturing were failing to achieve their lead time target, in spite of all the money that had been spent on new equipment. The process flow analysis he prepared demonstrated that virtually all orders were processed and entered on to the computer system on the day of receipt, as planned, and that Manufacturing completed nearly all the works orders on the 'want lists' within the specified three days. The delays were being caused by two functions that had been overlooked when the new 'quick response' arrangements were put in place:

- **Credit Control** continued to take up to three days to get clearance from the credit agency they used.
- **Despatch** continued to use the same delivery arrangements they had always used, which were based on weekly delivery schedules aimed at minimizing costs.

Once these problem areas were identified, management were able to take corrective action quickly. New quick response arrangements were made with a credit agency, and despatches were switched to a carrier who offered a country-wide 24 hour delivery service. Within a matter of weeks the late delivery problem was overcome, and *without any changes in manufacturing*.

It's easy to be wise after the event and say that management should have realized what the problem was. But it's not so obvious when it happens to you. Most people, in the circumstances described, would have assumed that it was a manufacturing problem: it's only when you get the facts, as the consultant did here, that the less obvious causes of delay are revealed.

11.3 REDUCING SET-UP TIMES

If you haven't tried the SMED technique yet, you may well have thought I was exaggerating when I claimed in Chapter 3 that 'Typically you can expect to cut set-up times by between 30 and 50 per cent within a matter of weeks *and at very little cost*'. My own experience, over a number of years, is that it would be unusual *not* to achieve reductions of this order. The two case studies that follow demonstrate how straightforward it can be, provided that you follow the simple procedure explained in Chapter 3. Even if you're not familiar with the machinery and processes involved, just by studying the information provided you'll probably be able to see for yourself how the set-up times can be reduced *even before you reach the part of the case study that describes the solutions actually adopted*.

Case Study: Set-Up Time Reduction for CNC Lathes

The machine shop concerned had for some time been suffering a severe bottleneck problem with a group of CNC turret lathes. Initial investigation revealed that in theory there was more than enough machine capacity to cope with the workload, but that time was being lost between successive batches 'waiting for setter'. The machine operators were not sufficiently skilled to undertake the set-up change themselves and in any case could be found other work to do. The root cause of the problem was the company's inability to recruit the full complement of setters allowed for in their staffing establishment, due to competition from other local employers.

Management realized that this skills shortage could be overcome if the setters' workload could be reduced significantly. They therefore decided to set up a team charged with the task of cutting set-up time in half.

As a first step the team arranged for a time study to be carried out on a number of typical set-up changes. The results of four of these studies are shown in Fig. 11.12.

As you will see from the 'Find' activities listed in the table, the setter wasted a considerable amount of time searching for information and equipment. Further investigation revealed that drawings often had to be fetched from the Central

Task	Time taken (minutes)			
	Study 1	Study 2	Study 3	Study 4
Find:				
–Process sheets	3	7	3	3
–Drawing	16	8	15	2
–Program set-up sheets	15	8	2	37
–Tape	13	2	2	—
–Material	—	—	—	15
–Fixtures/jaws/chuck	2	15	5	—
–Inspection equipment	2	—	—	—
–Cutting tools/inserts	—	—	7	7
Total find	51	40	34	64
Clean machine	30	8	20	44
Load:				
–Fixtures/jaws/chuck	8	40	30	23
–Cutting tools/inserts	—	8	17	—
–Tape and dry run	2	3	2	3
Check offsets and datums	16	36	43	12
Machining 'first off'	7	45	34	49
Wait inspection	13	35	35	12
Set gauges (inspector)	30	—	—	25
Other equipment – Miscellaneous	5	—	—	—
Total time	162	215	215	232

Figure 11.12 Analysis of set-up change times: CNC turret times.

Drawing Office which was situated at the other end of the factory; process layout and program instruction sheets were not always prepared in advance, in accordance with the shop planning; inaccurate stores location records made it difficult to find the right material; and the fitter had to look around the workshop for any special tooling or fixtures, since there were no properly indexed storage facilities for these.

Using the SMED approach, the team realized that all of these activities could be classified as 'external', i.e. they could (and should) be carried out while the machine was working on a previous batch. Furthermore, none of the activities really needed the special skills of a setter, so that all of them could be carried out in advance by someone else, thus completely eliminating all the time spent by setters on 'Find' activities. The team therefore introduced new arrangements for storing and retrieving drawings, process sheets etc.; proper storage facilities were provided for tools and fixtures; and procedures were introduced to ensure that all the information and equipment needed for the next set-up change was prepared in advance, in accordance with the forward production schedule, and located at or near to the machine well before the previous batch was completed.

At a later stage of the set-up changing process, the setter's work was interrupted by having to search for an inspector to check the 'first off', and sometimes there was a further delay because the inspector had to prepare special gauges before he could check the work. In the four studies summarized in Fig. 11.12 these two headings accounted for a further half to one hour. Better coordination between the setters and inspector was achieved simply by giving the inspector a copy of the forward production schedule (so that he could see which gauges need to be prepared in advance), and by the setter giving him advance warning of when the 'first off' was likely to be ready.

The changes described above can all be considered as the first stage of the SMED process. They took just under two months to complete and enabled set-up time to be reduced by about 40 per cent (sufficient to overcome the immediate bottleneck problem) and at minimal cost.

The team subsequently applied the second stage of the SMED process, looking for ways to convert internal time to external. Their solution was to propose the introduction of quick change block tooling, which would allow set-up change times to be reduced to a matter of minutes. Although the setters still had to pre-set the quick change tools, they could do this in advance at a time to suit themselves, thus spreading their workload more evenly. As is often the case with stage two of the SMED process, this required some capital expenditure: an initial expenditure of about £20,000, to cover the pre-setting equipment and the first machine, was approved for trial purposes, with further expansion (at a cost of about £10,000 per machine) being built into the capital expenditure budgets for future years.

The target reduction in set-up time was comfortably beaten; as a result the bottleneck problem was overcome, and there was no longer a need for the two additional setters originally allowed for to be recruited, even if the labour market subsequently eased.

Case Study: Reducing Press Set-Up Time

The example in Section 11.1 described how press down-time in a moulding shop was dramatically reduced, simply by making sure that a mould change fitter was made available without delay. The team appointed to study the problem subsequently introduced a number of other improvements aimed at reducing press down-time still further. The changes they introduced took several months to complete; for convenience I shall describe them here in the sequence of the original activities, as illustrated in Fig. 11.2.

'Mould removed from press' and *'assembly of new mould'*: analysis of past demand showed that there were a number of regularly ordered items that made up a family of similar parts, with only minor variations in dimensions. Each of these currently had its own mould assembly which had to be removed completely at the end of the batch run. The team developed a new 'family' outer mould which could be left permanently fixed to the press bed, with quick-change inserts to accommodate the differing dimensions.

Waiting for fork-lift truck: because of the weight involved, a fork-lift truck was used to remove the old mould from the press, take it to the mould stores, pick up the new mould from the mould stores, take it to the press and position it on the press bed. The delay arose because the mould stores were located in a different building, which meant that a fork-lift truck had to be used which was capable of travelling on the factory road: the only suitable trucks were 'owned' by the central rubber stores and their first priority was to keep the rubber mixing department supplied with raw material. Once they understood the problem, the team were able to come up with a simple low-cost solution which effectively eliminated the 'waiting for fork-lift truck' activity: a temporary storage rack was installed just inside the workshop; the fork-lift truck drivers were given details of moulds required on the next shift so that they could collect them from the mould stores at a time suitable to them, returning any 'finished with' moulds at the same time; the fitter then used a small lift truck (which was already available in the department) to move the old mould to the temporary storage rack and collect the new mould for mounting on the press.

Fitter called away to breakdown: normal practice here, as in most factories, was for maintenance staff to give priority to dealing with machine breakdowns. However, further investigation showed that in this case the machine that had broken down was only used for a few hours a week, and it wouldn't have mattered if the repair had been left until the next day. This led the team on to question the 'give priority to breakdowns' policy, particularly when an analysis of recent breakdowns showed that only a small proportion of the machines involved really needed to be repaired urgently. Rather than define a new set of rules, the team (which, you may remember, included both the Engineering and the Production Managers) decided to leave it to the people involved to decide on a day-to-day basis: while in principle priority was to be given to repairing breakdowns, a fitter would only be called off another job at the discretion of the Engineering and Production Foremen concerned. (I would hesitate to recommend such a solution in some factories, because the relationship between Production and Engineering isn't always as good as it ought to be! However, in this case team working had developed to the point where the traditional brick walls between these two departments had been broken down and they now cooperated well.)

Mould heated and first off approved: getting approval for the first off proved not to be a problem as there was a roving inspector in the press shop who was readily available when required. This left the mould heating time, which typically required between two and three hours for the mould to reach optimum operating temperature. Previously it had not been considered feasible to install mould pre-heating equipment since the mould was not available in the production area until the fitter was ready to install it on the press (as described above). With the new temporary storage rack installed and arrangements in place for moulds to be collected from mould stores during the previous shift, the team realized that it would now be feasible for pre-heating equipment to be installed alongside the temporary storage rack. This pre-heating enabled the final heating up stage on the press to be cut to less than 30 minutes.

The improvements described above reduced press down-time sufficiently for the immediate delivery performance problem to be overcome and the backlog cleared. Mould change time has been reduced to two to three hours, compared with as much as two shifts previously, but there is still considerable scope for improvement. However, this will require moving on to the SMED Stage 3 type of improvements, which the team decided could not be justified at this stage. Should demand increase significantly in the future, the team still have a number of ideas in reserve that will enable them to reduce mould change time still further. Although capital expenditure will be required on new mould designs and on better handling equipment, the team know that this will be a much cheaper way of increasing capacity than the alternative of buying an additional press, quite apart from the other advantages that can be gained when reduced set-up times enable smaller batches to be run.

11.3.1 Continuous Improvement

Using the SMED technique to reduce set-up time on a key machine will usually make everyone in the vicinity much more aware of how much time is wasted on changing set-ups, and help them to realize that something *can* be done about it. You should take advantage of this by inviting people to come forward with ideas for cutting set-up times in their own work areas. This method of involving the whole workforce in the process of continuous improvement is dealt with in more detail in Chapters 5 and 13.

Another method of raising awareness is to introduce monitoring of the time taken to change set-ups. You may well find that some such record is already made by operators as part of the data collection procedures used for calculating bonus payments, but the information needs to be presented in a different way if you want people to stop accepting delays in changing set-ups as 'normal'. Two reports that will help are as follows:

- *Average set-up time report*: a weekly report produced by simply adding up all the machine down-time booked to 'set-up', and then dividing by the number of set-up changes completed. The results should be plotted on a graph and shop management should be told that they are expected to achieve a clear downward trend on the graph.
- *Excessive set-up time report*: a weekly report listing details of all set-ups that took more than, say, one hour to complete (the cut-off time you choose will depend on your particular circumstances: the objective should be to pick the worst half dozen or so cases). Shop management should be required to conduct a post-mortem and include comments in the report explaining the reasons why the set-up took so long to complete. You will soon find an improvement, as people will do everything they can to avoid having to report a failure that could, and should, be avoided! This will enable you to adjust the cut-off point, for example from 'more than one hour' to 'more than 45 minutes'.

It's amazing how set-up times will drop once you start monitoring them in this way *provided that you are punctilious about following them up*. Cutting set-up times is such a key part of the JIT philosophy that it's worthwhile for management to show that they are interested in what's happening and are prepared to get involved if improvements are not being achieved. Remember that much of the reduction obtained through the first stage of the SMED process comes about simply by organizing the work better.

11.4 REDUCING INVENTORY

11.4.1 Inventory Analysis: The Starting Point

The first step when you're trying to reduce inventory is to get a good understanding of *what* inventory you have, and *which parts* of it are significant. In order to do this you will need to analyse your inventory records in a number of different ways.

You will probably be able to get all the information you need from your computer system. Although existing reports may not contain the precise details you require, this can normally be extracted from the system's database without too much difficulty: most computer systems these days have facilities for producing special reports, sorting and compiling information in whatever way you want. If this proves impossible, don't give up hope! You should still be able to prepare a reasonable breakdown using the information produced at the last physical stock check, which should be on file in your Accounts Department.

Beware of producing too much information at this stage, since the action you might need to take later in order to reduce inventory will almost certainly differ for different categories of inventory. There is little point in analysing *work-in-progress* in great detail, for example, if over 80 per cent of the total inventory value is in *finished stock*.

Your first objective, therefore, should be to get a 'feel' of your inventory. How much of it is in the form of finished stock? How much is raw material? Is the value of work-in-progress significant? If you have a number of different businesses on the site, do they have different inventory patterns? The Pareto Principle nearly always applies to inventories, so that a relatively small proportion of items will account for a major part of the total value of your inventory. The trick is to use the Pareto Principle in this first stage analysis to identify where this small proportion of items is in your particular case, and so help you decide where to concentrate your efforts; you can then analyse the inventory in much greater detail in the areas you have selected. The following example will illustrate what I mean.

11.4.2 Example: Inventory Analysis by Categories

Your company is currently experiencing difficult market conditions. Due to high interest rates, demand for your products has fallen significantly and this has forced management to consider what action it can take to improve an increasingly poor cash flow position. As part of this initiative, you have been asked to investigate the current high level of inventory, with a view to reducing stocks by at least 20 per cent.

As a first step you have decided to investigate what the main areas of inventory currently held are. The Accounts Department is able to provide details of the total value of inventory in each of the eight main areas of business. The figures are as follows:

Product group A: £120,000
Product group B: £800,000
Product group C: £50,000
Product group D: £600,000
Product group E: £40,000
Product group F: £80,000

Product group G: £400,000
Product group H: £100,000

You could probably decide where to concentrate further analysis just by looking at these figures, but it's better to draw a diagram. This makes it easier for your senior colleagues to see *at a glance* why you have selected some products for further investigation and ignored others. A histogram is the most suitable type of diagram to use here. You *could* use a pie chart, but this wouldn't be so suitable at the next stage when you want to compare components of stock in different product groups, so for the sake of continuity I'll stick to the straightforward histogram. Incidentally, most companies these days have facilities for producing both histograms and pie charts on a computer direct from the data.

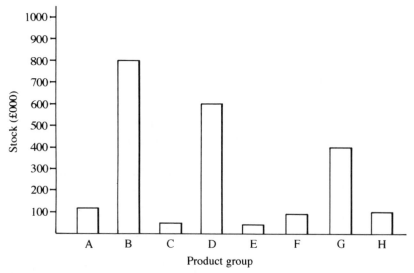

Figure 11.13 Histogram of inventory (by product group).

Figure 11.13 illustrates the data given above in the form of a histogram. Faced with this diagram, nobody is likely to quarrel with your decision to select just Products B, D and G for further investigation, particularly when you point out that they account for 82 per cent of the total inventory.

Let's continue with the example. Following the initial analysis of inventory described above, you have decided to obtain additional information regarding the current stock of the three Product Groups B, D and G.

In response to your request, the Accounts Department have provided the following information:

Product group	Raw material	Work-in-progress	Finished stock
B	£100,000	£400,000	£300,000
D	£200,000	£300,000	£100,000
G	£150,000	£250,000	—

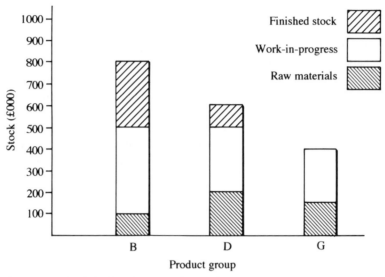

Figure 11.14 Analysis of product group inventories (stacked bar chart).

(The Accounts Department may well have had to do some work in order to extract this information from their records, which is why the more detailed breakdown wasn't requested previously for all product groups.)

It isn't quite so easy here to see from the stock values which areas should be given priority, but again a histogram makes it easier to decide, as you can see from Fig. 11.14 (this type of diagram is sometimes called a stacked bar chart). The most promising area seems to be work-in-progress, which is significant in all three product groups and accounts for 43 per cent of the total inventory; action here is also likely to have a spin-off effect in the other product groups.

You now need to find out *why* you have so much work-in-progress in these areas; the best way to do this is to prepare process flow diagrams, paying particular attention to where delays occur between processes. You can then decide which of the various techniques described in Chapter 3 will help to achieve the reduction in inventory you are looking for.

11.4.3 Inventory Analysis by Item

If you select Raw materials, Components or Finished stock for further investigation you will need to look at details of individual stock items. Most computer systems have facilities for producing a Pareto analysis of inventory (often referred to as an 'ABC Analysis'). This will list all stocked items in descending order of value, the 'value' being either the value of current stock or the value of issues over a given period, depending on which you specified. However, the standard printout is generally designed just to help you draw a Pareto diagram and make broad-cut decisions about stock control parameters: it may not include all the information which you will need to bring your inventory up to world-class standard, and some editing of the data will often be required, as I will explain in a moment. You may well find it easier to extract the basic data required from the main computer database and transfer this to a spreadsheet program, such as *Lotus 1-2-3*. You will then be able to select, sort, categorize and print subsets of the original data as required. This approach will allow you maximum flexibility while carrying out your in-depth investigations, and make it easier to evaluate the effects of different policy decisions.

Figure 11.15 shows a suggested layout containing the key information you are likely to need. At a later stage you might want to include additional information, for example 'standard order quantity' and 're-order point' (to enable you to calculate the change in average stock value resulting from new stock control parameters, or new supply methods such as Kanbans). However, I suggest you avoid complicating the analysis any further with additional information at this stage: this can always be included in the computer file if you think you are going to need it later, but it's probably best left out of the ABC listing.

If we go through Fig. 11.15 column by column you will see how useful this sort of analysis can be, and how you might need to edit the information extracted from the computer database before you can produce a meaningful analysis.

Column 1: Cumulative number of items You may decide to include all items in a listing, or you may select a particular category, sorting, for example, by lead time or by product group. Column 1 will give a count of the number of items included in each listing so that you can identify, say, the top 100 items, or simply see how many items are in that particular category.

Column 2: Part number The primary reason for including the part number, as you might expect, is to enable you to identify which parts need special treatment (because they have a high stock value) and which need investigating further (because they have an excessive number of weeks stock). However, you will probably find it useful to produce an additional listing in part number order for cross-reference purposes.

Column 3: Description Fitting 13 columns into the width of a page means that the space available for the 'description' field is necessarily limited; this can occasionally result in a vital part of the description (such as type number or dimensions) being cut off at the end of the allocated field. In most cases this will only matter for the more significant items, which are likely to be near the top of the listing. You'll probably have to edit the original data file anyway to correct information in other columns, so it's worth checking that the description is adequate as printed for, say, the first 100 items, editing this where necessary.

Column 4: Lead time category Lead times are included in the computer database to enable order requirements to be generated by the system at the correct time. Unfortunately, lead time information is all too often either missing or out of date and correcting it can be a major task. However, if you are using a special file that has been extracted from the computer database, there is a way in which you can simplify the task by using a lead time coding system which will be quite adequate for planning your world-class improvements – in fact, it will make this planning a lot easier. But make sure that you don't overwrite the existing lead time in the computer database with the coding system described below, or you could cause problems for the buyers and planners who rely on

1 Cumulative number of items	2 Part number	3 Description	4 Lead time category	5 Unit cost (£)	6 Average usage per year (qty)	7 Average usage value per year (£)	8 Current stock (qty)	9 Number of weeks stock	10 Value of current stock (£)	11 Cumulative value of stock (£)	12 Cumulative value of stock as % of total	13 Cumulative number of items as % of total
1	83246	Engine, type 3X	CO	2,205.00	1,560	3,439,800	90	3	198,450	198,450	23.7	0.63
2	73918	Thrust bearing	S	40.59	23,400	949,806	3,600	8	146,124	344,574	41.1	1.25
3	81367	Engine, type 3R	XL	1,976.72	33	65,232	43	68	84,999	429,573	51.2	1.88
4	85707	Controller, AVM	L	83.78	1,560	130,697	450	15	37,701	467,274	55.7	2.5
5	46139	Gearbox/transmission, AVM	CO	429.00	1,560	669,240	74	2.5	31,746	499,020	59.5	3.1
6	68418	Cable, type 39 (metres)	M	1.15	78,000	89,700	15,000	10	17,250	516,270	61.5	3.8

Figure 11.15 Inventory analysis: ABC listing.

the order requirement information produced routinely by the computer system. If you subsequently decide to include this new lead time code in the main computer database, you will probably find it best, if the system allows, to put it into a separate data field.

If you think about it, lead times generally fall into one of the following categories:

- **Short (code S)**: these are standard items, normally available from stock; delivery will typically require anything from two or three days up to about three weeks, depending on how well organized the supplier is.
- **Medium (code M)**: these are standard items, but normally made to order rather than supplied from stock; delivery will typically be anything from four to eight weeks, depending on the supplier's current workload.
- **Long (code L)**: these are typically items made to a customer's specification and may require special materials to be ordered; delivery will normally be in the range of three to four months.

These three categories will usually cover the bulk of items in your inventory, whether they are bought externally or made in-house. You can usually decide which category is relevant for each item without much difficulty. However, you will need two other codes:

- **Extra long (code XL)**: If you believe any of the items you stock require a lead time in excess of four months, then you should use this code.
- **Call-off (code CO)**: You may already be using call-off schedules for some of your major items (see Section 3.8 for more details): if not, you will almost certainly decide to do so as part of your JIT programme.

You will see later in this section how the coding system can be used to develop a set of stock control rules that are easy to understand and operate. Even more importantly, it will help you identify where you need to concentrate action in the initial stages of a JIT programme: your objective should be to remove all instances of XL, L and M (in that order of priority) from the top 100 or so items on the ABC listing. The techniques for achieving this are described elsewhere in this chapter and in Chapter 3; they include agreeing partnership sourcing arrangements with key suppliers, introducing more call-off schedules, organizing Kanbans, and perhaps even modifying the design to avoid 'specials'. Whichever solutions you adopt, if you can succeed in changing all the top 100 or so items to either S or CO you should achieve a dramatic reduction in inventory value.

Column 5: Unit cost Always check the last few pages of the listing to see if any of the items are shown as having a 'low' stock value simply because there is no unit cost recorded in the computer system database. This may be because the item has been obtained for a new requirement and the cost has not yet been entered, or it may be because there has been no demand for several years and the value of the item has been written off. Whatever the reason, it would be unrealistic to leave the item in your ABC listing without a value. If you are satisfied that the item is obsolete, it should be categorized as such, so that you can extract it to a separate list (see later in this section for how to deal with obsolete items). If the item is live, try and find the correct unit cost, so that the item will appear in the right position in the listing when you re-run the analysis programme after all the editing is finished. However, you may find it difficult or time-consuming to find the correct unit cost if there are a lot of items involved; if you are using a special analysis file (as opposed to working direct from the computer system database) there is a short cut that will usually be sufficiently accurate for inventory analysis purposes:

- First categorize each item, using the experience of the people involved, as 'High cost' (H), 'Medium cost' (M) or 'Low cost' (L).
- Agree a realistic price for each H category item by comparison with similar items for which you have a cost.
- Repeat the process for any M category items which have a significant quantity of stock.
- For all other items, select a suitable 'standard' value for the M category, and another for the L category, and use these standard values for analysis purposes.

You may well decide to repeat the analysis at a later date, returning to the computer database for up-to-date information on current stocks and average usage. If so, you might find some surprising results if the re-run happens to be done in a subsequent financial year. There are two reasons for this, both dependent on the year-end adjustments that are made in some companies:

- The unit cost may have been written down for items with no transactions during the previous financial year (from the point of view of your analysis this only matters when the product range has been changed significantly during the year).
- The standard cost for made-in items may have been changed to reflect the latest update in the overhead recovery rate.

As part of your world-class initiatives you may well be introducing updated or new designs much more frequently than in the past. This means that some of the items in your inventory will no longer be required. Eventually, the lack of issues will trigger the 'write down' procedure.

The benefits you will gain through applying the new world-class concepts will typically be reflected in lower overheads, which in turn means that the adjustment to standard cost can sometimes be quite significant. This is particularly so when overheads are recovered in the traditional way, by applying a factor to direct labour costs, since these may well be only a small part of your total costs. Fortunately, it's usually possible to adjust the *original* listing by re-running using the new standard costs, so that you can make direct 'before and after' comparisons.

Column 6: Average usage per year Remember that the computer analysis can only report information that can be extracted from the database. If the item is required for a new model that has only just been launched, then the 'average usage per year' may well be understated. In this case you will need to replace the original value, based on past usage, with a forecast demand, at least for the top 100 or so items on the list.

You should also look out for any items further down the list which have a high unit cost but low usage: if they, too, are new items, their usage may suddenly increase and this should be taken into account when preparing your inventory reduction plans. Or they may need to be reclassified as 'obsolete', for example if they are old items which have been replaced within the last year and are destined to be classified as obsolete at the next review (the reason for identifying them as obsolete at this stage is to ensure that any changes you may make to the stock control rules don't result in additional orders being placed for these high-cost items based on their past demand patterns).

Column 7: Average usage value per year This is simply Column 6 multiplied by Column 5. If you have changed the value in either of those two columns, the value in Column 7 should be recalculated automatically when you re-run the analysis program, but do make sure that this *is* the case with the program you are using. Following completion of the editing process, a list of all items in descending order of 'average usage value per year' will be needed when you come to setting new inventory control rules.

Column 8: Current stock The 'current stock' (and the corresponding 'value of current stock' in Column 10) is a snapshot in time: you need to know what this current stock is in order to quantify your inventory analysis. However, when you are looking for opportunities to reduce inventory, you will need to look at Columns 8 and 9 together.

Column 9: Number of weeks' stock This is calculated from Columns 6 and 8. In the initial listing this column will help you identify where editing might be necessary:

- If the number of weeks' stock is unusually high, check whether the item needs to be categorized *for the purposes of your analysis* as 'obsolete' (see below).
- Look out for items that are high in terms of annual usage value (Column 7), but have little or no stock: there may be a temporary supply problem, in which case you may decide to include the item in your action plans if it would normally be in the 'top 100'. You may need to assume an 'average' stock value for this purpose, taking this as half the normal stock replenishment order.

When you have completed the editing process for all columns, you may find it helpful to produce a list, in descending order of stock value, of the top 100 items for which the 'number of weeks' stock' is greater than, say, 15 weeks. If you can find out *why* the stock of these items is so high, you should be able to identify what changes need to be made in your current operating practices in order to avoid similar errors occurring in the future.

Column 10: Value of current stock This is derived from Columns 5 and 8: after the editing process is completed, make sure that the computer program you are using automatically recalculates the value for Column 10.

The values in Column 10 provide the basis for producing that most useful listing, the ABC analysis, which lists all the items in descending order of current stock value. This will be needed for preparing a Pareto analysis; it will also help you to decide where to concentrate your attention in the initial stages of an inventory reduction project.

Column 11: Cumulative value of stock (£) This is the cumulative sum of Column 10: the second line is the sum of lines 1 and 2; the third line is the sum of lines 1, 2 and 3, and so on. Its primary purpose is for calculation of figures for column 12; it also enables you to make statements such as 'The top 100 items account for £1,560,000 of inventory'.

Column 12: Cumulative value of stock (% of total) This is Column 11 expressed as a percentage of the total value for Column 11 for all items (see comments for Column 13).

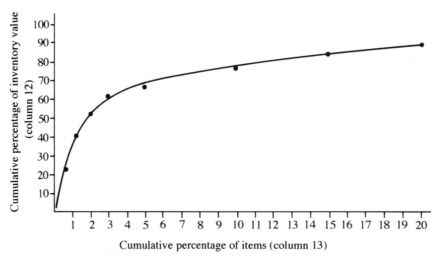

Figure 11.16 Pareto graph of inventory.

Column 13: Cumulative number of items (% of total) This is column 1, expressed as a percentage of the total number of items in the list.

The pairs of values in Columns 12 and 13 are used to plot a Pareto graph: an example of this is shown in Fig. 11.16, which illustrates that the top 10 per cent of items account for around 77 per cent of the total inventory value.

You could also read off similar pairs of values direct from the listing, without bothering to draw the Pareto graph: in the brief extract illustrated in Fig. 11.15, you could say that 'just 3 per cent of the items account for 60 per cent of the total inventory value'. However, drawing the Pareto graph will get the message across to people much more effectively, so that they will understand why you only intend to concentrate on a small proportion of the range of items stocked.

11.4.4 Dealing With 'Difficult' Items

When you've completed the analysis described above, you should have a good enough understanding of your current inventory to begin the process of bringing it up to world-class standards. Perhaps I should have said 'bringing it *down* to world-class standards', since *any* inventory should be considered a waste! Unfortunately, it's a waste that you can never hope to eliminate completely, though you should try to reduce it as much as you can.

I've explained that excess or unbalanced inventory is often the result of misunderstandings about how the ordering and control systems operate, and I've suggested how these misunderstandings can be identified and corrected. These are problems to do with how the system is used; when you've put these right you will still be left with problems to do with individual items. It's important that you don't try to solve these sorts of problem by just holding more stock of the 'difficult' items. Remember that a fundamental principle of JIT is that you should expose problems and then put them right once and for all, so that they don't keep recurring. If you can remove the underlying reasons why certain items keep running out of stock, then you will reduce the occurrence of stock-outs significantly.

The inventory analysis will help you identify where to start. You should be able to use the computer to extract a list of all items for which the current stock is less than, say, two weeks average usage (Column 9 of the analysis). Some of the items on this list will be random shortages due, for example, to an unusually large order having been satisfied recently, and some will be scheduled items which are delivered on a just-in-time basis; all these can be deleted from your problem list. The items you are looking for in the remaining list are those which keep causing problems: these are the ones you need to do something about. You may be able to identify which the persistent problem items are by looking at the stock history file, but it's usually easier to consult the 'experts', i.e. those who have to do something about shortages when they occur. This may be Production Control or Purchasing, or it may be the Stores who often keep an individual 'shortages' card for any item where a shortage has occurred in the past. Ask them to mark up your list to show which items have a shortage record on at least three different occasions during the last 12 months (they may also be able to identify some other items which didn't appear on your list because a new supply had just been received).

When they've finished you should have a list of the most troublesome items: now you have to do something to stop them being troublesome in the future.

One solution would be to reduce the risk of running out of stock by increasing target stock levels for 'difficult' items: but that would be contrary to the JIT philosophy. The *right* solution is to do something which will overcome the problem once and for all. For example, you might be able to overcome late delivery problems by introducing Kanbans, or by arranging 'scheduled deliveries', or by getting suppliers to top up your stocks regularly using the 'supermarket' method (further guidance on improving supplier performance can be found in Sec. 3.8). If none of these methods is feasible, you could re-source to a more reliable supplier, or you might even get the design modified, particularly if persistent manufacturing defects were the main reason for late deliveries. Whichever solution you adopt, pay particular attention to reducing lead time to a minimum, just in case problems do recur in spite of all your efforts: at least, then, it will take you less time to put things right.

11.4.5 Reviewing Inventory Parameters

Ideally, you will only order sufficient materials to meet known requirements, arranging for these to be delivered 'just-in-time' for when they are needed by Production. Unfortunately, for many companies this will never be feasible because they don't know far enough in advance what their customers will want. This is particularly the case with spare parts or products offered on an ex stock basis, for example from distribution centres, and also with spare parts held by a maintenance department in case of machine breakdowns; the only practical way in which these customers' requirements can be satisfied is to hold stocks. *Someone* has to decide how much stock of each item should be held; the problem is *who*. In most companies the task is left to the people who are responsible for controlling stocks; management may occasionally tell them 'your stocks are too high, you must reduce inventory by (say) 10 per cent', but management doesn't usually get involved in the detail of *how* the stock control staff should do this. This doesn't matter too much if the sort of reduction that's specified is relatively small, but management really ought to get more involved if the objective is to reduce the inventory significantly, i.e. to world-class standards.

Here's a simple analysis procedure that will enable *management* to make sensible policy decisions, which *stock control staff* can then implement accurately at the individual item level. It's based on two obvious, but important, principles:

- The more you increase an item's average stock level, the less the risk of stock-out
- The longer the re-order lead time, the greater the risk of stock-out

The inventory analysis procedure showed that a small percentage of stocked items accounted for a major part of total inventory value (refer to your ABC listing, showing items sorted in descending order of annual usage value, i.e. Column 7). If you want to keep total inventory value to a minimum you need to keep the stock of these high annual value items low; you can compensate for the increased risk of stock-out by improving supplier performance, by finding ways to reduce lead time and by keeping a close eye on the actual stock (possibly monitoring stock levels daily). In contrast, you can have much higher stocks of items with low annual usage value: this won't cost much in terms of total inventory value, and holding higher stocks will reduce the risk of stock-outs occurring, so these items are unlikely to need much attention from stock control staff.

You also need to take account of lead time, to reflect the second principle, *the longer the lead time, the greater the risk of stock-out*. In other words, you need to forecast (i.e. guess) what the demand will be while you're waiting for your supplier to deliver a new order quantity: the longer the period over which you have to guess, the greater the risk that you'll get it wrong.

Figure 11.17 illustrates an easy way of taking these two principles into account when deciding what stocks to hold of each item, by breaking them down into three ranges of annual usage value and, for each range, subdividing according to three categories of lead time (I'll explain what I mean by target stock in a moment: for now just think of it as the 'average' level of stock for each item over a period):

Annual usage value range	Lead time			Totals
	Short	Medium	Long	
High (over £.............)	Ⓐ W = TS = £	Ⓑ W = TS = £	Ⓒ W = TS = £	TS = £
Medium (from £...... to £......)	Ⓓ W = TS = £	Ⓔ W = TS = £	Ⓕ W = TS = £	TS = £
Low (under £.............)	Ⓖ W = TS = £	Ⓗ W = TS = £	Ⓘ W = TS = £	TS = £
Totals	TS = £	TS = £	TS = £	TS = £

W = No. of weeks' stock proposed
TS = Value of target stock

Figure 11.17 Inventory policy: Table 1 – proposed stock.

- Target stock in square C should be greater than in square B, which in turn should be greater than in square A. For example, if you set target stock for square A as 2 weeks, you might set square B at 4 weeks and square C at 6 weeks.
- Target stock for square G should be greater than in square D, which in turn should be greater than in square A. For example, if you set target stock for square A as 2 weeks, you might set square D at 4 weeks and square G at 6 weeks.

The actual values you set will depend on your particular circumstances, and in any case they will probably be adjusted by management, as you will see in a moment. Let's assume for now that you decide on values as follows: A = 2, B = 4, C = 6, D = 4, E = 6, F = 8, G = 6, H = 8, I = 12. You can see that such an arrangement satisfies the strategy of increasing stock for longer lead time items, while reducing stock for those which cost more (in terms of usage value).

If you now define values of annual usage (Column 7 of Fig. 11.15) for each of the three bands (High, Medium, Low), you can sort your inventory analysis table to show the following information *for each square of the matrix*:

- Number of items in the square
- Total average usage value per week (Column 7 ÷ 52)

You now need to produce two tables. The first (Fig. 11.17) should show the number of weeks' stock you propose for each square and the average inventory cost that would be required (i.e. the average value of one week's usage for the square multiplied by the number of weeks' stock proposed). Don't forget to include the totals for each row and each column, as shown in the diagram. The second table (Fig. 11.18) should show the number of items in each square and the total average usage value *per week*.

Management now have all the information they need to make any adjustments they think appropriate. For example, suppose management feel that the total cost of your proposed inventory policy is too great: they can decide precisely what changes they want to make, and calculate there and then what affect their changes would have. Supposing, for example, that there are only six items in square C, but the total cost of the proposed six weeks' average stock is £5,000: they might suggest that action is concentrated on reducing the lead time of those items so that they can be transferred to square B. Equally importantly, they will probably conclude that there's no point in trying to cut

Annual usage value range	Lead time		
	Short	Medium	Long
High (over £ . . . .)	No. = V = £	No. = V = £	No. = V = £
Medium (from £ . . . . to £ . . . .)	No. = V = £	No. = V = £	No. = V = £
Low (under £ . . . .)	No. = V = £	No. = V = £	No. = V = £

No. = Number of items in square
V = Total average usage value per week in square

Figure 11.18 Inventory policy: Table 2 – basic data.

the proposed stocks in squares G, H and I, because this would have little impact on total inventory value: they may even decide to increase the proposed stock in squares H and I, to reduce the risk of stock-out still further at little extra cost. Whatever changes they propose, they can see for themselves what the effect on inventory costs will be and, most importantly, decisions on inventory policy will have been made by *management* and not delegated to staff at a lower level.

There is one further step that needs to be taken: the target stock of each item needs to be broken down into 'order quantity' and 'safety stock'. As most readers will know, safety stock is held as an insurance policy to avoid a stock-out occurring while you are waiting for a new supply to be delivered, either because demand during the supplier's lead time is greater than you forecast, or because your supplier delivers late. The rest of the target stock is made up of 'working stock'; when you're reviewing inventory parameters this is usually assumed to be half the order quantity (because working stock is at a maximum when a full order quantity has just been delivered and, in theory, falls to zero just as the new order quantity is received from the supplier). Ideally, a separate table should be prepared for safety stock, so that management have direct control of how much money is being spent on 'insurance'; in practice, however, I've found that most people who use the simplified procedure described above prefer to specify the overall target stock figure, and leave it to the stock controller to set the re-order point for each item at an appropriate level to suit the desired safety stock, using the traditional 'max/min' method. This tends to be only a transitional problem, while you are at an early stage of improving suppliers' performance: the more successful you are at getting your suppliers to reduce their lead time, and the more reliable their delivery performance becomes, the less you will need to rely on safety stock.

11.4.6 Obsolete Stock

Section 3.5 included some suggestions on how to deal with obsolete stock. But first you need to identify which of the items in your inventory analysis should be classified as obsolete.

Most modern computer systems include a facility for identifying and listing obsolete stock items, but the information provided isn't always reliable. Watch out for the following:

- The rule for classifying an item as obsolete is 'any item for which there have been no transactions for x months'; with this rule an item will not be included if there has been a 'returned to stock' transaction (for example, as a result of a stock adjustment, or an item returned by a depot).
- The rule is 'any item for which there has been no *issue* for x months'; this takes care of the returns problem, but what about the case where you have 1000 of an item in stock and issue just 1 (perhaps written off because it was damaged in storage, or not found when the stock was checked)?
- Stocks received in preparation for the production of new designs may be listed as obsolete if the analysis report is produced before any of the items are actually issued to Production.
- Items which have been replaced by new designs within the x months period will not be listed, even if they will never be required again; this is a particular cause for concern,

since there may still be an opportunity of using up the old stock, provided you act promptly.

- Some items may no longer be required for new designs, but have a continuing demand for spares at a much lower usage rate.
- Many companies write down the value of obsolete or slow-moving items at the end of each financial year in order to maintain a realistic inventory valuation; if this is done at the individual item level then the unit price shown for the item may be unrealistically low, and not suitable as an indicator of its sell-off value.

Some of these problems can be avoided by making sure that you understand in advance how the computer program will identify items as obsolete; if necessary you should try to change how it does this, so that you get the results you want. You will also need to edit the full inventory analysis in the way I've suggested in the notes on Columns 5, 6 and 9 above. When you are doing these adjustments watch out for items that are no longer used in current production, but still required for spares at a much lower usage rate: if the number of weeks' stock (Column 9) is very high, you may need to transfer the bulk of the stock to your obsolete list.

Case Study: Archilighting GmbH

(At the request of management the name and geographical location of this company have been disguised.)

Background

Archilighting designs, manufactures and distributes a comprehensive range of high-quality lighting equipment, particularly for the architect-specified contract lighting market. At the time of this case study, annual sales to this market were around DM60,000,000 and employees numbered 380. The company has invested heavily in design in recent years and its latest catalogue includes many new world-class products which take full advantage of the latest technological developments in low-energy long-life light sources. To enhance Archilighting's market image as a leading-edge manufacturer, it has also developed a computer-based design system which architects and specifying engineers can use to help them design more efficient lighting systems.

There is a wholly owned subsidiary factory situated some 150 km from the company's HQ and principal manufacturing facilities, which supplies the specialist high-quality metal spinnings and pressings used in Archilighting's products. A central warehouse and distribution facility for finished products is located close to the main factory, and this supports a network of branches around Europe (within a distance of about 800 km of the factory). These branches act as both showrooms and local distribution centres. There are also two subsidiary sales and distribution companies overseas.

This case study starts at the point when a new range of products had just been launched and a major investment programme to improve manufacturing equipment had been completed. Management were ready to start on the final stage of their plan to become 'The fastest growing manufacturer of high-quality architectural lighting products in the world'.

Executive Vice-President Helmut Winter felt strongly that making investments in new designs and new manufacturing equipment was only part of what needed to be done: 'I was convinced that unless a corresponding investment was made in improving our *people*, Archilighting would never achieve the full benefits of all this investment we'd made in design and manufacturing, since it is *people* who determine how effectively manufacturing resources are used and how well customers are served'. The key to success, he felt, would be to break down traditional barriers between departments and get people at all levels working together with a common aim: to provide a world-class service to customers, to match the high quality of Archilighting's new product range.

A number of multi-disciplinary improvement teams were launched, involving people from all parts of the company, with two objectives in mind:

- To achieve specific improvement targets that would provide significant customer benefits
- To demonstrate how much could be achieved through effective teamwork, making full use of the skills and experience of employees at all levels

The remainder of this case study is concerned with the work of one of the teams, charged with improving inventory performance in the European branch network. A separate case study in Sec. 11.7 describes how another team, made up of design, production and purchasing staff, tackled the problem of material cost reduction.

Improving inventory performance

The main end users of Archilighting products are electrical subcontractors. They normally order the materials they need for each job either through a trade distributor or direct from Archilighting, and usually expect delivery either ex stock or within two to three days: if Archilighting fail to supply within this time-scale the order may be lost to a competitor. Large orders are sometimes sent direct to site from the central warehouse; all other orders are supplied via the trade distributor or Archilighting's branches, either from their own local stocks or by drawing additional supplies from the central warehouse.

Before the project started, distribution to customers and branches was via a mix of own vans and haulage contract, with most areas serviced on a weekly cycle. The team realized that this would have to be changed if customers' delivery expectations were to be satisfied. A new contractor was therefore appointed to look after distribution across Europe, with the new arrangements providing a 'next day' despatch service for all areas. Virtually all deliveries are now despatched within one day, compared with only 30 per cent previously. These new and vastly improved arrangements are very flexible, allowing volumes to vary from one day to the next without cost penalties, and the total cost of distribution is actually slightly lower than with the old arrangements. In addition, there has been a marked reduction in goods damaged in transit, thanks to the attention the new contractor and Archilighting's own despatch staff have paid to improving handling and packaging of consignments.

When the new 'rapid response' arrangements were in place, the team moved on to review stockholding policy at the branches, using the approach described in Sec. 3.5. Following a detailed analysis of past sales and stock levels, they decided to place particular emphasis on making sure that stocks of the most popular products were readily available at branches, with most of the remaining catalogue items available from the central warehouse on a 'next day' despatch basis (a small number of low usage products that management wished to retain in the range for commercial reasons were marked in the catalogue as 'available to order only'). The team realized that their proposals would result in a very significant reduction in the range of products that would be stocked at branches, with many items currently stocked being returned to the central warehouse. They didn't want to do this over the heads of the managers concerned: the problem was how to get their willing cooperation? Having one of the branch managers as a team member helped them decide how to proceed. This is what they did:

1. The first step was to introduce a new stockholding policy at the central warehouse for the full range of finished products and factored items. Stock classifications were agreed ('Top 200', 'Fast', 'Mid', 'Slow' and 'New') and a stockholding policy, approved by management, was specified for each category.
2. No action was taken at branches until the team was satisfied that the new 'rapid response' distribution service was working and warehouse stocks were at the planned levels.
3. All branch staff were invited to a series of seminars at Head Office, in which the Executive Vice-President and senior managers from each department explained Archilighting's world-class initiatives and how they would be able to contribute. They were shown the changes that were being introduced in production departments to improve customer service and were able to discuss any questions or doubts they had directly with the people involved. Finally, team members explained the proposed changes in stockholding policy and invited feedback.
4. One branch was selected as a pilot for implementation. The detailed stockholding proposals were discussed with the manager, leading to some minor adjustments. A key factor in gaining cooperation at this stage was the 'stock capping' option (explained in Sec. 3.5): the team proposed a list of core products which they specified should be held in stock; the manager could, if he wished, select a limited number of additional products with a specified maximum value; all other products currently stocked at that branch were to be returned to the central warehouse. This option proved more than sufficient to accommodate any changes the manager wanted and agreement was reached to proceed with implementation. The result was a reduction in the number of products stocked from 600 to fewer than 100, and a reduction in inventory value from DM250,000 to DM60,000.
5. The new arrangements were subsequently extended to all branches. As a result, inventory held at branches overall has been reduced by two thirds. Branch managers are reported to be very pleased with the changes, which have enabled them to improve customer service in spite of the lower level of stocks.

6. With all surplus stocks now concentrated at the central warehouse, the team was able to undertake a further analysis to identify obsolete stock, which was valued at a total of DM1,500,000. A separate team was instructed by management to find ways of using up or disposing of these obsolete products, and steps were also taken aimed at limiting the accumulation of obsolete stock in the future.

Although the team's main objective was to improve inventory performance, they didn't forget that an important part of their task was to improve customer service. During their investigations they found that staff at branches often had difficulty in finding information quickly to answer customer queries, and in many cases they didn't know who to contact at Head Office when they needed support. The team therefore compiled a loose-leaf 'Customer Service Compendium' for branch and sales staff, and got management to approve arrangements for this to be regularly updated in the future. As a result, Archilighting people in the field now have an up-to-date quick reference source of the sort of information likely to be needed when responding to customer queries, together with contact names for various 'experts' back at Head Office.

As a result of this project Archilighting are able to respond more quickly and effectively to customers' demands than ever before. Although total inventory value has been reduced significantly, stocks are better balanced and customer service has been improved. As the team reported to management at the end of their project: 'We are at last really getting control of our inventory. We know how much stock we have of each category and where it is, and we are able to influence this. With the changes we have made to our systems and procedures, not only do we now have buttons available to press, we actually know how to tweak them'.

11.5 IMPROVING LABOUR FLEXIBILITY

Case Study: Vokes Limited – Genflex Division

Background

The main work of Vokes' Genflex Division is the design and manufacture of bellows expansion joints. The product is used in any capital project involving pipework exposed to heat variation or vibration, and is sold either as original equipment or subsequently as spares. The project contractor specifies the operating conditions, and Genflex technical staff then translate this into a technical specification, with drawings, to meet the appropriate EN or BS Quality Standard. Although some applications can be specified with standard units for which drawings already exist, many require bespoke solutions for which new drawings have to be prepared.

Since the end product has to be produced according to a standard or code of practice which applies equally to every competitor, the Genflex product cannot effectively gain any competitive edge through quality alone. Getting business, therefore, depends on being known as a reliable supplier and on being able to compete on price – in some capital projects contractors will state in advance the price they are prepared to pay. Delivery performance is particularly important: in the case of original equipment, failure to satisfy contractors' delivery requirements would be fatal for any supplier who wished to remain in business, while orders for spares are often conditional on delivery to suit a planned maintenance shut-down, or the arrival of a ship in port. Competition is fierce, because there is overcapacity in the industry.

As part of Vokes' world-class programme, a team was set up charged with the task of improving the performance of Genflex Division. Having analysed lead time performance over a representative period, and looked in detail at the time required for each process stage, they realized that a major problem was caused by extreme variations in demand. For example, at times there would be a run of enquiries or orders which were relatively simple to specify and could be satisfied with existing designs; at other times there would be a surge of orders requiring bespoke designs which would overload the technical and design staff. Material procurement and Production were similarly also subjected to variable demand.

The team decided that the best way to improve competitive edge would be to find ways of coping with these extreme variations in demand *without allowing lead times to be affected*. They wanted to maintain a consistently reliable service to customers while at the same time taking advantage of every sales opportunity they could find. With this in mind they decided to concentrate on two areas:

- **Technical and administrative functions**, the objective being to spread the load by moving staff between jobs, so that temporary bottlenecks could be overcome
- **Shop floor operations**, with similar objectives of speeding throughput times by more flexible allocation of people to jobs

Technical and administrative functions

Following consultation with each member of the Technical and Administrative staff, the team prepared an analysis of all the tasks undertaken and who was able to carry out each task. The results of this analysis are shown in the resource/skills matrix they produced (Fig. 11.19). By comparing this matrix with the process flow charts they had prepared, the team were able to identify potential bottleneck activities and decide which members of staff could best be used to help overcome these bottlenecks, providing they were given the necessary training.

This wasn't quite as easy to decide as it sounds. They had to take into account what would happen to the tasks those people normally did: was it likely that an upturn in the activities they were diverted to would coincide with a downturn in their own workload? Or could their normal tasks be left for a few days without endangering customer service? And they had to make sure that the most versatile staff members weren't specified as back-up on too many tasks, because if they did that they'd simply be creating yet another bottleneck. The resource/skills matrix proved very useful in helping the team decide who should be trained in which tasks, and to what degree of competence:

- They considered each column in turn, looking to see which activities already had sufficient coverage at each skill level and which were inadequately covered; they also considered how critical that activity was to delivery performance, and whether it could be left for a few days when there was an overload elsewhere.

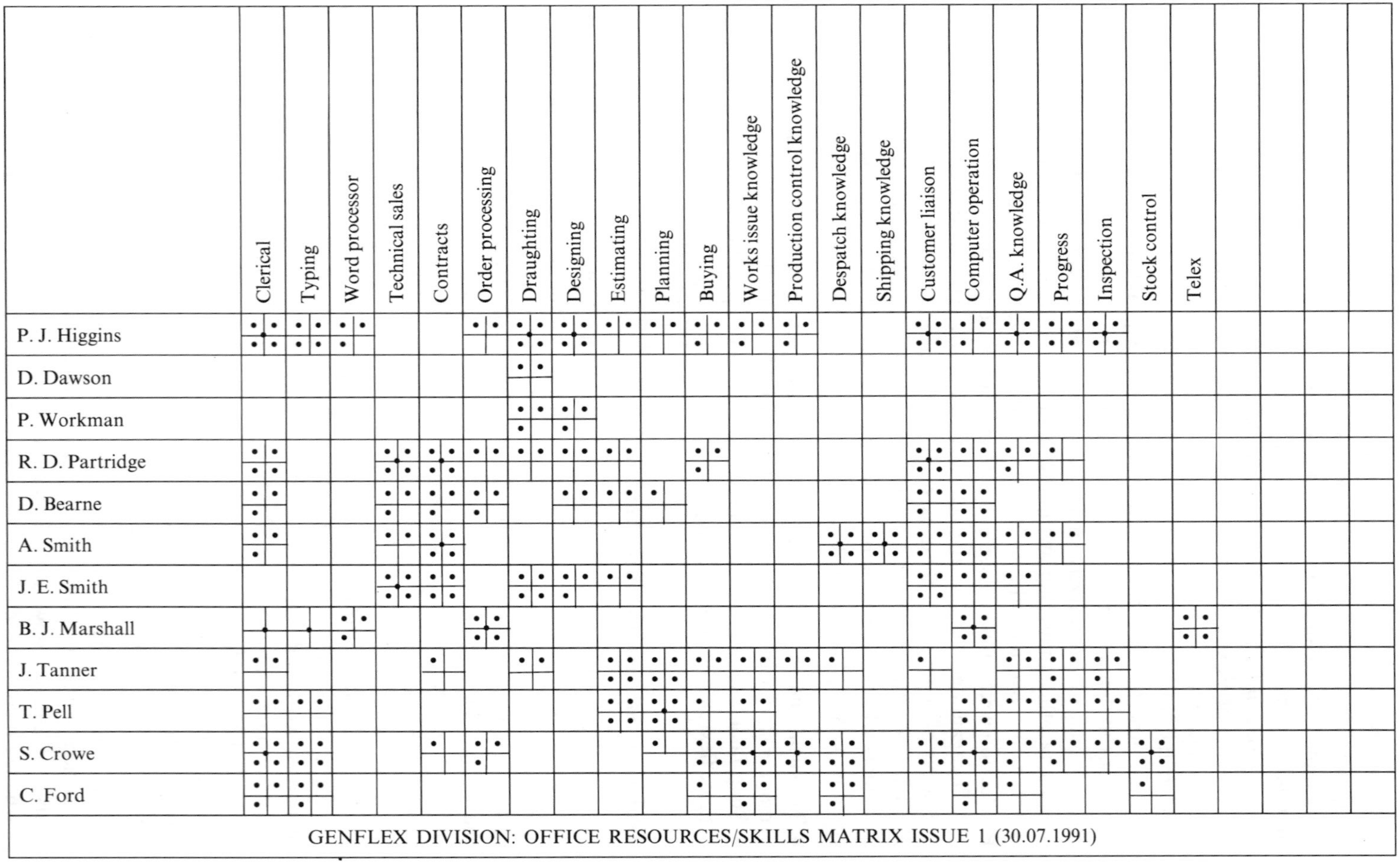

GENFLEX DIVISION: OFFICE RESOURCES/SKILLS MATRIX ISSUE 1 (30.07.1991)

Skills (rows): Clerical, Typing, Word processor, Technical sales, Contracts, Order processing, Draughting, Designing, Estimating, Planning, Buying, Works issue knowledge, Production control knowledge, Despatch knowledge, Shipping knowledge, Customer liaison, Computer operation, Q.A. knowledge, Progress, Inspection, Stock control, Telex

Resources (columns): P. J. Higgins, D. Dawson, P. Workman, R. D. Partridge, D. Bearne, A. Smith, J. E. Smith, B. J. Marshall, J. Tanner, T. Pell, S. Crowe, C. Ford

Figure 11.19 The resource/skills matrix at start.

- Where they felt that an activity was not adequately covered at present, they looked to see if it could be broken down in any way, so that re-training of back-up resources could be limited to just part of the job.
- They also looked at each row of the matrix to see how many tasks each person could currently undertake; they didn't want to allocate additional tasks to those who already had a wide range of work, but at the same time they didn't want to divert a scarce resource from a key activity which was already overloaded.
- They paid particular attention to the existing range of skills of senior members of staff: ideally, they should be able in emergencies to do the work of anyone they supervised, and they were the obvious ones to provide training to others.
- They noted any personal preferences mentioned in their discussions with each staff member: they felt that if someone expressed an interest in learning a particular new task, they would probably respond more positively to training, and on the other hand they didn't want to put pressure on individuals to learn a new task against their will.

Having completed the review, the next task was to set priorities. Much of the training could only be done 'on the job', and that necessarily takes time in a busy department. The first stage training programme prepared by the team is illustrated in Fig. 11.20, which shows the planned completion date for each training task; the progress to date after five months is shown in Fig. 11.21. This programme is updated every three months: at each review, target completion dates are revised to reflect current priorities, and the training programme is extended to ensure that there is continuous improvement in workforce flexibility.

Shop floor operations

The process flow charts prepared by the team showed that welding was a critical part of manufacturing. They wanted to reorganize the welding section into cell manufacturing units because they knew this would improve delivery performance by cutting throughput time, and reduce overheads by cutting work-in-progress and space occupied. However, they found difficulty in doing this because of the complexity of the fabrications produced and the special materials that were often required, which meant that a wide diversity of welding skills was needed.

To conform with the technical requirements laid down in the various standards and codes of practice, welders have to be independently certified as competent to perform the specific category of weld with the specific type of material called for in the job. With the existing organization of manufacturing, a welder with the appropriate skills moved to the job: with cell manufacture, in order to keep work moving freely a welder needed to be able to undertake any work allocated to the cell. A training programme would therefore be needed to increase the range of skills of those welders selected to work in the proposed cells.

The first step was to get an independent assessment made of what skills were available at present, which welders appeared to be both capable and willing to learn additional skills, and what training they would need. A training programme was then drawn up, specifying for each welder what training was planned (type of weld, type of material and size), in what priority sequence each type should be learnt, and

GENFLEX DIVISION W.C.M. OFFICE TRAINING

Trainee	Subject	Target ability level	Teacher	Training period	Completion target date	Training completed	
						Teacher	Trainee
R. Partridge	Sales Order entry	[ability level]	B. Marshall	Live	28.2.92		
	Couplings/Sales	[ability level]	D. Bearne	½ hr/day	28.2.92		
D. Bearne	Bellows Data Sheet Compilation	[ability level]	R. Partridge	Live	28.2.92		
D. Dawson	Planning	[ability level]	T. Pell	1 hr/day	20.12.91	T. Pell	D.F.D.
P. Workman	Planning	[ability level]	T. Pell	When DFD trained			
C. Ford	Raising GRNs	[ability level]	S. Crowe	Live	31.1.92		
	Purchase Order entry	[ability level]	S. Crowe	½ hr/day	31.1.92		
A. Smith	Purchasing	[ability level]	R. Partridge	1 hr/day	31.1.92		
B. Marshall	Purchase Order entry	[ability level]	R. Partridge	½ hr/day	20.12.91	R. Partridge	B.J.M.
J. Tanner	Compilation of Q.A. Contract Dossiers	[ability level]	S. Crowe	Live	20.12.91	S. Crowe	J.Tanner

Note: Live training means training on actual work as it arises. All training to continue until target ability level reached.

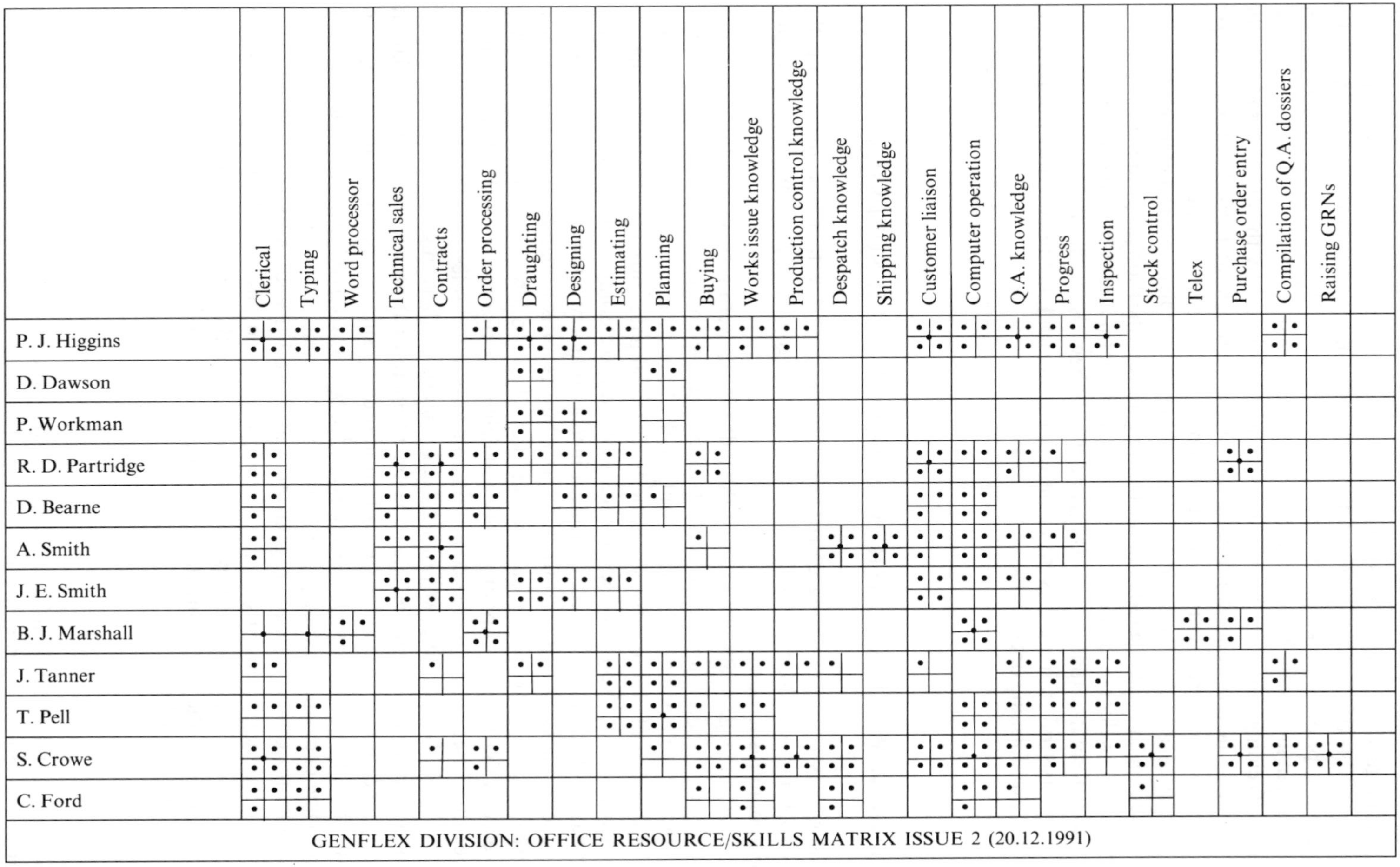

GENFLEX DIVISION: OFFICE RESOURCE/SKILLS MATRIX ISSUE 2 (20.12.1991)

Skills (columns):
Clerical, Typing, Word processor, Technical sales, Contracts, Order processing, Draughting, Designing, Estimating, Planning, Buying, Works issue knowledge, Production control knowledge, Despatch knowledge, Shipping knowledge, Customer liaison, Computer operation, Q.A. knowledge, Progress, Inspection, Stock control, Telex, Purchase order entry, Compilation of Q.A. dossiers, Raising GRNs

Resources (rows):
P. J. Higgins, D. Dawson, P. Workman, R. D. Partridge, D. Bearne, A. Smith, J. E. Smith, B. J. Marshall, J. Tanner, T. Pell, S. Crowe, C. Ford

Figure 11.21 The resource/skills matrix after five months.

the target date by when he should be ready to take the certification test. Since as far as possible this training was to take place alongside normal work, welders were also given a priority ranking for each test type, so that in the event of any delay the foreman knew which should be trained first.

Welding cells were eventually established, manned by the most versatile of the welders, the remainder continuing to work in fixed welding bays. Temporary surges in workload were accommodated by allocating an additional welder to a cell, or by calling on additional resources from another Vokes Division on the same site, some of whom had been included in the training and certification programme.

The welder training programme is still continuing, where individual welders have the ability to learn new skills and where they wish to do so. However, the main emphasis of training has now shifted to the next manufacturing priority, the bellows-forming operations.

11.6 HOW WELL ARE YOU MANAGING YOUR SUPPLIERS?

How well is *your* purchasing department functioning? Are they already well on the way to being world-class? Or do they offer you a golden opportunity for improving profitability? And how can you tell?

Most managements would have difficulty in answering these questions with any confidence; financial and management reporting systems will show whether material cost targets are being met, but these will usually have been set on the basis of past costs or, in the case of new products, on the basis of estimates provided by the purchasing department itself. You may be satisfied that they are doing well, because the annual purchasing spend has reduced, or at least increased at a rate lower than inflation: but is this due to the skills and hard work of your buyers, or is it mainly due to competition between suppliers in an over-supplied market? And are low material costs only being achieved at the expense of poor quality and delivery performance, so that these 'savings' have to be offset against increased production costs or lost sales?

A simple, but effective, way of assessing what scope there might be for improvement is to look at how your purchasing department operates at present and, in particular, at what proportion of their efforts goes into improving supplier performance as opposed to simply placing orders. I've suggested, below, seven levels of development of a purchasing department, ranging from an 'order placing' service at one end of the scale to a fully fledged world-class organization at the other end. And, to help you make an impartial judgement on where *your* company lies on this scale, I've suggested some questions you should ask your purchasing managers: their answers should indicate the extent to which the requirements of each level really are being satisfied in your present purchasing operations.

Level 1

- Buyers spend so much of their time on order placing and expediting that they have little time left for improving purchasing performance.

- They have generally poor relationships with suppliers, the main concern being to drive prices down, often at the expense of quality and poor delivery performance.
- Time is often wasted chasing up suppliers when the parts have actually already been delivered, but not yet processed through Goods Received.
- There is often conflict between Purchasing and Production staff, the latter claiming that shortages of purchased materials are the main reason for their own poor delivery performance.
- There is no systematic analysis of material costs, no performance measurements, and no management reporting of purchasing performance.

Questions None, because Level 1 is the baseline. You should start by assuming the worst, and only rate your own purchasing function at a higher level if you get positive answers to the questions suggested for that level.

Level 2 (Levels 2, 3 and 4 should be considered together)

- As Level 1, but there is a list of 'approved suppliers': buyers are normally required to use this list when selecting which suppliers should receive enquiries or orders; if they wish to use a supplier who is not on the list they have to obtain the approval of the Purchasing Manager or Senior Buyer.
- Suppliers are included on the approved list on the basis of familiarity rather than formal appraisal; acceptance therefore tends to be judgemental rather than quantified.
- Level 2 is better than Level 1 because it allows the more junior buyers to look after the bulk of the day-to-day business, but limits them to using suppliers who are considered 'satisfactory'. However, you need to assess whether the senior staff are adequately monitoring the performance of suppliers on the approved list; if so, they may qualify for a higher rating – see below.

Questions Ask to see the list of approved suppliers. Make sure that every buyer has a copy of this list *and uses it* (is it close to hand and showing signs of use, or is it filed away? Cross-check orders placed over the last few days against the approved list, and look for signs that any placed with non-approved suppliers have been properly authorized). You should also look to see if the list shows clearly what type of materials each supplier on the list is approved for.

Level 3

- Supplier performance is regularly monitored (i.e. some form of vendor rating is in place), and the approved list is adjusted as a result.
- Some form of management reporting exists, but this is usually limited to analysis of quality failures and lateness.
- Information on supplier performance may be suspect, due to inadequacies in the computer systems from which the analysis is compiled.

Questions Ask to see the (monthly?) vendor rating report and ask what action was taken as a direct result of last month's report; see if any suppliers have been removed from the approved list recently as a result of persistently poor performance (the fact that vendor rating reports are produced is not sufficient to justify a Level 3 rating: there must also be evidence that the information in these reports is actually *used* to improve supplier performance).

Check the validity of the reporting systems by asking:

- What happens if you ask a supplier to deliver in much less than his (or her) normal lead time? For example, consider the case where something goes wrong with your production process, as a result of which you need to replace some scrapped material urgently; your supplier's normal lead time is six weeks, but he promises to do his best to get the replacements to you within two weeks, and the delivery date requested on your official order is therefore entered as 'two weeks'. In the event the supplier takes three weeks: this is half the normal lead time, but in many vendor rating systems the delivery would be recorded as one week late. This is a common problem and the purpose of the above question is to determine whether your buyers are aware of it and make appropriate adjustments before showing the delivery performance analysis to the supplier.
- What adjustments (if any) do you make to requested delivery dates when our master production schedule is changed? If suppliers are asked to deliver earlier than previously requested, is this reflected in the subsequent delivery performance analysis? If you are told that it *is* allowed for, ask a supplementary question 'How?' (it's notoriously difficult to do this within a computer-based vendor rating system: any allowances usually have to be made manually).
- What happens when bought-out parts are identified as faulty and have to be returned to the supplier for correction or replacement *after their receipt has been entered on to your computer system*? When the corrected parts are returned, are they included a second time in the quality performance analysis? They probably *will* be included again and, since they will have a better chance of being right on the second try, this will have the effect of improving the quality performance average, particularly if it happens often (to make the point clear, consider the extreme case of a supplier who *always* has to have two goes to get it right: his failure rate will be reported as 50 per cent, when in reality his first-time failure rate is 100 per cent).

When asking these questions, remember that you are mainly trying to find out whether your buyers are using what vendor rating information is available to them *intelligently*, as a means of improving supplier performance, or whether they are just paying lip service to the vendor rating concept. If their answers show that they *are* interpreting the information intelligently and with a degree of caution, they may well deserve a higher, Level 4, rating.

Level 4

- Suppliers are only admitted to the approved list after an appraisal visit in which a formal audit procedure is followed.
- Once approved, a supplier will normally remain on the approved list, subject to satisfactory performance (inclusion in the approved list does not guarantee that orders will be placed, the latter being subject to the normal enquiry/quotation process).

- Supplier performance is monitored routinely; failure to maintain an adequate quality and delivery performance leads to a reappraisal visit in which the formal audit procedure is repeated.
- Care is taken to check the validity of vendor rating reports *before* approaching suppliers.

Questions Ask to see examples of appraisal reports, selecting suppliers' names from the approved list yourself so that you can check that the audit process is being carried out systematically (be realistic about this: make sure you select suppliers who are used frequently).

Select examples of poor performers from *last* month's vendor rating report and ask what action has been taken with the suppliers concerned: has the validity of the reported data been checked, and have any reappraisal visits been arranged?

Level 5

- The Purchasing Manager and/or Senior Buyers spend a significant part of their time on monitoring the performance of key suppliers; they keep in close touch with them by telephone and visit regularly.
- A Pareto listing of the worst offenders is produced (i.e. suppliers are listed in descending order of poor performance rating).
- Suppliers are made aware of how poorly they are performing compared with other suppliers, particularly their direct competitors (to preserve commercial confidentiality the suppliers' names on this list should be replaced with a coded reference; care should be taken not to use the computer system's supplier code if this includes the first letter(s) of the supplier's name).
- Suspending a supplier who is performing badly is recognized as the last resort; the preferred solution is always to help the supplier to improve ('What can *we* do to help?').

Questions Ask to see examples of 'before' and 'after' reports, demonstrating how suppliers with a poor record have improved their performance. If your purchasing function warrants a Level 5 or higher ranking there should be formal 'visit reports', minuting what has been agreed, and evidence that agreed actions have been acted upon.

At this level there should also be evidence that suppliers are able to satisfy JIT delivery requirements. In particular, ask which supply on a 'zero defects' basis, i.e. have been formally approved for 'certificated supply' deliveries.

Level 6

- 'Partnership sourcing' agreements are in place with a number of key suppliers, confirming a mutual long term commitment between supplier and purchaser.
- The number of suppliers used regularly has been reduced significantly, many materials now being obtained on a sole-source basis.

Questions Ask for a list of suppliers with whom a partnership sourcing agreement has been negotiated, and what proportion of the annual purchasing spend this represents. Look at a typical agreement document, to see how it compares with the guidelines suggested in Fig. 3.10. Make sure that the new arrangements have enabled purchasing procedures to be simplified in order to reduce administrative work and associated delays. Above all, ask what *quantifiable* benefits have resulted.

Level 7

- As Level 6, but with considerable emphasis placed on working closely with suppliers to achieve *continuous improvement* in purchasing performance.
- Your Production, Engineering and Design staff are encouraged to keep in close touch with their opposite numbers at suppliers and visit each other whenever appropriate.
- Materials purchased through a partnership sourcing agreement are periodically benchmarked with alternative sources (to ensure that the arrangement doesn't become too cosy); if a cheaper source is identified the results are openly discussed with the existing supplier on the basis of 'What can we do together to bring your price into line?'.
- Materials not purchased through a partnership sourcing agreement are reviewed annually, typically by re-negotiating for families of materials.
- A list of 'high risk' items is maintained, with availability of all items on the list closely monitored on a daily basis by a Senior Buyer.

Questions At this level you shouldn't need to ask for evidence! The Purchasing Manager will ensure that you get regular reports on purchasing performance; these should include a summary of new savings achieved since the last report and a comparison of 'cumulative savings agreed to date' with the 'continuous improvement' targets previously agreed with management. However, there are three questions that you should ask if the answers haven't been volunteered:

- How many suppliers have we used during the last three months, and how does this compare with the same period last year?
- What proportion of the top 50 items (by annual purchase spend) are covered by partnership sourcing agreements, and are deliveries of all these items called off against a scheduled order, bypassing the buyer?
- How many materials have been eliminated as a result of a material rationalization programme (e.g. standardization of fastenings)?

Finally, don't stick too rigidly to the seven levels of development as defined above. They are intended simply as a way of helping you to make an informed judgement on how world-class your own purchasing function is, and at the same time they should give you and your purchasing experts some ideas on what you *should* be doing if you want to improve.

11.7 IMPROVING DESIGN

The task of improving design performance can be considered under two headings:

- '*New product development*': this includes deciding what new designs are needed to enable the company's strategic objectives to be achieved; setting design parameters that meet customers' needs (through market research) and that offer a competitive edge (through competitive benchmarking); developing the design concept into detailed designs, ready for production, on a very short time-scale and with minimum teething problems (through simultaneous engineering); and improving manufacturing, purchasing and control systems to ensure that they don't let the new products down.

- *Improving existing designs*: a systematic review of existing designs, covering both products and (particularly) components. This might include reviewing past 'make vs. buy' decisions; value analysis to reduce costs, set-up times and quality problems; rationalizing the range of standard materials such as fastenings; standardizing dimensions to reduce the range of tooling and gauging equipment needed in production; reviewing standard practice on tolerancing; and looking for opportunities for replacing design details with proprietary items.

Both types of improvement will usually be needed to bring your designs, and the way in which your Design function operates, up to world-class standards. Which you choose to start with will depend on the action priorities you selected when reviewing strategy (see Sec. 2.5); if you have sufficient resources you may even decide to tackle both together. Two case studies are included below: one in which the priority was to develop a completely new range of products, the other in which the prime objective was to reduce the manufacturing cost of existing designs.

The first case study describes how Cincinnati Milacron used the simultaneous engineering approach to develop a new world-class product range in record time; this follows the case study in Sec. 10.3, which described the strategic issues involved, and the steps taken by Cincinnati Milacron to develop a design specification for a range of products that would enable it to compete successfully in world markets.

The second describes how Archilighting GmbH tackled the problem of bringing manufacturing costs into line with what customers were prepared to pay in highly competitive world markets; a systematic review of design details led to significant reductions in the costs of existing products and components, and the lessons learnt are now being applied whenever new product designs are being developed.

Case Study: Cincinnati Milacron UK Limited

Background

It's a familiar story: a long-established company, world leader in its field for many years, fails to update its product range fast enough; competitors from other parts of the world, many of them new to the scene, capture more and more of the company's traditional market by offering products that are both cheaper and, increasingly, technologically competitive; and by the time management realize that they can no longer depend simply on the company's name and past reputation to get orders, future survival may well be at stake.

Cincinnati Milacron reached just such a realization in 1987. The case study in Sec. 10.3 describes how they faced up to the challenge and developed a new strategy to re-establish their company as a world leader in its field. Central to this strategy was the need to produce a completely new range of CNC machining centres that could compete successfully with the best in the world. Market research helped to identify a potential product range with good long-term prospects, and competitive benchmarking established the design parameters that had to be satisfied. But serious doubts were raised as to whether the UK factory could continue to survive for the number of years normally needed, based on past experience, to design and develop a completely new range of products. Somehow the whole process had to be speeded up dramatically. This case study describes how Cincinnati Milacron were able to do this through application of the 'simultaneous engineering' approach. The result is the new Sabre range of CNC machining centres which has already succeeded in capturing a significant share of its target market. Incidentally, the term 'team engineering', rather than 'simultaneous engineering', is preferred at Cincinnati Milacron, to emphasize their belief that the key to success lies in getting a team of all the experts working together effectively throughout the project.

The project team

A multi-disciplinary team was established with a brief to design and develop a range of new products which satisfied the design, cost and delivery criteria specified as a result of the market research and competitive benchmarking study. 'There's nothing unusual about that' you might say; 'That's how *we've* always managed the development of new products'. What made Cincinnati Milacron's approach different was *who* was included in the team, and how the skills and experience of every member of the team were used to the full *right from the start of the project*:

- Care was taken to ensure that the project team included representatives from every function in the business: Marketing and Sales, Electrical Engineering, Mechanical Engineering, Manufacturing Engineering, Production, Finance and Purchasing; representatives of some key vendors also joined team meetings when appropriate.
- End users were represented through the part-time involvement of the company's own Applications Engineers; they are the ones who demonstrate machines to customers and train operators, and are therefore themselves expert operators.
- A representative of the quality function joined team meetings as appropriate, to deal with quality control aspects. Apart from this, management stressed repeatedly that the traditional view that 'quality is someone else's job' was no longer appropriate to a company that wanted to be world-class: the new message was that 'quality is *everyone's* job', and each team member was therefore instructed to keep his own personal responsibility for quality in mind throughout the project.
- All members of the team were involved in the many brainstorming sessions that were held during the progress of the project; those who were not experts in the particular subject of a brainstorming session were encouraged to participate, challenging traditional ideas and introducing lateral thinking to stimulate the development of new solutions.
- No one was allowed to miss meetings or fail to complete their allotted tasks on time because of 'pressure of other commitments': those concerned, and their managers, were continually reminded that the future survival of the factory depended on the project's success.
- The team's efforts were 'customer benefits'-oriented throughout.

- In parallel with the main design project, a separate team was set up to develop a new world-class business system, and the manufacturing facilities were reorganized to improve materials flow, new equipment being installed where needed.

Achieving the design objectives

No dilution of the benchmark targets was permitted: if an initial design solution fell short of a target, new ideas were sought until the target was met. An example of this was the development of a low-cost automatic pallet transfer system, specified in the original design brief as 'must not exceed 25 per cent of the cost of the basic machine'. This compares with traditional solutions that typically add 50 per cent to the machine cost, and the first design solution was indeed in that sort of cost range. It must have been very tempting for the team to say 'it can't be done'; but they persevered, re-examining the design and considering other ways of solving the problem until, eventually, they succeeded. This low-cost feature now gives Cincinnati Milacron a significant price advantage over most of their competitors' products.

Value engineering techniques played an important part in driving down the manufacturing costs. Right from the start it was recognized that fundamental changes in past design practices would be needed to achieve the very challenging design and cost parameters that had been set. For example, the hydraulic systems that had always been used in past designs were replaced by high-efficiency pneumatics incorporating sophisticated electrical and mechanical elements, resulting in a significant reduction in cost without affecting performance.

Achieving maximum cost-effectiveness was not the only consideration: quality and lead time were equally important. Finite element analysis techniques were used to ensure the integrity of the main structures, and quality of manufacture was ensured by involving both external suppliers and in-house production specialists at the design stage. Efforts to achieve a high degree of commonality of parts and sub-assemblies between different machines enabled new models to be developed more quickly, with two important additional benefits: many of the components in the new model were already 'quality proven' with assured supply, and at the same time production flexibility was improved, enabling the production programme to be modified at short notice to provide a quick response to customers' requirements.

The 'partnership sourcing' approach was used to improve supplier performance. A great deal of effort was put into weeding out unreliable suppliers, reducing the number used to those who were able to show the capability of meeting required quality and delivery performance standards. 45 suppliers who survived this selection process now supply the 80 per cent of Sabre parts that are out-sourced. Many of these suppliers were involved at the design development stage and are still actively involved with Cincinnati Milacron staff in the ongoing continuous improvement process.

The results

The first machine in the new Sabre range was completed and ready for shipment to a customer within 12 months of the project being launched. Cost and performance targets were all achieved. Nine months later the second machine in the range was launched, and six months after that the third. By the spring of 1993 four vertical and one horizontal machining centres in the Sabre range had been released. The complete design process now takes between six and nine months and there is a continuous programme of new machines under development.

For each new model, the first stage in the design process is to update the competitive benchmark analysis; this is to ensure that the design specification continues to be competitive with the best that competitors can offer. Technical improvements are consequently introduced as each new machine is released and, since these usually involve parts which are common to other machines in the range, the opportunity is taken to incorporate these improvements in all models. This ensures that all Sabre machines are kept right up to date with the latest technology: Cincinnati Milacron are determined to ensure that anyone buying their machining centres has the benefit of all the latest developments.

When the project started there were serious doubts about the future viability of Cincinnati Milacron's Birmingham factory. Now, in spite of a serious world recession, its fortunes have changed: it has a new range of products which can compete successfully in world markets against the best of its competitors and sales are growing steadily. The company has clearly achieved its objectives of re-establishing itself as a world leader in its field.

Project Manager Colin Davis is understandably proud of what has been achieved: 'We've secured a strong competitive position, reduced costs by 40 per cent, halved the time to market, shortened lead times by more than 75 per cent in some cases and improved cash flow and margins despite lower selling prices'.

When I last visited the factory I sensed another benefit generated by the project which will become increasingly important in years to come: employees at all levels have regained their sense of pride. So many people were involved in the project, all aware that the future survival of their factory was at stake, and they achieved what most of them would have sworn was impossible. The project has succeeded far beyond their expectations and *they were the ones that did it*. They know that without the very high level of commitment they all gave to the project it would not have happened. They can deservedly be proud of their products and proud of the company they work for, a world leader in its field.

As I explain elsewhere in the book, using your people effectively is the key to becoming world-class. Cincinnati Milacron seem to me to have found the way to do just that.

Case Study: Archilighting GmbH

(At the request of management the name and geographical location of this company have been disguised.)

Background

The case study in Sec. 11.4 of this chapter included information about Archilighting and its products, and explained why management decided to set up a number of improvement teams as part of its plan to become 'The fastest growing manufacturer of high-quality architectural lighting products in the world'. Archilighting's strategy at the time of the case study was to increase market share by offering better technological solutions than other lighting system manufacturers while remaining competitive on price.

The new range of products developed by Archilighting's designers was therefore launched initially at market-driven prices, regardless of the cost of manufacture. The task of the improvement teams was to bring these manufacturing costs into line as quickly as possible, so that the margins necessary for supporting the business could be restored.

This case study describes the work of the team charged with the task of reducing material costs by 20 per cent, the amount calculated as necessary in order to bring costs back into line with selling prices.

Material cost reduction project

The team consisted of senior members of the four departments directly involved: Design, Production Engineering, Manufacturing and Purchasing; a Product Manager representing the interests of the sales force and their customers; a management accountant to help the team evaluate costs and savings; and three 'non-owners' whose primary role was to challenge traditional thinking.

The first question the team had to consider was the very challenging target of achieving a 20 per cent reduction in material costs: was it *too* challenging? And, if they succeeded, would this lead to management questioning the professionalism of the designers and buyers who had previously accepted costs that would, as a result of the project, appear to have been unreasonably high? Executive Vice-President Helmut Winter personally intervened to answer this second concern. He reminded the team that over the past two or three years all the emphasis had been on getting a whole range of new products launched in the shortest possible time; he accepted that as a result the designers had been unable to pay as much attention as they normally would have done to minimizing production costs, and the buyers had not had time to follow their normal enquiry and negotiating procedures. In other words, they had not, as yet, had the opportunity to apply their professional skills to the full because of the emphasis placed on getting so many new products to the market in such a short time: they could now do so, and they should be able to do better than ever before because they would be combining their skills with the skills of all the other departments involved through this material cost reduction project.

(*Author's comment: I've explained this in some depth because it's often vital to the success of a world-class project that you recognize that some of the key people involved will feel that their professional ability is being challenged; it helps if, as in this case, you can answer their (often unspoken) fears.*)

All members of the team accepted the point made by Helmut Winter: the new range of products by now accounted for a major part of sales value and they should, indeed, be able to achieve considerable savings by re-examining the design details and procurement arrangements which had been made in such a rush. Various computer listings were produced to help them assess the scope for improvement and identify where to concentrate their attention first. For example, products and components were listed in descending order of 'forecast sales value', 'forecast quantities', 'more than three months' stock', 'Archilighting-designed items only' (i.e. excluding factored and proprietary items), 'currently made in-house' and so on. With the help of these reports and a subsequent brainstorming session, the team decided to set up three sub-teams, co-opting other people who could contribute specialist knowledge and skills:

- Make vs. buy
- Value analysis
- Purchasing cost reduction

How each of these sub-teams tackled their respective tasks is described below. Some aspects, particularly in the case of the third team, could have been described separately in Sec. 11.6 on improving suppliers; they are included here partly for reasons of completeness and continuity, but also because many of the cost reductions achieved depended on the cooperation of design staff in testing alternative proprietary components, and their willingness to consider modifying specifications.

Make vs. buy

This sub-team identified a number of component families in which some items were currently obtained from external suppliers and others manufactured in-house. They examined each of the externally purchased items in these families to see if it could be made in-house on existing equipment and, if so, what effect this would have on cost, whether additional tooling would be required and whether sufficient capacity would be available. They also considered the possibility of modifying the design detail to make it easier to manufacture in-house and assessed the justification for installing some additional production machinery. They were able to identify a number of opportunities:

- **Turned parts**: 15 components were identified that could be made in-house on existing equipment, saving DM40,000 per year (tooling cost DM1,400); further savings could be achieved by purchasing a new CNC lathe, but this was rejected by the team as the payback period was too long.
- **Mitre sawing**: Archilighting uses a large quantity of aluminium extrusions which have to be cut to length and ends mitred. The team identified a special-purpose machine which would enable this process to be automated. This gave a direct saving of DM36,000 per year for a total capital expenditure of DM45,000. In addition, stocks were reduced because the new equipment enabled just-in-time cutting of standard stock extrusions to suit each day's production requirements.
- **Press parts**: external purchases of pressed parts amounted to approximately DM900,000 per year; although some of these parts required specialist skills and equipment, many could be manufactured equally well in-house. The seven highest spend items were brought in-house immediately, enabling their cost to be reduced by 63 per cent (DM60,000 per year). The team then went on to consider the justification for purchasing a further two presses and ancillary equipment at a cost of DM240,000, which would enable an additional 140 parts to be manufactured in-house, saving DM150,000 per year.

The make vs. buy sub-team estimated their total cost savings, once all proposals were implemented and existing stocks used up, to be in the order of DM1,200,000 per year. In addition, lead times for the parts involved have been reduced significantly, enabling customer service to be improved and inventory reduced.

Value analysis

This sub-team's objectives were defined as 'To examine manufactured products and components for opportunities for value analysis, component rationalization, standardization and deletion, and with a view to the possible use of lower cost processes or new tooling'.

Their initial examination showed that the top twenty or so components offered little opportunity for improvement, since these had already been studied carefully at the design stage even during periods of maximum pressure. Better opportunities for improvement were to be found further down the list, not just in components with a high unit cost, but particularly in quite low unit cost components which were significant because of their high annual usage. They also identified a number of families of components where a design improvement in one member of the family could be extended to the whole group.

Some examples of the improvements they made are as follows:

- **Metal spinnings**: many of Archilighting's products include one or more spun components; conformance to design specification is particularly important from the point of view of both appearance and technical performance, so that as far as possible they are manufactured at a wholly owned subsidiary factory which specializes in this work. The team were concerned that a significant amount of spinning work was currently subcontracted because of insufficient capacity at the subsidiary factory; they therefore looked to see what they could do to enable process time to be reduced, thus freeing up additional capacity. Technical, Production Engineering and Manufacturing experts cooperated in a detailed review of every component required for the current product range. They achieved a major breakthrough when they realized that many of the dimensional tolerances currently specified were tighter than they needed to be and difficult to achieve with the spinning processes used; the new values set reduced the final polishing time significantly without any detrimental effect on product performance and, in some cases meant that the component could be finish-machined on the CNC spinning lathe, without the need for a subsequent manual polishing operation. Further savings were achieved by redesigning some of the more complex shapes, replacing them with a two-part spinning that was simpler to produce. As a result of these design changes and the purchase of a limited amount of additional low-cost equipment, sufficient capacity was made available to enable all subcontract spinning work to be brought in-house at an annual saving of about DM300,000.
- **Improving existing processes**: examples of the team's work under this heading include improving press tools from single operation to progression tools; modifying design details for ease of assembly; redesigning components for ease of manufacture (e.g. altering the dimensions of a nylon spacer to suit available raw

material so that a machining operation could be eliminated); and designing better assembly jigs to improve quality and to reduce the 'learning curve' delays experienced at the start of a new batch run. The team estimate savings from improving existing processes to be in excess of DM90,000 per year.

- **Modifying component design**: two low-cost components, a gear tray and cover, used in large quantities, were redesigned to allow the use of pre-coated steel instead of painting, and assembly with 'Riv-screws' into pre-formed holes instead of the original machine screws which required the components to be bushed: in addition to simplifying the assembly operation, this saved DM21,000 per year for an initial outlay on tooling of DM3,400. Another example of a low-cost/high-usage component was a simple slip washer, previously manufactured by a sub-contractor; designing new tooling and bringing manufacture in-house enabled the annual cost of these slip washers to be reduced by DM30,000 and, in addition, lead time and inventory were both reduced. A third example showed the benefit of including production experts in the design review team: one of the components looked at was a brass fabrication costing DM210,000 per year; at the suggestion of the production expert this was redesigned as a pressing which could be manufactured in-house, saving DM63,000 per year for a one-off tooling cost of DM24,000 and at the same time lead time and stock holding were reduced.

The team kept careful records of their work, logging each item under review so that they could report progress to management at regular intervals, and so that the buyers and material controllers had advance warning of items that were likely to become the subject of an engineering change. After 1500 manhours of work, at an estimated cost of DM80,000, they had achieved annual savings of over DM800,000 with more in the pipeline. For the longer term, they had succeeded in generating an encouraging enthusiasm and spirit of cooperation between Design and Production staff that should ensure that the same care is given to the value analysis of any future new products while they are still at the design stage.

Purchasing cost reduction

This was a particularly successful team, probably because they accepted right from the start that a fundamental change was needed in the way the Purchasing Department operated. A world-class company needs to treat its suppliers as an important resource, and to manage this resource as effectively as it manages other parts of its business. As in so many manufacturing companies, this was certainly not the case at Archilighting when this project started:

- Buyers spent so much time on order placing and expediting that there was little time left for cost-reduction programmes or for developing Archilighting's supplier resources.
- They had only limited controls, with no systematic analysis of cost, few performance measurements, and inadequate reporting to management on purchasing performance.
- They had poor relationships with their suppliers.
- They did not provide adequate support to their users, Production and Design; the responsibility of buyers ended when goods were delivered to the receiving door.

The team decided that they needed to get these problems sorted out first, so that they had a sound foundation to underpin their subsequent cost-reduction initiatives.

Their first step was to reorganize the Purchasing department into two sections: Inventory Control would be responsible for the day-to-day activities of order placing and expediting; Buying would concentrate on negotiation, cost reduction and alternative sourcing. This structure ensured that the more experienced buyers were no longer tied down with routine work, and could spend all their time on improving 'value for money'.

The next task was to improve the computer system so that it could be used more effectively to monitor supplier performance. They found difficulty at first in getting the sort of information they wanted because the system was overloaded with old data: details of 3364 suppliers were held on the system, but only 811 of these had been used in the last four years; the system still maintained full details of every order placed on suppliers for the past four years and there were 830 product/supplier links in the database for products that were now obsolete. All this surplus data was purged from the system. New vendor rating procedures were then introduced, to provide regular information to buyers on the performance of individual suppliers in terms of both quality and delivery performance. The team felt strongly that the primary purpose of monitoring supplier performance should be developing a basis for helping suppliers to improve, rather than providing a stick to beat them with.

Many of the items in the top section of the 'annual usage value' listing were found to be factored products, i.e. products purchased from another manufacturer as 'ready for sale'. Most of these were obtained from suppliers in other countries, and high stocks had to be held because delivery performance (and occasionally quality) tended to be unreliable. The team therefore decided to apply the new vendor rating procedures initially to suppliers of factored products.

At first they found that suppliers tended to be defensive when faced with a factual account of their shortcomings, but through exchange of visits and open discussions all but a few soon showed that they understood and welcomed Archilighting's new approach; as a result, problems have been brought to the surface and ways found to overcome them in order to reduce lead time, improve quality and delivery performance, and find more cost-effective solutions. For most factored products Archilighting are now able to provide a better service to customers than previously, in spite of inventory value being cut by 24 per cent. There were still a few factored products where the suppliers failed to respond and where the service they provided fell short of the standard required by Archilighting. The team decided either to re-source these products, or to design replacements which could be manufactured in-house.

With the review of factored products completed, the team moved on to other high annual cost items, using a similar approach.

Some of the savings achieved in this first stage review of product sourcing were as follows:

- Three whole groups of products were re-sourced at an annual saving of DM120,000.

- Suppliers of three other groups of products agreed to price reductions in return for a longer term commitment and simplified ordering procedures, involving the placing of annual contracts with monthly call-off schedules; these new arrangements saved over DM200,000 per year.
- Investigations revealed that insurance on shipments from an overseas supplier was being paid by both Archilighting and the supplier; removal of this double insurance payment saved DM30,000 per year.

Finally, the team started on a process of systematically reviewing the whole range of materials purchased. All materials used in the current range of products were marked up in the computer database to show a 'material commodity group'; each month one commodity group was selected and a list of all materials in that group was produced, showing usage and supplier details; current sources were then reviewed and negotiations initiated with possible alternative suppliers, the objective being to reduce the number of suppliers used, with the selection reflecting supplier reliability as well as cost. The team found that suppliers were much more willing to reduce prices and agree to shorter lead times once they realized that Archilighting were willing to give them better information about planned purchase requirements for a whole group of materials and for a 12 month period, instead of the past practice of negotiating for one item at a time as each order was placed. Many of the items included in this review process were of relatively low cost and would not have been given much attention in the past. However, by grouping them with other items and then negotiating with the supplier for the whole group, agreeing cost and delivery details for a year at a time, significant savings were achieved.

This approach of reviewing complete commodity groups is now undertaken on a continuous improvement basis. A programme is established for the whole year and cost reduction targets agreed with management; each commodity group is therefore reviewed once a year. For example, targets agreed for the first year were as follows:

- **May**   Plastic mouldings; target cost reduction DM150,000
- **June**   Emergency modules; target DM100,000
- **July/Aug** Gear/electrical hardware; target DM180,000
- **Sept/Oct** Transformers; target DM120,000
- **Oct/Nov**   Emergency gear; target DM90,000
- **Jan/Feb**   Springs; target DM60,000
- **March**   Fastenings; target DM75,000
- **April**   Turned parts; target DM75,000

Designers played an important part in helping to achieve these savings. In many cases a specific manufacturer's proprietary product was called for; with the help of Design staff these specific requirements were replaced with a generic description or, where this was not feasible, alternative manufacturers' products were included, which enabled the buyers to identify alternative sources.

The purchasing cost reduction sub-team reduced material costs by over DM1,200,000 in the first year, and at the same time managed to shorten lead times and reduce inventory. They expect to continue to achieve similar benefits in the future, but increasingly the emphasis will be on getting Archilighting's own designers and production experts to work more closely with their opposite numbers at key suppliers, in order to find ways of improving product performance and reducing cost.

Manufacturing Vice-President Hans Romer has been delighted by what has been achieved so far, and is confident that there are a lot more benefits to come: 'We have only just started to develop that great untapped resource, *our suppliers' skills*. The partnership sourcing approach which we have now begun to adopt will help us unlock this potential, and ensure that our products are kept at the leading edge of our industry. We've already reduced material costs by DM3,000,000, which is 15 per cent of our annual purchasing budget, and I'm convinced there's a lot more to come'.

11.8 RELIABILITY-CENTERED MAINTENANCE

There are two stages to the RCM process:

Stage 1: deciding what types of failure might occur, what effects these failures would have, and how critical each would be in respect of both safety and economic consequences

Stage 2: for each failure risk identified, deciding what action needs to be taken either to remove the risk of the failure occurring, or to minimize its effects

The first stage makes use of Failure Modes and Effects Analysis (FMEA); this is a well-established process and is already used by many companies when designing new products, particularly in the defence and aviation industries. For the benefit of readers who are not familiar with FMEA, a brief summary is included below; information on where to obtain a more detailed description of FMEA can be found in the Bibliography at the end of the book.

The second stage builds on the FMEA results by using the RCM decision diagram to develop a maintenance strategy which is aimed at maximizing safety and getting the best value for money from maintenance activities. The main elements of this stage are described below; information on where to obtain a more detailed description of RCM, including sample analysis forms and worked examples, can be found in the Bibliography.

11.8.1 Failure Modes and Effects Analysis

FMEA is a very detailed process, involving a great deal of work. Fortunately, for RCM purposes we only need to apply it to a limited range of equipment identified as 'significant'. How to decide which equipment should be considered as 'significant', and which as 'non-significant', is explained later. First I'll describe the eight steps contained in the formal FMEA process, when this is carried out at the design stage.

Step 1: Define the equipment to be analysed This includes details of what the equipment is supposed to do, and what performance standards are expected of it, so that a benchmark is established against which a shortfall in performance can be identified. The operating context also needs to be clearly shown, so that you can decide (in Step 2) what effect any failure of this machine or equipment will have on other parts of the production process.

Step 2: Construct block diagrams This is, in effect, a process flow diagram showing the operation, interrelationships, and interdependencies of each step in the production process.

Step 3: Identify failure modes and effects All possible functional failures are listed, drawing on general engineering nous, and experience of similar equipment; there may be several ways which could give rise to a particular failure condition and each of these must be listed (they are referred to as *failure modes*). The effects of each potential failure mode are then assessed in terms of the ability of the equipment to continue to achieve its own performance standards safely, *and* in terms of any effects that the failure might have on other parts of the production or operating process.

Particular care needs to be taken to try and identify every potential failure mode. The FMEA standard recommends that the following check-list of typical failure conditions is applied to each failure mode and output condition:

- Premature operation
- Failure to operate at the prescribed time
- Intermittent operation
- Failure to cease operation at a prescribed time
- Loss of output or failure during operation
- Degraded output or operational capability
- Other unique failure conditions, as applicable, based upon system characteristics and operational requirements or constraints

Step 4: Determine the 'criticality' of each failure mode You need to assess the worst potential consequences of the failure occurring, and assign a criticality rating accordingly. The most severe rating is assigned to failures that could result in someone being injured. Next most critical is where there would be severe economic consequences: for a world-class company this would include any production stoppages which would have an unacceptable impact on customer service, as well as the more obvious instances where the value of lost production plus the cost of repairing the equipment would be high.

Step 5: Identify failure detection methods Some types of failure are immediately obvious to the operator; others may need to be identified through instrumentation, or through condition monitoring equipment which gives advance warning of an impending failure. Particular care needs to be taken to identify *hidden* failures. An example of this would be a condition monitoring device, designed to give a visual or audio warning of a potential failure condition, which itself fails: if the operator cannot detect that the device has failed, the more serious failure which it was designed to prevent could be the first indication that something had gone wrong with the warning system.

Step 6: Identify action required This may be redesign to eliminate the potential failure condition, or other action to minimize the risk and so make the equipment more failure tolerant.

Step 7: Assess effects of actions taken The analysis of failures and effects carried out previously needs to be changed to take account of any changes made as a result of Step 6.

Step 8: Documentation The analysis finally needs to be documented for future reference. There should also be a summary of potential failure problems that the designers have been unable to resolve, and their recommendations on condition monitoring or other measures necessary to reduce the failure risk, or the effects of the failure should it occur.

So much for the FMEA process as applied at the design stage. When used as part of RCM, Steps 4–8 are replaced by the RCM decision diagram process, described below.

11.8.2 Developing an RCM-Based Maintenance Strategy

The RCM decision diagram in Fig. 11.22 is reproduced from the US Department of Defense report *Reliability-Centered Maintenance* (see Bibliography); this is the definitive work on RCM, and the diagram is the one normally used by professional RCM practitioners. However, the wording reflects the purpose for which the diagram was originally developed, i.e. developing a maintenance policy for civil aircraft prior to the aircraft entering service. When applied to the maintenance of factory equipment the logic remains the same, but some interpretation of the wording is necessary. This applies particularly to the recommended action 'redesign required': that's fine if you're dealing with equipment while it's still at the development stage, but in a factory we're usually dealing with existing equipment for which redesign isn't a feasible option. Alternatives have to be found, either by incorporating additional safety equipment, or by using condition monitoring techniques to reduce the risk of failure occurring.

In the explanation of the RCM decision diagram that follows I've adapted the *wording* of the decision questions to suit a manufacturing environment but, for ease of understanding, the *purpose* of the question is explained in terms of functions of a motor car, with which most readers should be familiar. The sequence of questions in the decision diagram must be applied to every failure mode listed in the preceding FMEA stage.

1. Is the occurrence of a failure evident to operators during their normal duties?

The purpose of this question is to identify potential 'hidden failure' conditions which, if not recognized, could allow other more serious failures to develop without warning.

For example, if the braking system of your car were to fail the results could be disastrous, but the failure would certainly be evident to you! Designers have reduced the risk by introducing dual circuit braking, but suppose one of the circuits fails and you don't notice it? You are now relying on the one remaining circuit and, if you don't realize this and so don't get the fault repaired, you could be in real trouble if the second circuit failed some time later. In other words, a hidden failure has occurred, which in itself doesn't matter, but its occurrence has opened up the possibility of a more serious and unexpected failure subsequently causing a serious problem.

These questions must be asked for each type of functional failure listed for the item. The first three questions determine the consequences of that failure, and hence the objective of preventive tasks

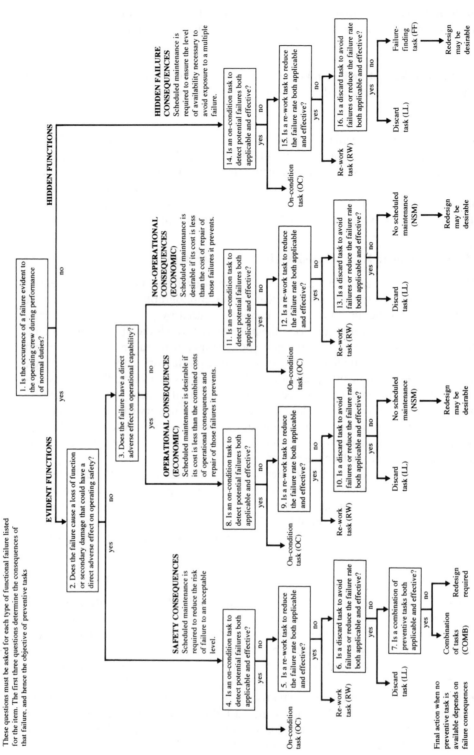

Figure 11.22 RCM decision diagram. (*Source:* Reproduced from F. S. Nowlan and H. F. Heap: 'Reliability-Centered Maintenance', US Department of Defense report No. AD-A066-579, December 1978.)

Hidden failures which could allow a serious secondary failure to occur have to be identified and suitable protection provided: in the braking system example this protection is provided by means of a red warning light showing on the dashboard.

If the answer to Question 1 is 'Yes', go to Question 2. If the answer is 'No' (i.e. it *is* a hidden failure condition), go to Question 14.

2. If this failure occurs, would it affect personal safety?

In other words, is there a risk that someone could get hurt? In a manufacturing environment such a risk should be considered unacceptable: if the answer to Question 2 is 'Yes', then something has to be done to avoid the failure occurring.

In the example of the braking system on your car, if you only had a single circuit system (as was the case some years ago), then there certainly was a risk of someone getting hurt! Hence the development of dual circuit braking systems.

If the answer to Question 2 is 'Yes', go to Question 4; if the answer is 'No', go to Question 3.

3. Would the failure have serious economic consequences?

This is normally interpreted as 'If the failure is allowed to occur, will the cost of lost production *combined with* the cost of repairing the equipment be high?'. However, in a JIT environment you should also consider the consequences to your customers (and perhaps your suppliers too) if your production processes are interrupted.

In the car example, if the engine failed there wouldn't necessarily be a risk to personal safety, but it could be expensive to repair, and the cost of hiring a car in the meantime could also prove expensive: the answer to Question 3, therefore, would be 'Yes'. If the radio broke down, however, the consequences wouldn't be serious and the answer to the question would be 'No'.

If the answer to Question 3 is 'Yes', go to Question 8; if the answer is 'No', go to Question 11.

4. Could the potential safety risk failure be avoided through an on-condition task?

An 'on-condition task' means carrying out an inspection of the part of the equipment involved at set intervals: if the inspection reveals that the condition is satisfactory, then the equipment can continue to be used; if not, the specified action must be taken, typically carrying out adjustments or replacing the parts affected. *Note that you should err on the side of safety when asking this question: if you're not completely confident that the potential problem can be avoided, then you should answer 'No'*. Some maintenance experts recommend that you temper your judgement by assessing the risk of the failure occurring – if the failure condition is considered to be just a theoretical risk with a very low probability of occurring in practice then, they say, you don't need to be quite so certain that the on-condition test will protect against the failure. I don't agree: I believe that you should never take *any* risks where personal safety is involved.

Returning to the car example, a tyre blow-out could have serious safety consequences. You are therefore recommended to carry out regular on-condition checks on the tyres to make sure that the tread depth and general condition are satisfactory: action is only required if you find something wrong. Brake pads are another example: the service schedule includes an inspection of the remaining thickness; the pads are left as they are *on condition* that they have a specified thickness remaining; if the thickness remaining is less than this, then a 'scheduled discard' task (to replace the pads) is specified. Although both these examples are of age-related failures, on-condition tasks may also be specified for other failure patterns based on, for example, abnormal noise, temperature or vibration.

Be careful in answering 'Yes' to this question: even if you can identify a sufficiently reliable warning of impending failure, this must still leave you enough time to take appropriate action. This is sometimes referred to as the 'P–F interval': the time interval between when the *potential* failure condition starts and the time when the actual *functional failure* is likely to occur must be greater than the time interval between inspections.

If the answer to Question 4 is 'Yes', record the required on-condition task(s) for incorporating into maintenance schedules; if the answer is 'No', go to Question 5.

5. *Could the potential safety risk failure be avoided through a re-work task?*

'Re-work' in this context means repairing or adjusting the part or parts affected. If a safety risk failure can't be avoided by an on-condition task, then see if any repair or adjustment tasks can be identified which would stop the failure occurring; as above, if you have any doubts as to whether a re-work task would be effective, play safe and answer 'No' to this question.

Re-work tasks are particularly appropriate when you believe the failure to be age-related but there are no advance indicators of failure which could be identified through an on-condition task, or you are not confident that such a task will be sufficiently reliable to avoid the risk of the safety-related failure occurring. However, re-work tasks aren't often specified as a means of protecting against safety risk failures, because you can't usually forecast the age at which failure will occur with sufficient accuracy.

If the answer to Question 5 is 'Yes', record the required re-work task(s) for incorporating in maintenance schedules; if the answer is 'No', go to Question 6.

6. *Could the potential safety-related failure be avoided through a discard task?*

A discard task simply means replacing a part after a certain time; it is only appropriate for protecting against an age-related failure, when the safe life of the part can be estimated with some degree of confidence. An example of a discard task to protect against a potential safety risk failure is the replacement of aircraft turbine engine discs after a specified number of running hours: these discs are known to be subject to metal fatigue after a certain number of running hours, and the safe life can be determined with confidence by testing-to-failure during the development stage. However, this is an exception; discard tasks, like re-work tasks, are not commonly feasible as a means of protecting against safety risk failures.

If the answer to Question 6 is 'Yes', record the required discard task(s) for incorporating in maintenance schedules; if the answer is 'No', go to Question 7.

7. *Could the potential safety risk failure be avoided by a combination of preventive tasks?*

This question is included in the diagram because a combination of two or more on-condition, re-work or discard tasks might in some circumstances reduce the risk of failure to an 'acceptable' level. When applying RCM in a manufacturing environment, however, it's most unlikely that you could answer 'Yes', since the only acceptable level in the case of a potential safety risk failure is 'no risk at all'.

If the answer to Question 7 is 'Yes', record the required on-condition, re-work or discard tasks for incorporating in maintenance schedules; if the answer is 'No' you have reached the end of the line! Assuming that you are not prepared to risk your employees getting hurt, you must find some other way to stop the failure happening: *no amount of maintenance will do this for you.* If the equipment is still at the development stage you may be able to alter the design to avoid the problem; if it's already in use you will have to consider urgently whether you can avoid the safety risk failure either by installing some additional safety equipment, or by changing the operating procedure.

8. Could the failure be avoided through an on-condition task?

Questions 8–10 all refer to failure modes identified through Questions 2 and 3 as having no safety implications but serious economic consequences. As the questions are identical to Questions 4, 5 and 6, the explanations which follow are limited to illustrations.

Applying Question 8 to a car, engine seizure would be an example of a failure with serious economic consequences, and one of the failure modes that could give rise to engine seizure would be a lack of oil. Using the dipstick to check the oil level is an 'applicable and effective' on-condition task, which most manufacturers recommend should be done each time the fuel tank is filled: if the car is serviced regularly according to the manufacturer's specification the oil level will probably be between the 'high' and 'low' marks, and no action by you is required; if it's low, the on-condition instructions are to top up with oil and continue to use the car, taking particular care to check again when you next take on more fuel; if the oil level continues to drop between successive checks, you are advised to take the car to your garage for a check-up.

If the answer to Question 8 is 'Yes', record the required on-condition task(s) for incorporating into maintenance schedules; if the answer is 'No', go to Question 9.

9. Could the failure be avoided through a re-work task?

A heavy truck tyre is expensive. Its life can be extended at much less cost by re-treading, but only if it is removed before the tread has worn out completely. Catching it in time and sending it for re-treading is an example of a re-work task.

If the answer to Question 9 is 'Yes', record the required re-work task(s) for incorporating in maintenance schedules; if the answer is 'No', go to Question 10.

10. Could the failure be avoided through a discard task?

In the example given in Question 8, the functional failure was 'engine seizure', and the failure mode was 'lack of oil'. Another failure mode which could also give rise to engine seizure would be 'poor oil condition': oil deteriorates gradually as a result of contamination and working conditions and, since the failure pattern is age-related, a safe life can be determined; the car manufacturers specify that the engine oil should be changed (i.e. 'discarded') whenever the car is serviced, because they know from research that this will be within the safe life of the oil. It would be technically possible to take a sample of oil from the sump, test it, and only discard it if it failed a specified on-condition test, but that would be expensive and the cheaper 'discard' solution is therefore preferred.

If the answer to Question 10 is 'Yes', record the required discard task(s) for incorporating in maintenance schedules; if the answer is 'No', you may need to consider changing the design of the equipment in some way either to overcome or to reduce the risk of the failure occurring – but only if the cost of these avoidance measures would be less than the costs incurred if the failure were allowed to happen.

11. Could the failure be avoided through an on-condition task?
12. Or through a re-work task?
13. Or through a discard task?

Questions 11–13 all refer to failure modes that have been identified through Questions 2 and 3 as having neither safety implications nor serious economic consequences. This means that the definition of when scheduled maintenance is worthwhile changes to a straightforward choice: would it be cheaper to follow a policy of 'If it ain't broke don't fix it', or would *total* costs be less if some form of on-condition, re-work or discard tasks were scheduled?

In a manufacturing environment there are two circumstances in particular in which scheduled maintenance is likely to be worthwhile even for failure modes classified as not having serious economic consequences:

- There is an age-related failure pattern for which the useful life can be readily predicted. A typical example is circular knives on rubber or paper processing machinery: production can be slowed down if the knives aren't kept sharp, so the normal practice is to replace them at the end of each shift with a spare set which have been reground (i.e. a 'scheduled re-work' task is specified).
- Failures which would occur frequently if you didn't do something about them; although the consequences of these failures may not be serious in cost terms, production operators become frustrated at having to cope with unreliable equipment in their efforts to maintain output and keep their customers satisfied.

If you decide that it *is* worthwhile to proceed with the RCM analysis for some failure modes in this category, the procedure is identical to that in Questions 8–10.

14. Could the potential hidden failure be avoided through an on-condition task?
15. Or through a re-work task?
16. Or through a discard task?

Hidden failures can be potentially serious, because the operator is unaware that failure has occurred: the danger arises if the initial hidden failure exposes you to the risk of a related failure that might have serious consequences; in some circumstances a hidden failure can even lead to subsequent multiple failures occurring, without anyone being aware of the danger.

For example, suppose your car develops an oil leak in the hydraulic braking system. When the leak starts it would be a hidden failure condition since you wouldn't be aware of it until the oil level in the reservoir dropped to the point where the subsequent failure condition occurred, causing your brakes to fail. Designers cater for this hidden function by incorporating a 'low oil level' warning light in the instrument panel. But suppose the bulb on this warning light was faulty: that in itself would be a hidden failure; as long as the oil level in the reservoir was normal you wouldn't be aware of it, and you could be happily driving for days unaware that the warning system you rely on wasn't working. Modern car design therefore includes a periodic check that the warning light is working, by getting it (and other system warning indicators) to light up each time you turn the key in the ignition prior to starting the engine.

This use of instrumentation, and/or a periodic check that equipment is working satisfactorily, is a common way of providing protection against hidden failure conditions. Where the part that might fail is known to have a safe life (i.e. the failure pattern is age-related), a re-work or scheduled discard task may be specified instead of an on-condition task.

Potential hidden failure modes must never be left unresolved. If on-condition, re-work or scheduled discard tasks are impracticable (for example because the failure pattern is *not* age-related), then some form of failure-finding task must be specified, such as the display of warning lights on a car instrument panel each time the ignition is switched on, referred to above.

11.8.3 Preparing the RCM Maintenance Schedules

That completes the analysis of potential failures, and the process of deciding what preventive maintenance tasks are either necessary or worth doing. All that remains is to prepare a scheduled maintenance programme which incorporates all these tasks. The programme should, of course, make clear the criticality of each task ('safety-related' etc.), and also the maximum time interval permitted between inspection tasks to ensure that the specified on-condition checks provide sufficient warning to enable the potential functional failure to be avoided.

You will also need to arrange for any condition-monitoring equipment or processes, specified during the analysis stage, to be implemented: these may be manual procedures, such as maintaining process control charts or recording instrument readings at specified intervals; or it may be the installation of expert systems to monitor the process output and adjust equipment automatically, or systems for continuously monitoring vibration, oil or temperature.

There are also routine tasks such as lubrication and walk-around checks to be considered. Strictly speaking, the primary objective of a lubrication task is to replace the lubrication film, which normally has an age-related failure pattern, i.e. lubrication can be thought of as a scheduled discard task. However, the cost of frequent lubrication is usually minimal and it is therefore not generally considered as part of the RCM analysis process. The lubrication schedule *may* include some tasks identified through RCM, such as the example quoted above which required the oil dipstick level to be checked each time you fill up with petrol. Walk-around checks are usually aimed at looking for problems such as accidental damage or leakages, typically in an informal 'when I've got time' way; you may need to make these walk-arounds more formal and consistent, so that they can include some of the required on-condition inspections specified during the RCM process. Ideally, in a JIT environment as much as possible of the lubrication and walk-around schedules should then be allocated to operators, rather than maintenance staff, in line with the 'total productive maintenance' concepts described in Sec. 3.10.

11.8.4 Reducing the Maintenance Workload

As you will have realized by now, an RCM analysis of every item of equipment in a factory could be a daunting task. Fortunately, there's an easy way of reducing the analysis workload significantly which will, at the same time, ensure that you keep the resulting maintenance workload to a minimum. This short cut method is possible because the RCM process can be applied using a top-down approach, as I will explain using the example illustrated in Fig. 11.23.

The first step is to consider the piece of equipment as a whole (the process plant, the production machine, the motor car or, as in Fig. 11.23, the complete aircraft). Decide

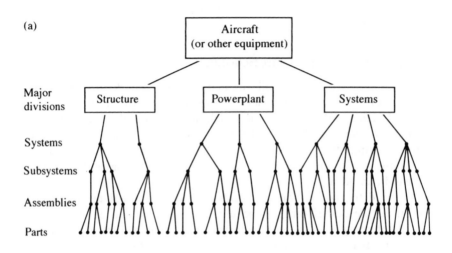

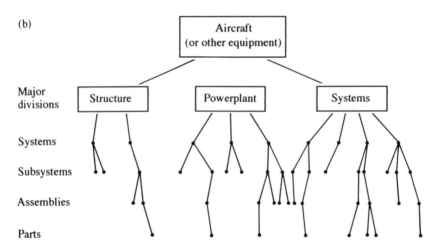

Figure 11.23 Reducing the maintenance workload. (a) The bill of materials structure; (b) the scheduled maintenance requirements, specified by RCM. (*Source*: Reproduced from F. S. Nowlan and H. F. Heap: 'Reliability-Centered Maintenance', US Department of Defense report No. AD-A066-579, December 1978.)

what functional failures and failure modes could occur *at this equipment level* and apply the decision diagram process to each of these failure modes: if one or more failures are considered to involve a safety risk or serious economic consequences, then proceed to the next level down; if neither of these potential consequences applies, consider whether the failure could still have serious consequences because of its interrelationship with other equipment; if there is still no problem, ignore the rest of the equipment structure, since the whole equipment can be specified as 'No scheduled maintenance'.

By working through the 'bill of materials' structure in this way, *stopping as soon as you reach a level where the consequences of failure are identified as non-significant*, you will probably only need to consider around half the equipment in your factory. Even if an item of equipment is identified as significant, you will probably only need to look in detail at fewer than half of the equipment components. This thinning out process is illustrated in Fig. 11.23: part (a) of the figure shows the full bill of materials structure for a piece of equipment (an aircraft) for which both safety risk and high economic cost failure modes were identified at the equipment level; part (b) of the figure shows the components remaining after the thinning out process has been completed. Scheduled maintenance procedures will only be required for the parts shown in part (b) of the figure.

Using this approach, you should now be able to take a quick 'rough cut' look at the equipment in your factory. Don't follow the chain down through each machine at this stage, just go far enough to enable you to assess whether maintenance *is* significant in your circumstances and, if it is, to see where the priorities lie.

11.9 CELL MANUFACTURE

11.9.1 The Cell Manufacturing Concept

Let's start by clearing up any confusion there might be over terminology. You'll hear some people talking about 'cell manufacture', while others refer to 'cellular manufacture'; in either case, there will be people who prefer to replace 'manufacture' with 'manufacturing'. There's actually no difference between any of these, other than the name used. From now on I'll use the abbreviated form 'CM', which should keep everybody happy!

CM is usually defined as:

> The grouping of manufacturing facilities into a production cell, in order to produce a family of parts which require a similar sequence of processes.

For many years the usual way of organizing manufacturing facilities has been to group them *by process*, particularly where machine tools are involved: all the milling machines are put together in one part of the factory, lathes in another, grinding in another, and so on. Batches of work move from one specialist section to the next, criss-crossing the factory, even at times doubling back to a section visited earlier in the sequence. This approach has the advantage of bringing all the expertise and special tooling equipment for each type of process together in one place, enabling both machine and operator utilization to be maximized. However, it's very inefficient in JIT terms, because it introduces a number of serious wastes, all generated as a result of the excessive movements around the factory; six out of the seven categories of waste defined by Toyota (see Sec. 3.2) are generated as a direct result of grouping manufacturing facilities together by process. CM, as you will see in a moment, gets rid of this problem by grouping manufacturing facilities together *by product category*, thereby cutting the distance parts have to travel during the manufacturing process to an absolute minimum.

The origins of CM can be traced back to the Group Technology (GT) approach developed over 30 years ago. The original idea behind GT was to try to convert jobbing work to semi-flow line production by identifying parts which required similar processing. The initial planning stage usually involved a detailed examination of all current drawings, and the application of a complex coding and classification system to every part, to enable families of similarly shaped parts to be identified. For example, one family might be 'turned parts not more than 24 inches long and with external diameter between 2 and 4 inches'; all parts which fitted this specification would be listed as members of the family and manufactured on a group of machines dedicated to that family. GT cut out the need to move parts around the factory during processing and so reduced some of the wastes of traditional manufacturing layouts; but the limitations of machine design at that time, particularly the lack of quick change tooling, prevented full advantage being taken of the new arrangements to reduce batch sizes significantly.

GT never really caught on, partly because of the amount of detailed work involved at the planning stage, but also because too much emphasis was placed on sorting parts into families, without sufficient attention being paid to the *sequence of operations*. As a result, the families didn't always fit together very well. However, it provided the basis needed when Toyota and others started to introduce JIT concepts in their factories, and led eventually to the development of CM as we know it today. Toyota were exploring possible ways of reducing all types of waste, including both set-up and travel time: the GT concept, they realized, would certainly help them reduce travel time (and the associated work-in-progress stocks) and at the same time it would enable them to virtually eliminate the need for some set-up changes, provided they made sure that the families of components followed essentially the same sequence of operations. It would also bring successive operations close together (even in some cases enabling them to be done by the same operator), which would be a great help in picking up quality problems quickly. They were able to make the concept work because the introduction of CM was combined with action to reduce set-up time, thus overcoming the temptation to push work through the cells in large batches.

Although CM started with machine tool-based manufacturing processes, it has since been applied to virtually any type of production process. The objective is to keep work flows and set-up changes to a minimum by grouping machines and process equipment close together, with a minimum of conveyor lengths or storage space between process steps. CM is essentially a *product-oriented* layout, with families of similar materials or parts all allocated to a cell which provides the types of equipment and sequence of processing required for their manufacture.

Shigeo Shingo, who pioneered most of what we now call JIT, believed that CM was a fundamental requirement of the JIT approach to manufacturing. CM does away with the hard work part of GT: all that complex coding and classification of parts. It's much easier to set up than GT, because it uses the experience of shop floor people to identify suitable families of components, and because a simple tabular method which everyone can understand is used to work out the best cell configuration.

11.9.2 Planning For CM

There are five stages to planning for CM:

- *Stage 1*: Product quantity analysis (volumes and values)
- *Stage 2*: Process route analysis (process steps and times)
- *Stage 3*: Analysis of products into cell groupings
- *Stage 4*: Planning the layout
- *Stage 5*: Planning the control systems

The actual work that you will have to do in planning the introduction of CM will depend very much on the manufacturing processes involved. I'll explain the five stages in terms of the machining of metal parts, since the number of different parts involved in this tends to be much greater than with a sequence of assembly operations, or if you are working in a process environment.

Stage 1: Product quantity analysis The first step is to make a list of all the parts you manufacture; it helps in subsequent stages if you use a computer spreadsheet program for this, rather than listing the parts manually. Don't waste people's time in trying to be too precise about this task, by trying to include in your list every single part that you're ever likely to have to make: remember that CM is supposed to do away with the hard work part of GT. You need to make sure that you've included all the parts in regular demand, but it doesn't matter too much if you leave out parts that are only occasionally used; their omission is unlikely to affect subsequent decisions on cell design, since the volumes involved will be too small to have any appreciable effect on cell capacity. In any case, your final plans should include a general machining area for manufacturing those parts that don't fit easily into any of the family groups allocated to cells; requirements of parts omitted from your analysis can, if necessary, be produced in this general area.

You now need to add, for each part on your list, details of expected demand quantities and values (value = quantity × unit cost): you will need this in Stage 3, when the Pareto Principle will be used to ensure that the most significant parts (in terms of both quantity and value) are given priority in the process of allocating parts to cells. In practice you may well find that this information can be obtained from your computer manufacturing database at the same time as you are compiling the list of parts.

Stage 2: Process route analysis For each part on the list you now need to add details of the manufacturing process; this should show the work centre or machine identity, and the process time, for each successive process step. You don't need to include detailed process instructions, since the objective is to identify a family of parts which require a similar sequence of processes.

Before proceeding to Stage 3, use the 'value' column of your list to identify the most significant parts (i.e. the top 15–20 per cent of the list after sorting it in descending order of value). Get a team of production experts together (including at least one operator), and ask them to look at the list and decide if there are any obvious improvements that can be made to the existing production process. I'm not suggesting that you carry out a full value engineering study (although that would be a good idea if you have time); I'm simply suggesting that there's no point in going to all the trouble of building up a nicely balanced cell family, only to be told by production staff that some of the processes really ought to be changed in order to improve manufacturing efficiency!

Stage 3: Analysis of products into cell groupings The objective at this stage is to form families of parts by grouping identical and similar process sequences together. In theory you could write a computer program for this, but in practice you'll get near enough to the optimum by using the experience of the team of production experts referred to above (Stage 2); this will have the added advantage that the people who have to implement the new cells will have been personally involved in the planning stage and so feel fully committed to making the plan work. This is how to do it:

- Start with the list completed in Stage 2, sorted in descending order of expected demand quantity: it's useful also to refer to the list sorted in descending order of value, which you used in Stage 2 for reviewing manufacturing processes, just in case some parts near the top of this list have too small a demand to appear on the quantity list (their high value being due to high material cost).
- Select the first part on the quantity list and enter it, together with its sequence of processes, in a table (see Fig. 11.24); mark the original list to show that the part has been extracted.
- Find the next part on the list *which has the same sequence of operations* and add that to the table, marking the list again to show that the part has been extracted.
- Continue to add parts with the same sequence until you reach the end of the list, marking the list as you go to show which parts have been extracted.
- Return to the top of the list and select the next part which has not yet been extracted; enter this in the table ... and so on.

When you have marked up the list in this way your table will be sorted into blocks of parts, with each block having an identical sequence of processes. In theory, you could now transfer this information to your computer listing and produce a summary table as shown in Fig. 11.25: the percentages can be calculated as a percentage of total quantity, total value or total process time. However, this would involve a lot of work and it wouldn't necessarily provide the best groupings for cell planning purposes, particularly since several cells are likely to be needed.

A much better way is to use the experience of your team to decide the best allocation of parts to cells, using the process families listing as a starting point, but applying considerable discretion based on their specialist knowledge. For example, they may decide to combine some parts from process routes b and c in one cell, because they know that in practice it will make little difference to the operators whether process step 1 is

Part no.	Quantity per period	Value per period	Process sequence (work centre nos.)
73918	1,950	79,150	L3 → M1 → J2 → B1 → D4 → G2
85061	500	47,500	L3 → M1 → J2 → B1 → D4 → G2
46429	1,200	29,364	L3 → M1 → J2 → B1 → D4 → G2

Figure 11.24 Process route analysis table.

Process routes	Percentage of total	Sequence					
		L	M	J	B	D	G
Route 'a'	35	1	2		3	4	
Route 'b'	25	1		2	3	4	
Route 'c'	15			1	2	3	4
Route 'd'	10	1	3		2		
Route 'e'	5	1	2	3	4	5	6
Other routes	10	.	.	.	.	.	.

Figure 11.25 Process route summary table.

done on machine A or machine B, providing that these are placed alongside each other in the cell layout. They may also prefer to omit some parts from the cell family, because of some peculiarity in tooling or processing of which they are aware. And, above all, when they are scrutinizing the list of parts in this way, they may well be able to identify further opportunities for improving the manufacturing process.

Stage 4: Planning the layout This stage will in practice generally overlap with the second part of Stage 3, since the team who are allocating parts to cells will find the task easier if they can picture the cell layout and have some idea of how tasks will be allocated to operators.

Cells may consist of a sequence of machines or equipment in a straight line, or in an L-shape, but the layout most commonly used is U-shaped as shown in Fig. 11.26. Operators are normally trained in a number of processes to be undertaken in the cell, preferably all of them. The latter makes 'one-piece' production possible: instead of completing a whole batch at a time, the operator takes one piece at a time through all eight machines in the cell, and then starts on the second piece in the batch, and so on. The layout of the cell ensures that when operation 8 is finished the operator is close to the starting position and ready to start the circuit again with the next piece.

If throughput levels require more than one operator in a cell (as is usually the case), the operators could follow each other round. However, if one operator is slower, or has difficulty at any point, the operator following could get held up. A better way is to get one operator to carry out the initial process steps and then hand over to a second operator to complete the process sequence. In Fig. 11.26, operator A is able to operate machines 1 to 5 and operator B is able to operate machines 4 to 8; the overlap of skills on machines 4 and 5 provides the flexibility required to keep the flow of work through the cell in balance.

Flexibility can be improved still further if you are able to allocate some parts to more than one cell. For example, suppose you have two similar cells, with one set up primarily for high volume parts and the other for low volume: each of these cells should have a core set of parts that are always made in that cell, typically accounting for about two thirds of the cell's capacity at *average* demand levels; the remaining parts can be manufactured in *either* of the cells, the decision being made on a day-to-day basis to smooth variations in cell loading.

If you are unable to build in much flexibility, and your production equipment is bulky and expensive to move, you may need to take extra precautions to make sure

Short conveyors
linking machines

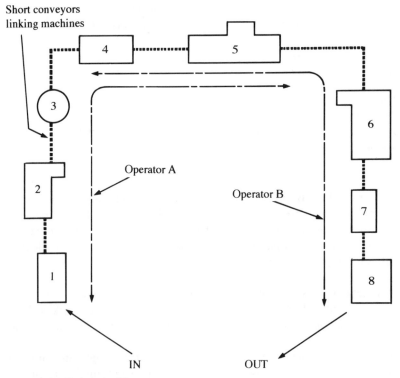

Figure 11.26 U-shaped cell layout.

you've got everything properly balanced *before* you implement the cells you have planned. In this case you should consider using simulation, which will enable you to check the effects of likely variations in throughput, and decide whether you have sufficient capacity and the right balance of operators. A practical application of this is illustrated in a case study in the next section of this chapter.

Don't try to do everything in cells. For example, if parts have to leave the cell for heat treatment and then return for finish grinding, consider instead having a dedicated grinding section adjacent to the heat treatment area. You will probably also have to plan a general manufacturing area for those parts which don't fit readily into cells, or to cope with occasions when a cell is temporarily overloaded. You should also be careful to ensure that cells don't become too complex: if you find that you have more than about ten machines or processes in a cell you are probably trying to include too wide a range of parts in the family group; or you are over-dependent on dedicated machines and should be considering replacing them with simpler, but more flexible, machines. This concept of using simpler, but more flexible machines reflects one of the principles underlying CM: work should flow quickly through the cell with maximum utilization of human resources, even if this means that machine utilization suffers: the cost of a machine is incurred only once, when you first buy it; thereafter its maintenance and running costs are, for most manufacturers, relatively insignificant; people costs, however, go on for ever, so that people costs are the ones which in most environments need to be minimized.

Further guidance on planning cell layout can be found in Chapter 6 of Suzaki's book *The New Manufacturing Challenge* (see Bibliography).

Stage 5: Planning the control systems Planning and control systems can be greatly simplified when you introduce CM. Work moves through the cell so quickly that there's no point in trying to monitor its progress: it's either 'awaiting Op 1' or it's finished! The computer record of routing through a number of machines can therefore be replaced by just one 'machine' – the cell.

More importantly, switching to CM will often provide an excellent opportunity for introducing cyclical planning. Since the parts have already been listed in blocks of parts, all of which require the same sequence of processes, see if you can take this a stage further by getting your team of production experts to sort the items into the optimum sequence, i.e. the sequence which will minimize set-up changes. Ask them to consider this question:

> If you had to make every single part that is allocated to this cell, in what sequence would you want to process them in order to minimize set-up changes?

You can then use this list as a master schedule: production control can fill in the quantities to be made each week (or day, or month, depending on your particular needs), crossing out those parts for which there is no requirement for that time period. If you use this method, don't be too rigid about what constitutes a 'week's' production capacity; if you have a slack week, be prepared to finish the 'week' on a Friday morning and start on the next week's production schedule; if you have a heavy demand, let it run over to Monday. You will sometimes find that it's worth marking some blocks of parts in the cycle for inclusion only in alternate weeks' schedules, in order to avoid a difficult set-up occurring too frequently. But remember that the objective is to satisfy your customers' requirements with the minimum changes of set-up *and within the promised time-scale*.

Even when you've implemented CM as far as possible, there are still some situations where the use of a finite scheduling software package can give further advantages, for example in large jobbing shops or with processes requiring complex set-ups, such as weaving sheds in the textile industry. Here you need to know the earliest date that you can complete an order given the existing load – and you must do this calculation frequently and quickly. A scheduling package loads orders forward in time taking account of resource constraints and the relative priorities between orders. The resulting 'work-to' lists are the programmes for each cell which, if followed, will allow you to achieve the promised delivery dates. Modern packages are very sophisticated, taking account of, for example, multiple priority rules and individual operator–machine performances. Their speed of calculation allows you to assess the effects of unexpected events very quickly.

Finally, when introducing cells, you should consider whether your existing management organization is still appropriate. Many companies which have introduced CM have taken the opportunity to strip out one or more layers of middle management, replacing them with Team Leaders who have full responsibility for every aspect of planning and processing work through their cell. The Barr & Stroud case study in Sec. 13.6 is an example of this.

11.10 AVOIDING CRISES

11.10.1 Overcoming Persistent Problems

Are you learning from past mistakes? Are you continually improving how you anticipate and react to crises? Remember that the very first of the key elements of just-in-time
philosophy, listed at the beginning of Chapter 3, was:

> 'exposing fundamental problems and then putting them right once and for all, so that they don't keep
> recurring'.

This applies as much to the big problems, the major crises that afflict every manufacturer from time to time, as it does to the little problems. The difference is that in a world-
class company the little problems will usually get taken care of automatically by the
people involved. The bigger problems are more likely to involve people from different
departments, each of whom typically sees and accepts responsibility for only part of the
underlying problem. If you want to improve the way in which you anticipate and react
to crises, you need to manage each occurrence just as thoroughly as you manage any
other part of your operations.

That means you need to make sure that everyone knows in advance who is responsible for what, you need to plan what action to take, you need to monitor what
subsequently happens, and you then need to revise your future plans to take account of
any new lessons you have learnt. One way of doing this is to appoint a 'crisis avoidance
team', consisting of experts from each part of your factory, so that when something goes
wrong everybody knows whose job it is to deal with the problem. Their responsibilities
should include *anticipating* problems as well as coordinating activity when something
goes wrong; their role, in fact, should be rather like that of a public fire service, which is
responsible not just for fire-*fighting*, but for fire *prevention* as well. (I'm not talking here
about a crisis of the magnitude of Bhopal, in India, or the Mississippi floods in the USA.
In this chapter we're more concerned with the sort of crisis that threatens your
JIT objectives, i.e. 'to provide a fast, *reliable* and flexible response to customers'
requirements at least cost and with minimum dependence on inventory'.)

Most problems can be solved without too much difficulty once you understand
what is causing them; the difficulty lies in getting that understanding. Typically the information you need never seems to be there when you want it, either because it hasn't been
recorded or because the compilation and reporting of data lags too far behind the event
to be of any use in an emergency. The crisis avoidance team should be given authority
to organize whatever record keeping is appropriate to ensure that the information
they need is available quickly whenever an emergency arises or, better still, *before* the
situation has slipped out of control. For example, condition monitoring equipment for
complex process plant, and manually prepared control charts elsewhere, may well
provide advance warning of an impending problem long before it has a chance to
develop into a crisis; in addition, information provided by these techniques can be
invaluable in pinpointing exactly when things started to go wrong, which can be a great
help in identifying the cause. Depending on the nature of the process, it can also be
helpful to know the ambient temperature at the time, whether operators had just been
changed, whether the problem had arisen gradually or suddenly, whether a new batch of
materials had just been started, whether the problem first occurred on starting up after

maintenance work, and so on: all these are simple to record, but rarely are; and yet, with many processes it could be vital information. The Alexander Iron Founders case study, below, is just one of many instances I've seen where this was the case.

Case Study: Alexander Iron Founders Inc.

(At the request of management the name and geographical location of this company have been disguised.)

This North American iron foundry periodically suffered from a sudden increase in faulty castings, with defects increasing by 100 per cent or more overnight and lasting for several shifts. The problem had occurred on numerous occasions over the last year or two and each time the problem was overcome without anyone really knowing why. Significantly, they didn't know whether the situation improved as a *result* of how they reacted, or *in spite of* it! Nor were they really sure that the problems were the same each time, or whether they had the same cause. When something went wrong, the supervisors and technicians at each stage of the process tried various remedies, depending on their personal theory as to the cause of the problem. Actions taken in different areas weren't coordinated, and they were very much on an *ad hoc* basis. Perhaps it's not surprising that the same problems recurred again and again!

All that changed when new management introduced world-class principles to Alexander's operations. A task force was appointed to tackle the periodic quality problem and clear it up once and for all. They started by asking for a breakdown of the daily scrap report, to help them get a better understanding of where problems were arising. Unfortunately, the only information available was the Inspectors' scrap report at two stages: after heat treatment and after grinding; in both cases the inspection activity took place at least one day after casting and since neither of the operations preceding inspection occurred in a strict sequence of operations after casting, it was difficult to relate the scrap to a specific casting time. Even worse, on average two days had elapsed before management knew that something had gone badly wrong.

However, it did prove possible to break the scrap reports down by type of defect, and this additional analysis revealed that by far the most important cause was 'sand-related'. Although various tests were carried out on the moulding sands at regular intervals throughout each day, the team found that the results of the tests were not routinely reported to management and, in particular, there was no procedure for relating scrap figures to sand conditions at the time of moulding (this was because of the time delay in identifying scrap, referred to above).

As a first step, in order to establish a clear point of reference, the team arranged for graphs to be produced, and updated daily, for the main high-volume plant. These showed the results of the five tests on sand condition carried out routinely by the Sand Technician, namely: moisture; green strength; permeability; shatter index; and compactability. Using the 'factorial experiment design' method, controlled tests were carried out to determine optimum operating conditions, so that upper and lower control limits could be shown on each graph.

Arrangements were then made for random samples to be taken from the track several times a day, these being sent for grinding and inspection as soon as they had cooled sufficiently. This enabled a direct link to be established between the time when defects occurred and the sand conditions at the time. The results of this comparison indicated that compactability seemed to be the most significant factor. Three additional sand tests were then introduced: loss on ignition; volatility; and active clay.

Once the main cause of the problems was identified, correcting the sand condition was relatively straightforward. The normal process routine was to recycle the sand, replacing any losses with new sand as necessary; additives, such as bonding agents, had to be injected at this point to restore the sand to optimum moulding condition. Investigation showed that the problems they had been experiencing were only partly the result of not getting the proportions of additives right; more important was the *way* in which they were added: one of the operatives from the area, who was a member of the team, reported that the present method didn't distribute the additives evenly and some fell off the conveyor on to the foundry floor. A new vibrating conveyor was ordered immediately to overcome the problem, the cost of this being recoverable within a few months just from the saving in the cost of additives previously lost through spillage. Meanwhile, temporary equipment was installed to ease the problem until such time as the new vibrating conveyor arrived.

During the course of the investigations an incident occurred which explained why sudden increases in scrap levels sometimes happened. One such surge was picked up quickly one Monday morning as a result of the random sampling. Investigation revealed that the main sand-hopper had been emptied over the weekend for repairs and cleaning; some of the sand was lost in this process and the hopper had to be topped up with new sand. However, the correct procedure had not been followed and as a result no additives were included to bring the new sand to the correct operating condition. Because the problem was picked up quickly, and tests were in place that enabled the cause to be identified, corrective action could be taken before too many scrap castings were produced, and preventive measures could be planned to avoid a similar problem occurring in the future.

As a result of the actions described above, average scrap levels at Alexander Iron Founders reduced significantly, and any sudden surges were quickly nipped in the bud. At the time of writing, the team have moved on to investigate the other categories of scrap (i.e. those which are not sand-related), in order to bring scrap levels down further. For example, arrangements have been made to improve the care and maintenance of pattern equipment, and to install new equipment to enable core boxes to be cleaned whenever necessary to ensure a consistently high standard of surface finish on cores produced; in addition, a detailed analysis of scrap castings is being used to identify specific pattern equipment that may need redesign or repair.

11.10.2 Anticipating Problems

To start with you may well prefer to appoint a crisis team to look at just one problem, as in the above case study. However, once you've gained experience through this first task, you would be well advised to appoint a team with a much wider brief. As I suggested in Chapter 3: 'Don't wait until a disaster happens before considering what you need to do about it. The effects are felt so much more quickly in a JIT environment that you can't afford to waste time in deciding a plan of action on the spur of the moment'. So, what can you do to anticipate problems?

You can start by getting your crisis avoidance team to brainstorm what sort of problems could cause you real difficulties in keeping your customers happy. You should aim at identifying all aspects of your operations in which you are potentially vulnerable, even if some have not as yet caused a problem; a good way to stimulate your people to come up with these theoretical weaknesses is to start by listing all the major problems you've actually had to cope with over the last year or two.

Typical of the problems you might end up with on your list are:

- A major breakdown on a piece of key equipment.
- Intermittent quality problems that seriously affect production, as in the case study above.
- Short-term interruptions of key supplies, for example because of bad weather or production stoppages at the supplier's factory.
- Longer term interruption of supplies, for example because of a supplier going into liquidation, or as a result of an overseas supplier being affected by civil unrest or even local war.

Some of the potential problems identified will require immediate attention. For example, the team's review in the foundry case study, above, revealed that their only sand mill was nearing the end of its useful life: if it were to break down before the replacement was installed in the following year, it would take two weeks to obtain spares and complete the repairs, during which time production of castings would be completely stopped and the furnaces would have to be shut down. Once the risk was identified by the team, arrangements were made for the mill to be checked particularly carefully during the next holiday shut-down, and plans to replace the equipment were advanced.

You should also take the opportunity to assess how well you've handled major problems in the past. Look at each of the problems on your list which have actually occurred in the last year or two: with the benefit of hindsight, consider what *could* have been done to avoid them; if they couldn't have been avoided, what pre-planning could have been done to minimize the effects and to speed recovery; and what specific preventive action was taken as a result of the crisis to avoid recurrence or, if it was unavoidable, to minimize the impact and speed recovery should it happen again?

Finally, since you probably won't be able to deal with every potential crisis on your list immediately, you will need to decide on their relative priority, taking into account how high you assess the risk of each occurring and the severity of the effects if it does. The failure modes and effects analysis (FMEA) method, described in Sec. 11.8, can be a great help in this, because the procedure will enable you to identify the precise ways in which failure is likely to occur, and which of these potential failures will directly lead to the serious problems that you are trying to avoid. You can then plan appropriate action either to give you advance warning of trouble or, better still, to stop it happening (as previously described in Sec. 11.10.1).

11.10.3 Avoiding Problems in the Future

So far, I've concentrated on what you can do to reduce the risk of crises arising based on where you are now. You can reduce future risks even more if you apply the same sort of fire *prevention* thinking whenever you are planning any major changes.

A typical example would be when considering proposals for the supply of new process plant which you know will be critical to your future operations. Suppose that you've narrowed the choice down to Option A and Option B: before making your final decision, use the FMEA method to assess how they compare in terms of both the *risk* of failure, and the *effects* of failure; check if one of the options has more effective condition monitoring equipment which will give sufficient warning of a potential failure to enable corrective action to be taken before a real problem arises. Consider also what would happen if you've got some of your key assumptions wrong. Suppose production requirements turned out to be higher than you've allowed for: would one option be able to cope better than the other? Similarly, if the product mix assumption was incorrect, would one option offer more flexibility than the other? In each case, if some of your key assumptions turned out to be wrong, what would you *then* have to do to recover the situation, how much would it cost and what other penalties would be incurred meanwhile? If there's little otherwise to choose between Options A and B, then this sort of risk assessment could well tip the balance by helping you to anticipate, and hence avoid, problems in the future.

Another problem that occurs frequently when JIT is being introduced is getting the right balance of resources, for example in a 'cell' (see Sec. 11.9 for further details of the cell manufacturing concept). Simulation can be used to work out in advance just how many machines of each type and how many operators are required to ensure that work flows freely in the cell. Simulation is also useful if you are introducing a completely new range of products, for example when you are planning to rationalize production between factories, or diversifying into a new field to compensate for declining demand for your existing product range. The particular strength of simulation is that it allows you to let your crises happen on the computer – not in the real world, where getting it wrong can be very expensive.

The following case study describes how one company avoided a potentially serious problem when introducing a new type of production into an existing factory: simulation enabled them to identify the danger in time, and to install additional equipment to ensure that the potential problem was avoided.

Case Study: Using Simulation to Avoid Problems

This company had for many years specialized in the design and manufacture of boilers, particularly for marine applications. Faced with a declining market for their traditional products they had diversified into work for the defence and nuclear industries, building on the fabrication and welding skills for which they already had a high reputation. When this market also started to decline they realized that further diversification would be needed.

In recent years their work for the defence and nuclear industries had led them to develop highly specialized skills in welding unusual materials, and this experience enabled them to secure a contract to manufacture components for an aluminium smelter plant that was to be built in the Middle East by a large European-based contract engineering company. They knew that if they were able to complete this first contract successfully to the tight time-scale required, they would be able to open up many similar opportunities in the future.

The components they were to manufacture consisted of sets of aluminium bus bars which provide the electrical connections to the melting pots. These were large fabrications made from a very pure form of aluminium. To enable them to flex in operation the design was similar in construction to the traditional leaf springs used in the rear suspension of cars before the days of independent suspension – but much larger.

Management didn't anticipate any particular problems since they had already manufactured prototypes as part of the contract qualification stage. However, partly to reassure the main contractor, and partly because of the importance of the contract to the company's long-term strategy, they decided as an insurance policy to retain a consultant to support their own project management team.

The consultant found that the necessary production arrangements had already been planned in meticulous detail by the project management team. However, he was concerned that no one in the team had practical experience of the type of batch production that would be involved: the short time-scales between receipt of material from the aluminium mills and the planned shipping dates, the number of fabrications in each batch and the size of the fabrications all meant that each assembly would require a series of continuous welding operations so that it could be completed and moved out of the way before the next set of components arrived from the bending and forming section. In effect, the assembly welding would have to operate virtually as a flow line, whereas the type of work with which they were familiar always involved large fabrications that remained in the same place throughout the fabrication process, with welders going to the work, instead of the work coming to the welder as was planned for the new products. Furthermore, the time-scale they were accustomed to for each fabrication was several months, as opposed to a few days for the new products.

Because of the risks involved, and because the production staff involved were clearly unable to assess those risks adequately from their own experience, the consultant suggested that a simulation model of the new production arrangements should be developed. All the relevant production experts got together over a weekend and, with the help of the consultant, drew up a simulation model, testing this manually to ensure that it was an accurate representation of the proposed production arrangements. The model was then input to a computer and run, first with the planned schedule of batches and then with variations to test the effects of material being delivered late.

The results showed that the project management team had correctly assessed the production resources required in respect of both manufacturing equipment and people, and that they could cope with reasonable variations in material receipts – all aspects which they understood and could relate to their past experience. However, the model revealed one highly significant deficiency which, if not corrected, would have jeopardized the whole operation: the team had failed to recognize the frequency with which handling equipment would be needed to rotate the heavy assemblies during the welding process, and to move them down the line between work stations – something which was outside their experience. They had assumed that all lifting would be done by the three travelling cranes, not realizing that these were often tied up for half an hour at a time and would be completely unable to cope with the number of movements required each day.

Once recognized, the problem was solved quickly. A member of the team knew of another factory in the group which had recently been mothballed, and which had a number of wall-mounted jib cranes available. These were duly installed in the new production area to provide dedicated lifting facilities for each work station, just in time for the first batch.

If the new operations had not been tested in advance with a simulation model, the problem with the cranes would never have been anticipated. The initial batches would have been despatched to the Middle East several weeks late, holding up a major construction project, and the company's diversification plans would have suffered a serious setback. Instead, the project was completed to schedule (in spite of some batches of material arriving late), and the company was successful in establishing an important new source of work for the future.

TWELVE

TOTAL QUALITY – THE FIRST STEPS

Linked to Chapter 4, this chapter explains some of the methods and procedures which are likely to be needed in the first year of a total quality programme. The first section describes how to establish a benchmark of where you are now as a basis for setting action priorities; the remainder of the chapter describes some of the key techniques that are likely to be relevant to a total quality programme, namely cost of quality analysis, department purpose analysis, Taguchi methods and SPC control charts. Training is dealt with separately, in Chapter 13.

12.1 WHERE ARE YOU NOW?

If you're about to launch a total quality campaign, don't jump in with both feet – make sure that you have some specific objectives in mind. If you've decided to go for total quality as a result of your strategy review (described in Chapters 2 and 10), you should already have a clear idea of what those specific objectives are. If not, then this section will help you to decide which is the more important to you: to provide better quality to your customers, or to reduce the quality-related costs you are currently incurring. In practice you will probably want to go for both; after all, trying to provide better quality to your customers without at the same time trying to reduce the costs incurred in achieving that quality doesn't make sense, since the 'costs of quality' are a *waste* and any waste should be a target for improvement.

Before getting started you need to find out where you're starting *from*, so that you have a benchmark against which to measure progress in the future, and to help you decide where to concentrate action first in order to get the most benefit in the shortest time. In essence, you need to find the answer to three questions:

- *What do your potential customers think about your current quality performance?* How well do you meet their perceived quality requirements at the moment, and how does your performance compare with that of your main competitors? What particular aspects of quality are most important to them? How much extra business might you be able to win if you improved your performance in these aspects?
- *What do your employees think about your current quality performance?* Do they believe that your customers are, on the whole, satisfied? How do they think their quality performance compares with that of their competitors? Do they think that quality is being sacrificed because of cost or time constraints, or in order to meet monthly production targets? And, most importantly, to what extent do *they* think sales would increase if quality was improved?
- *How much is it costing you to achieve and monitor your current quality performance?* How much money are you wasting on correcting errors caused by work not being done 'right first time, every time'? How much are you spending on prevention? Where are quality costs being incurred (in which departments, and on which products or processes), and which of these are the most significant?

I'll consider each of these in turn.

12.1.1 Customers' Perceptions

However convinced you may be that customers will respond to improvements in your quality performance (by giving you more orders than they would otherwise have done, or by being prepared to pay higher prices for your products), you still need to make sure that you know which particular aspects of quality are more important to them than others. For example, by 'improved quality' are they talking about problems that occur after the goods are delivered to them, as a result of manufacturing defects, or are their concerns directed more at the basic design of the product and its functional capabilities? If you're going to spend time and money (and a great deal of management effort) in improving quality, you want to make sure that you concentrate on improvements that will bring the most rewards and, preferably, rewards that come sooner rather than later!

If you've not already done so during the strategy review process, consider commissioning a customers' attitudes survey. I suggest you treat information gleaned from distributors and from your own sales force with extreme caution: more often than not market research studies reveal different, and generally more accurate, answers. 'Competitive benchmarking', or the 'problem ranking process', described in Chapter 2, should provide the guidance you need; both will provide a benchmark of where you are now, at the start of your improvement campaign, and so provide a basis later on for measuring what success you have achieved; and they will also highlight the quality problem areas that you need to attack first.

12.1.2 Employees' Perceptions

It helps if you can find out what your people really think about their current quality performance. An employees' attitudes survey should provide the answer: I say 'should', rather than 'will', because it all depends on how you carry out the survey and, in particular, whether it is entrusted to someone from outside the company who has specialist skills in conducting such surveys and who is seen by employees as independent of the management structure, i.e. someone they can trust to respect comments made in confidence. A properly conducted employees' attitudes survey should provide answers to the sort of questions posed earlier; this will give you a good idea of how much work you will have to do to get the total quality message across. If you repeat the process after six months, and again after a further six months, you will be able to see how far you have succeeded in changing people's attitudes.

An alternative way of finding out what employees think about their current quality performance is to combine this with a company-wide programme of quality awareness seminars. You can start the seminar by explaining the total quality concepts, and then split the audience into 'workshop' groups with no more than about ten people in each group. The groups should each be given the same topic to consider – the precise wording will depend on your particular circumstances, but will be something like:

> How well does our present quality performance satisfy our customers' needs? Do we need to improve? If so, list the five most important ways in which we can do this.

I suggest that you ask for five ways, rather than two or three, because you'll probably find that they identify 'management commitment' and 'better communication' as the first two; asking for five should ensure that more specific ideas for improvement are brought out.

It's best if you can arrange for each workshop group to be made up of members of the same department, so that they can think in terms of their own department's 'customers', who may well be another department rather than external customers. They can then concentrate on things that go wrong in their own area and suggest ways of avoiding such problems in the future.

It will also help you to get the message across about the significance of quality-related costs if you include a second question (making sure that they don't know the true answers until they've made their own estimates):

> How much do you think the company as a whole spends on quality-related costs each year, expressed as a percentage of our annual sales revenue? And what do you think the actual amount is in your own department?

I'll explain the importance of this in a moment.

Whether you opt for an employees' attitudes survey or for seminar workshops, you should recognize that by inviting their views you will have raised their expectations. You will therefore need to take note of what they are saying: both their specific suggestions for improvement *and* their comments on your management style (however uncomplimentary!); if you don't want to lose all credibility for the future, you will need to do something positive in response. A good way of doing this is to issue a *Total Quality Newsletter*, repeating the key message that you gave at the start of the seminars, and then summarizing the responses from the workshop groups; if you included the second question, about quality-related costs, you can then reveal the actual costs (which will usually be very much greater than any of them realized). Finally, you can explain which aspects of quality you plan to tackle first (and, preferably, why) and what contribution employees will be expected to make.

Further guidance on getting employees involved can be found later in this section, and in more depth in Chapter 13.

12.1.3 Quality Costs

It may be that customers are not directly involved, because any quality problems are nearly always picked up in good time before the goods leave your factory; your decision to highlight quality improvement will then probably be motivated by a recognition that the cost of not 'getting it right first time, every time' is unacceptably high. In this case you may be tempted to launch a company-wide campaign to improve quality generally. There are several reasons why, in my view, you shouldn't:

- If you simply declare open warfare on quality problems, wherever and whatever they might be, management's attention will inevitably be spread over too many areas; it's far better to concentrate on a smaller number of key problems first, so that all involved know that those specific production activities are being monitored very closely.
- Exhorting workers to pay more attention to quality may well be effective in Japan, but it doesn't seem to have the same effect in the West; I suspect that's because people don't like to admit that there's anything wrong with how they do their job at the moment – if there's a quality problem it's probably 'someone else's fault'.
- You've probably tried a broad-based quality improvement approach in the past and you may even have seen an improvement – but I doubt if it lasted once management's attention switched to something else (like improving delivery performance); what makes you think it will be any different this time?

If you want to achieve a *lasting* improvement in quality performance, I believe strongly that you must first convince your people that their current perception of what level of quality is right is no longer good enough if they want their company to survive and prosper in an increasingly competitive world. You need to shake them out of their complacency, and one way of doing this is to let them know how much money is being spent on quality-related costs at present. Because the true costs of quality are buried under numerous headings in the company's accounts, few people have any idea of how much is involved (if yours is a typical manufacturing company it will probably be between 15 and 25 per cent of sales turnover).

Once they realize the sums involved, most people will have little difficulty in understanding that money spent on quality is money that can't be spent on new equipment or on employee rewards or benefits, and they will then usually accept that everyone's attitude to quality (including their own) must change. Start by telling everyone how much money is being spent on quality-related costs in the company as a whole; then tell them how much it is costing *just in their department* – that will really shock them! The 'cost of quality analysis' procedure, described in the next section, will provide the figures you need.

It will also help convince people that their standards must change if you can demonstrate that the company is losing sales because of problems with quality. They might not believe this when it comes from your own sales force, but it will usually get through to them if you show them the results of a customer attitude survey – it can really hurt their pride to hear that customers think that their work is of a poor quality compared to that of their competitors (particularly if the competitor is from abroad!). The customers' attitudes survey, referred to above, will provide the evidence.

12.2 COST OF QUALITY ANALYSIS (CQA)

12.2.1 CQA Methods and Procedures

Section 4.4 explained what should be included in the calculation of quality costs, gave an outline of the process for assessing them and suggested who should be involved. This section describes the process in more detail. To save you turning back to Chapter 4, relevant passages are repeated here.

The references to British Standard BS 6143, both here and in Chapter 4, are to the 1981 version which had the title 'The Determination and Use of Quality Related Costs'. This publication has recently been revised and extended, with a new title of 'Guide to the Economics of Quality'. Part 1 of the new standard was issued in 1992 with the subtitle 'Process Cost Model'; Part 2 was issued in 1990 with the subtitle 'Prevention, Appraisal and Failure Model'. Details of where copies of these can be obtained are included in the Bibliography (according to the British Standards Institute, there are no corresponding ISO or EN standards). While these new versions of BS 6143 are un-doubtedly more comprehensive and reflect the latest thinking on the subject, I suggest you stick to the old 1981 version if you can get hold of a copy: this should prove quite sufficient to start with and much easier for the first-time user to understand; although the process is simple enough once you are used to it, most people find it a fairly for-midable task the first time, even with the 1981 version. If your Quality Manager has a copy of the BS Quality Manual issued prior to 1990 you will probably find that this includes the 1981 version of BS 6143.

The CQA process is really quite straightforward. All it involves is getting into the nitty-gritty of your accounts files and extracting details of those costs that are in any way related to quality, classifying these under a number of different headings (more on that in a moment). In practice it may not be quite that easy the first time you try it, since the accounting records will have been collected with different purposes in mind. You should find it a lot easier when you come to repeat the CQA process at a later date, since you will know by then what information you are likely to want and will be able to give your accounts staff advance warning; they can then record and collate data in a way that makes it easier for them to extract the information you need, using a special memorandum account.

BS 6143 recommends that you classify quality-related costs under four headings:

- *Prevention costs*: the costs of any action taken to investigate, prevent or reduce defects and failures.
- *Appraisal costs*: the costs of assessing the quality achieved.
- *Internal failure costs*: the costs arising within the manufacturing organization of failure to achieve the quality specified (before transfer of ownership to the customer).
- *External failure costs*: the costs arising outside the organization of failure to achieve quality specified (after the transfer of ownership to the customer).

You will find Appendix A of BS 6143 particularly helpful in identifying what costs to include, and under which heading they should be recorded. Further guidance on this is included in Sec. 12.2.2.

The importance of activities summarized under the heading 'Preventive costs' is often overlooked. Failures, whatever their cause, cost you money. You can reduce the incidence of failures by paying more attention to preventive measures; these, too, will have a cost, but this will nearly always be compensated for many times over by the reduction in failure costs that results.

Some people combine the two types of failure cost under one heading: I prefer to keep them separate as the Standard suggests, because a quality problem that the *customer* has to tell *you* about is potentially far more damaging than one that you identify yourself and can rectify while it is still hidden from the outside world.

When you carry out a CQA for the first time you will usually have three objectives in mind:

- To assess the size of the problem, so that you can make people aware of how important it is to reduce your quality costs
- To establish what your quality costs are at the start, so that you have a basis for measuring improvement in the future
- To identify where quality costs are particularly high, so that you know where corrective actions are likely to bring the greatest rewards

I explained earlier that you may have some difficulty in extracting the required information from your accounts files when you first attempt a CQA, because data will have been recorded with different purposes in mind. Fortunately, it doesn't matter too much the first time round, since 'ball park' figures will usually be good enough to satisfy the above objectives; if necessary, having completed the first rough cut analysis, you can go back over the main high-cost areas, examining just these in greater detail. If your primary purpose in the first CQA is solely to assess the significance of your current quality-related costs (for example, if you are having difficulty in convincing people that it's worth the effort), you may be able to limit the amount of work involved by concentrating initially on just one group of products or one department; the results from such a pilot study will usually provide sufficient evidence to gain management approval and commitment for a more detailed CQA study.

The full CQA process should be repeated initially at intervals of about six months, so that you can see what improvements have been made and identify any changes in priorities that may be necessary. Later on in your improvement campaign you will probably find that an annual review is sufficient. As soon as you have identified positive results, make sure that you publicize these across the company, to provide visible proof that the attention paid to improving quality is working, and so that your people can see the savings that their own efforts so far have achieved and will thus be encouraged to double their efforts.

The next two sections give advice on how to prepare and present the CQA information, based on the four quality cost categories explained above. The method recommended in BS 6143 should always be the preferred approach, not least because it carries with it the authority of a formal standard procedure; this method is described first. However, there is an alternative method if you find that your accounting records are unable to provide the information you need; this is based on an analysis of actual quality problems identified at the point where they occur, the end results being presented in the same way as with the BS 6143 method. This alternative method is described in the second section below. Whichever method you select, I suggest that you consider using a computer spreadsheet to assemble your source data so that you can summarize the results in a number of different ways, changing these if necessary to suit management's requirements.

12.2.2 The Standard CQA Method

This section should give you enough information to understand what is involved in the CQA process, but I strongly recommend that you read BS 6143 before you actually attempt to analyse your own quality-related costs in any detail; you will also find some useful 'Dos and Don'ts' advice on p. 37 of the DTI publication *The Case for Costing Quality* (see Bibliography).

The first step in the CQA process is to search through your accounts records, extracting all the quality-related costs you can find. Start by getting your CQA team to brainstorm a check-list of the sort of costs you are looking for; you can save time by giving them the following list, which they can then amend or extend to suit your particular needs.

Prevention costs

- The cost of any quality management and quality assurance functions and activities .
- The cost of design improvements aimed at reducing the risk of errors occurring in production or in use (including the costs of carrying out a failure modes and effects analysis (FMEA)
- The design, development and installation of quality measurement and process control equipment
- Costs associated with the introduction and subsequent supervision and analysis of statistical process control procedures and control charts, where these are used primarily as a means of anticipating and, hence, *avoiding* errors
- Maintenance and calibration of test and inspection equipment
- Vendor assessment
- Quality training
- The cost of hiring external consultants to assist you with assessing quality costs, or with your quality improvement projects
- The costs incurred in preparing a 'department purpose analysis' (described later in this chapter)

Appraisal costs

- The cost of inspectors and their equipment throughout the company, including those in Goods Inwards
- Costs associated with the application of statistical process control procedures and control charts, where these are used primarily as a means of *identifying and rejecting* defective products
- The cost of inspectors seconded to suppliers (I prefer to include these here, rather than under the 'vendor assessment' heading in the 'Prevention costs' list, if their primary task is to identify quality errors, i.e. if they are, in effect, acting as an extension of Goods Inwards inspection)
- Costs associated with activities such as conducting field performance tests, carrying out periodic product quality audits, or evaluating field stocks of spare parts
- Producing computer reports of inspection and test results

Internal failure costs

- Scrap costs incurred as a result of failure to meet quality requirements (net proceeds from the sale of such scrap can be included as a credit)
- Re-work and repair costs incurred in order to meet quality requirements
- The cost of re-inspection or re-testing
- Costs associated with modification permits or concessions
- The loss of value as a result of downgrading of products, resulting in a reduced selling price, but only if this occurs as a result of failure to meet normal quality requirements
- The cost of carrying out defect/failure analysis studies (including Taguchi, 'multi-variate analysis' or FED) to determine the causes of quality problems
- The cost of management time spent on troubleshooting, i.e. sorting out problems that have arisen because of faulty materials or workmanship (an appropriate proportion of managerial, technical and supervisory staff costs will need to be assessed and included under this heading)

External failure costs

- The administrative costs incurred in handling customer complaints
- Customer service activities, including the costs of correcting faulty products
- Product liability claims, insurance, or protective measures
- Product recalls, or allowances granted
- Warranty costs and costs associated with replacement
- A proportion of the costs of the Managing Director, Technical Director or Sales Director (for example) should also be included, if they get involved in dealing with after-sales complaints from customers

While extracting cost data from the accounts records you should, of course, keep your eyes open for any other quality-related costs which were not included in your check-list.

When you are satisfied that you have extracted all the relevant costs, the final task is to separate them into the four categories above and present the results in a number of summary tables, to show the costs for the company as a whole and a breakdown by, for example, product groups and operating departments. The precise form of these summary tables will depend on your particular circumstances; the remainder of this section shows some typical examples.

The illustrations are taken from an actual CQA carried out by a manufacturer of domestic appliances. This was the first time that the company had attempted such an analysis. The results were issued with a caveat to management that the costs shown probably underestimated the true costs, due to limitations in the accounts records from which the information was extracted; however, since the main element of missing cost was the allocation of management time spent on quality-related activities, it was considered that the relative importance of each category of quality costs was not affected.

Figure 12.1 shows the table summarizing current quality costs under the four standard headings. An overall quality cost of just under 20 per cent of net sales value was not unusual in this type of company; however, the cost of external failures, at 8.8 per cent of sales value, was clearly unacceptable, both because of the amount of potential

Type of cost	Cost ($)	% of net sales value
1. Prevention costs	249,132	0.4
2. Appraisal costs	2,314,208	3.8
3. Internal failure costs		
3.1 Rectification, labour	1,091,748	
3.2 Unrecorded re-work, labour (estimated)	1,445,887	
3.3 Materials	1,533,568	
Subtotal	4,071,203	6.7
4. External failure costs		
4.1 Repairs Department	345,160	
4.2 Service Department	1,078,875	
4.3 Warranty costs	3,971,388	
Subtotal	5,395,423	8.8
Total quality costs	12,029,966	19.7

Notes:
(1) The basis and the calculations for the above figures are contained in the detailed report prepared by the CQA coordinating team. Copies of this report, or specific sections, can be obtained from the CQA Facilitator, Al Mitchell, or from the Cost Accounts Manager, Dean Morrell.
(2) The figures quoted do NOT include any allowance for 'lost' sales, or for production delays, due to quality problems.

Figure 12.1 Example of CQA Summary table.

profit that was being lost and because of the poor image that was being presented in the market-place. Prevention costs, at less than 1 per cent of net sales value, were particularly low; reference to the back-up document giving a breakdown of these costs (not reproduced here) revealed that a third of the prevention costs were incurred in obtaining external electrical safety certification to satisfy the regulatory requirement in various countries, which meant that the company was currently spending very little money voluntarily on the prevention of quality problems.

Figures 12.2 and 12.3 show the breakdown of Service Department and Warranty costs respectively, these being the two main constituents of the external quality costs. Note that the source of the data is shown in order to establish their credibility, and any assumptions made are clearly stated.

So far, all the analysis has done is to show that external failures are costing the company a lot of money and, probably, a great deal of customer goodwill; what it hasn't really done yet is to identify *why* the costs are so high. Figure 12.4 shows an analysis of the same external quality costs, but broken down this time by product family; this helped management get a much better understanding of where problems were occurring. At the time of this study an average failure call rate of around 20 per cent was not unusual for this industry (that was before competition from more reliable overseas suppliers forced them to do something about it!). However, even by the poor standards which generally prevailed at the time, the failure rate on products B and C was clearly an

Expense category	Cost ($)
1. Salaries and associated costs	674,096
2. Operating expenses	19,320
3. Travelling expenses	63,030
4. Consumer compensation	11,995
5. Service manuals	35,615
6. Servicing receipts	(22,125)
7. Materials	131,015
8. Distribution/transport	116,220
Total expense	1,029,166
Allocation of company expense overhead at 4.83%	49,709
Total departmental cost	1,078,875

Notes:
(1) The Spare Parts Department (Cost Centre 270) is not included in the above figures
(2) Source of data: Accounts records, Cost Centre 280

Figure 12.2 Example of analysis of Service Department costs.

Expense category	Cost ($)	Source of data (see below)
1. In-guarantee spares allowances	378,255	1
2. Service and pre-commissioning allowances	826,775	1
3. Chargeable service scheme payments	2,563,242	1
4. Chargeable service rebates	32,243	1
Subtotal	3,800,515	
5. In-guarantee allowance (home)	43,295	2
6. In-guarantee allowance (export)	77,020	2
7. Warranty insurance schemes at 5% of NSV	50,558	3
Total warranty costs	3,971,388	

Sources of data:
(1) Management Accounts, sheet 7, Actual
(2) Management Accounts, sheet 9, Actual
(3) Includes new 'extended warranty' scheme for which no figures are yet available. Figure of 5% of net sales value (from Management Accounts, sheet 1) has been agreed by Sales and Marketing and Commercial Directors as 'best guess'

Figure 12.3 Example of analysis of warranty costs.

Product family	Number of units sold to date	Number of 'in-guarantee' failure calls	Average failure calls* %	Average failure calls* $ per call
A	83,609	12,635	15.1	—
B	32,238	15,538	48.2	—
C	50,776	17,183	33.8	—
D	28,159	6,233	22.1	—
Totals	194,782	51,589	26.5	104.58

* No information is available on the actual number of units involved; since some units are known to have failed on more than one occasion during the guarantee period, the actual proportion of units involved is less than the % figures shown in the table.

Source of data:
Service Department records, which include claims from overseas distributors and agents. No information is currently available to enable separate 'average cost per call' figures to be calculated for individual product families: the average cost per call for product family C is known to be significantly higher than for other product families, due to the complexity of the product and the higher cost of replacement parts.

Figure 12.4 Example of external failure costs analysed by product family.

unacceptable performance which would inevitably have a serious impact on future sales if it wasn't corrected quickly.

These first rough cut results illustrate why a more detailed analysis might not be needed when you attempt a CQA for the first time: in the example illustrated, 'External failures' stood out as the area that must be tackled first, probably by putting more effort into 'Prevention', and it was clear that the place to start was with product families B and C; there would be little point at this stage in trying to define costs in the three other areas more accurately. The company concerned had, in fact, originally intended to carry out a more detailed analysis; however, having seen the results illustrated in Figs. 12.1–12.4, they decided instead to set up a strategic improvement team urgently, tasked with finding out what was causing so many failures to occur and then identifying what action would be required in order to achieve a significant improvement in the reliability of products in the field. Further collection and analysis of data was requested, to determine whether the problems being experienced with product families B and C were due primarily to manufacturing faults, or to damage at the distribution and installation stage, or to fundamental design weaknesses. At the same time, the administrative procedures were modified to enable average cost per call figures to be calculated for each of the product families.

The extracts shown in Figs. 12.1–12.4 will, I hope, help you to understand enough about the CQA process to convince you of the value of assessing your own quality-related costs. The results of this should provide a great deal more information than I have room to illustrate here. For example, the report from which these illustrations have been taken also included:

- Tables showing a breakdown of the information from which the summaries were compiled

- An explanation of the method by which overhead allocations had been derived
- An analysis of quality-related costs by departments
- An analysis of internal and external quality-related costs by product line
- An analysis of causes of internal quality faults identified at final inspection
- A table showing a comparison of call rates and costs per call recorded by one of the main distributors for the company and its main competitors
- A summary of quality-related cost categories that were not currently recorded, but should be in the future

12.2.3 The Alternative Method

So far I've explained how you can determine your current quality-related costs by extracting the relevant details from your accounts records, following the guidelines explained in BS 6143. It's the method generally recommended, not least because it helps if you can quote known accounts sources as the basis for your calculations when you're trying to convince management that the true cost of quality is so much higher than most of them had expected. However, if you have difficulty in obtaining the data you need from your accounts records, the alternative approach, which uses an analysis of fault occurrences as its basis, should enable you to end up with similar summary tables, although rather less comprehensive and without quite the same authority as you would get with the first method.

This alternative method was originally developed as a means of focusing departments' attention on specific opportunities for quality improvement opportunities in their respective areas. Total quality practitioners often prefer it to the first method because they can use the 'fault analysis summaries' (described in a moment) as a basis for preparing a list of quality problems for each department; this list can be sorted into a priority sequence which takes into account both cost and customer implications, and which can then be given to the department's quality circle as their 'hit list'.

The key stage in the procedure is to prepare a comprehensive list, by department, of all the faults and errors that are known to occur. These should be summarized on a 'fault analysis summary sheet', such as the one illustrated in Fig. 12.5; in the example illustrated this consists of two sheets (simply because there's too much information to get it all on to one sheet!); where necessary, separate back-up documents (not shown) are used to record additional information about each fault and possible ways of overcoming the problem. Don't go into too much detail about the fault at this stage; this should be left for the quality improvement team to do at a later stage if the fault is considered sufficiently important for it to be included on their hit list. Hopefully, you will find that there are records of faults held in the department which you can use to compile your list; if not, you will need to get people in the department to use the brainstorming technique to identify the most frequently occurring or most significant faults. You will find that some faults are actually caused in a different department from where they are first noticed: in this event, normal practice is for the faults to be recorded on the sheet for the department where they are first noticed. You will probably have to rely on estimates for determining how much labour and materials are needed to correct the faults, but don't forget to include overheads.

A	B	C	D	E	F	G	H	I	J	K
Fault category number	Fault description	Frequency (per period) WEEK	Detection point	Correction point	Estimated time (man hours)	£ Estimated cost Labour	Material	Origin of fault	Signifi- cance of fault	Potential benefits of elimination (£ and comments)
MS1	drilled too short	150	MS	M12	5	42.5	—	M4	B	£60 per week (incl. recycling costs)
MS2	cast hole won't clean up	320	M1	(REJECT)	5.3	48.8	—	Foundry	B	£483 per week (casting returned to foundry)
MS3	grub screw cross threaded	10	CUSTOMER	(SCRAP)	—	—	120	M7	D	£130 per week (including admin cost)

Fault analysis summary – sheet 2

A	L	M	N	O	P	Q	R
Fault category number	Nature of solution	Degree of difficulty	Time- scale (months)	Potential cost £	Probable benefits %	£	External benefits
MS1	Improve setting gauge	LOW	ONE	20	100	60	NONE (9)
MS2	Persuade foundry suppliers to improve pre-delivery inspection	HIGH	SIX	NIL (to us)	70	34·16	NONE (7)
MS3	Retrain operators; introduce sampling inspection?	MEDIUM	ONE	50	60	78	ENHANCED QUALITY/RELIABILITY (9)

Figure 12.5 'Fault analysis summary': sheets 1 and 2.

299

You may prefer to use a form of your own design, in preference to the one illustrated in Fig. 12.5; if you do, remember that your key objectives in preparing the analysis of faults should be to:

- Identify as many types of fault occurrences as you can
- Identify the point (department, section, machine) at which each fault is caused
- Assess the costs of scrap or re-work that result from each of these faults
- Assess the significance of each fault (see below)
- Estimate the potential benefits of eliminating each fault (so that you can decide which are the most important to tackle first)
- Assess the feasibility of overcoming each fault, and the cost and time implications

In assessing the significance of each fault I suggest you use the following codes:

A = low cost, no customer impact
B = medium cost, no customer impact
C = high cost, no customer impact
D = some customer impact
E = high customer impact

If all you are trying to do is to prepare a 'hit list' for your quality improvement team, you don't need to go any further with this alternative method. However, before launching your quality improvement initiatives you should make sure that everyone realizes *why* it's important for them to get involved. The sort of training and briefing seminars that might be appropriate are described in Sec. 13.4; you may also find it helpful to introduce the 'department purpose analysis' (described in the next section) at this point, to focus everyone's attention on the need to improve their own personal customer/supplier links.

If you want to complete the 'cost of quality analysis', you will need to complete the other two forms, illustrated in Figs. 12.6 and 12.7. The results will not be as comprehensive as with the previous method, but they *will* indicate how significant quality-related costs are to the company's profitability, and they will also show where the main opportunities for improvement lie. Because the analysis is based on a bottom-up approach, in which costs are determined separately for each department, the usual practice in this case is to relate the current costs of quality to the operating costs of each department, instead of the sales revenue basis used in the previous method.

The form shown in Fig. 12.6 is used to determine each department's operating cost (columns A to C); the total staff costs in column C should include the appropriate overhead allocation. Details of correction costs are obtained from the Fault analysis document, but appraisal and prevention costs will need to be assessed by estimating the proportion of time each group of staff typically spends on that type of activity (columns E, F, H and I are included to cover instances where inspectors spend most of their time on appraisal or prevention activities, but also spend some time on correcting errors they've detected). The Total quality costs (column K) can then be found by adding together columns D, G and J.

Finally, data can be extracted from the previous two documents to complete the Quality cost–benefit analysis form, shown in Fig. 12.7.

DEPARTMENT:..................

DEPARTMENTAL COST SUMMARY

COMPILED BY:..................

DATE:..................

A	B		C	D	E	F	G	H	I	J	K	L	
	Staff		Total staff costs	Total correction costs	Appraisal costs			Prevention costs			Total quality costs	% quality to total costs	Comments
Department and section	Number	Category/grade			Gross	Correction	Net	Gross	Correction	Net			

Figure 12.6 Departmental cost summary.

301

DEPARTMENT:............

QUALITY COST–BENEFIT ANALYSIS

COMPILED BY:............

DATE:............

A	B	C	D	E	F	G	H	I	J	K	L	
Department and section	Total costs	Total quality costs	% quality to total costs	Potential benefits (£)			Potential costs (£)			Total potential benefits (£)	Total potential costs (£)	Comments
				Correction	Appraisal	Prevention	Correction	Appraisal	Prevention			

Figure 12.7 Quality cost–benefit analysis.

12.3 DEPARTMENT PURPOSE ANALYSIS (DPA)

DPA is a structured method for getting your people involved in the quality creation process. It forces them to think in terms of how their tasks form a vital link in their department's 'chain': their 'customers' (i.e. the next link in the chain) depend on receiving good quality output from them to enable them do their own job; and they in turn are dependent on receiving good quality output from *their* 'suppliers' (i.e. the preceding link in the chain); if one person's link breaks down, the whole chain is affected. To save you turning back, the diagram is repeated here in Fig. 12.8.

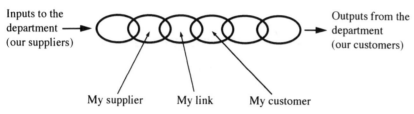

Inputs to the
department ⟶
(our suppliers)

Outputs from the
department
(our customers)

My supplier   My link   My customer

Figure 12.8 The department's chain.

Section 4.3 describes the DPA process in more detail and explains when it might be appropriate to use it; this chapter explains how to put it into practice.

The objectives of the DPA process are:

- To agree the purposes of a department, i.e. why it exists (Form A)
- To list the key activities undertaken by the department in order to achieve its purposes, i.e. deciding what the key chains are (Form B)
- To identify the various links in each chain which enable the department to convert its inputs into the desired outputs (Form C)
- To produce for each individual a list of his or her main tasks, which make up the links in the department's chains (Form D)

The examples of Forms A, B, C and D shown below are based on a Personnel Department, since most readers will be familiar with the functions described. Many of the day-to-day Personnel tasks in this particular company were carried out at the operating division level; the Personnel Department illustrated here was the central support function, consisting of just three people.

Form A Form A is used to make sure that all involved understand *why* the department exists (i.e. its purpose), so that they can think of their own tasks in future in terms of helping their departmental team to achieve this purpose.

The form should be completed by a team consisting of the department's managers and supervisors (in a small department the team may include everyone involved). Make sure that it *is* a team effort, and not just done by the manager: the whole point of the DPA process is to get everyone involved so that they contribute to, agree with and are personally committed to the end result.

The purposes listed on Form A should *not* be a detailed list of activities – that comes in Form B. Figure 12.9 illustrates a typical statement of purposes. When the team

DIVISION: _____CENTRAL_____

BUSINESS OR
DEPARTMENT:_____PERSONNEL_____

THE PURPOSE(S) OF OUR ~~DIVISION / BUSINESS~~ / DEPARTMENT
IS / ARE TO:

_____Contribute to the achievement of the company's_____

_____overall 'mission' by providing a Human_____

_____Resource service which will :_____

_____— improve the training and development_____

_____of all employees_____

_____— foster better industrial relations between_____

_____management and employee_____

_____— improve health and safety standards_____

_____— maintain a staffing level which will_____

_____meet the business requirements of_____

_____each Division_____

Prepared by (list all participants): _____

Mary Williams (Department Manager) _____

Frank Oliver _____ _____

Jenny Denton _____ _____

Approved by: _John Walton_ Date: _4. May 1992_
(Chief Executive)

Figure 12.9 Example of DPA Form A.

members are agreed that the completed form is a correct summary of the department's purpose(s), it needs to be approved by the Head of the Department or Division, who is responsible for ensuring that the statement of purposes fits in with your company's overall mission statement. In the example the form was approved by the Chief Executive, since he was also the Head of the Central Division.

Form B This should be prepared by the same team as Form A. Only the main activities of the department should be listed, with an absolute maximum of ten activities (preferably fewer). The example in Fig. 12.10 illustrates the list of activities agreed for the Central Personnel Department; it also shows who the team have agreed should act as DPA Coordinator for each activity, with responsibility for organizing the rest of the DPA process (i.e. the preparation of Forms C and D) and delivering the results to the department-level team.

Form C For each of the activities listed on Form B, you now need to draw a chain, showing the various links that contribute to the carrying out of the activity. In effect, this means drawing a process flow diagram, then listing all the steps of the process flow on Form C, illustrated in Fig. 12.11. For each step, there is a space on the form for listing:

- **Who does the task**, i.e. the name(s) of the individual(s) concerned
- **Who supplies the input**: remember that there may well be more than one supplier, and that inputs can include information and instructions as well as material
- **Who receives the output**: again, there may well be more than one customer who is dependent on the output of the task

The entries on Form C should not be too detailed: if necessary, show the process in summary form, then prepare a separate form to expand one or more of the process steps into more detail. Where you do this, write 'see data sheet no. ....' across the Suppliers and Customers columns on the first form to direct readers to the more detailed process analysis.

In practice, you may have some difficulty in deciding which process steps are worth breaking down into more detail, and which can be dealt with satisfactorily at the summary level. You may also find when you come to prepare Form D that you have accidentally left out some individuals' tasks, which could be rather upsetting for them! The solution is to do Forms C and D together, involving everyone in the department in the process. If your department is too large for this, get a representative team together and prepare a first draft of Form C, and then get sub-teams to expand any steps that need it into greater detail, together with the corresponding Form D for the individuals concerned.

Form D When the team, or sub-team, is ready to prepare Form D they should *always* involve the individual concerned. The example in Fig. 12.12 illustrates the tasks for which one member of the Central Personnel Department was responsible.

In addition to ensuring that *someone* is responsible for every task listed on Form C, you also need to make sure that every individual is responsible for at least one such listed task (if not, how else is that person contributing to the department's purpose?). Remember to ask each individual what else he or she does, and make a rough

DIVISION: _____*CENTRAL*_____

BUSINESS OR
DEPARTMENT:_____*PERSONNEL*_____

THE MAIN ACTIVITIES OF OUR ~~DIVISION/BUSINESS~~/DEPARTMENT ARE AS
FOLLOWS (NOT NECESSARILY IN ORDER OF IMPORTANCE OR EFFORT):

ACTIVITY No.	ACTIVITY DESCRIPTION	DPA COORDINATOR
1	Salary and Pensions Admin.	Mary Williams
2	Recruitment (Staff & Works)	" "
3	Training	" "
4	Health & Safety	" "
5	Employee Services (Switchb'd/Telex)	" "
6	Canteen	" "
7	Security	" "
8	Personnel Records	" "
9	Industrial Relations	" "
10		

Prepared by (list all participants): _____

Mary Williams _____ _____
Frank Oliver _____ _____
Jenny Denton _____ _____

Approved by: _*John Walton*_ Date: _*4 May 1992*_

Figure 12.10 Example of DPA Form B.

DPA: ACTIVITY ANALYSIS - SHEET No. 3

Division: _CENTRAL_   ~~Business~~/Department: _PERSONNEL_

Activity Description: _RECRUITMENT (WORKS)_   Activity No. 2

(The following table should list all the process tasks required in order to complete the activity, in the sequence in which they normally take place; i.e., it is a 'process flow' description.)

STEP No.	PROCESS TASK	WHO DOES THE TASK	SUPPLIER(S) (INPUT SOURCE)	CUSTOMER(S) (OUTPUT SENT TO)
1	ADVERTISE	Frank Oliver	Mary Williams/Dept Mgr	Job Centre
2	SELECT & INTERVIEW CANDIDATE	" "	" "	Dept. Mgr.
3	SHORT-LIST CANDIDATES FOR INTERVIEW BY SHOP FOREMAN/ DEPARTMENTAL MANAGER	" "	Foreman/Dept. Mgr.	Frank Oliver
4	OBTAIN REFERENCES	Jenny Denton	Frank Oliver	Mary Williams
5	JOB OFFER	" "	Mary Williams	Applicant
6	ARRANGE MEDICAL EXAMINATION	" "	Company Doctor	Mary Williams
7	STARTER PACK	" "	Mary Williams/ Frank Oliver	New Starter
8	INDUCTION	Frank Oliver	Mary Williams	New Starter

Do NOT list more than a maximum of 10 steps. It is better to show the main steps on this table, then use a separate sheet(s) to expand to greater detail where necessary. Where you do this, write 'See DPA sheet no......' across the 'Suppliers' and 'Customers' columns above.

Figure 12.11 Example of DPA Form C.

DPA: INDIVIDUAL'S ACTIVITY ANALYSIS SHEET

My Name is: *FRANK OLIVER*   My Division is: *CENTRAL*   My ~~Business~~/Department is: *PERSONNEL*

My main tasks are as follows:

My tasks:	Activity Ref No.	Step No.	I get my inputs (materials, instructions etc.) from these 'suppliers'	I give my output (materials, instructions etc.) to these 'customers'	Average hours per week			
					Under 2	2 to 4	4 to 8	Over 8
INDUCTION • Terms and conditions of Employment • Safety Instructions • Issue of PPE • Initial Job Training • Tour of factory • Assessments (1, 3 & 6 months)	2	8	Mary Williams Mary Williams/Safety Mgr. Mary Williams/Safety Mgr. Mary Williams/Shop Foreman Mary Williams Shop Foreman	New Starter New Starter Storeman New Starter/Time Office/ Shop Foreman New Starter Mary Williams/ Jenny Denton				

Agreed: *Frank Oliver*   Approved: *Mary Williams*   Date: *19 May 1992*

Figure 12.12 Example of DPA Form D.

assessment of what proportion of the person's time is spent on each task, so that you can check that most of each individual's working time has been accounted for. If the individual is responsible for a large number of tasks you can show which take the most time by putting a tick in the appropriate column of the 'average hours per week' section of the form. This is only necessary if you have difficulty in picking out the significant tasks: if you know which these are you can ignore the 'average hours' columns. The objective is to concentrate on the tasks that take up most of a person's time (I'll explain why in a moment): only include other tasks, which only take a small part of the individual's time, if they are recognized as particularly important in terms of the department's overall purpose(s).

When you've completed a Form D for everyone in the department, they should all be asked to sign the relevant sheets to confirm that they understand and agree with the details recorded, and accept responsibility for doing their best to make sure that *their* link in the chain doesn't break.

That completes the analysis stage of the DPA process, but you can't just leave it at that or all you will have achieved will be an administrative white elephant that will have cost you a lot of time and effort to create. You now need to use the information you've collected as the basis for a company-wide campaign to improve quality and to eliminate wasteful activities. But before you start getting everyone involved in quality circles or continuous improvement groups, don't forget that there are two important sources of improvements that can be identified and acted on *immediately you have completed each individual's Form D*:

- As those readers who are familiar with the preparation of process flow charts will know, the very act of putting down on paper what happens at present will nearly always reveal opportunities for improvement. If preparing Form C helped you to see a better way of doing things, *do something about it!*
- Form D shows how individuals spend their time at present. In most manufacturing companies only about 50 per cent, on average, of what people do actually adds value; the rest is a waste, and this will provide a useful source of ideas for your improvement programme. You will probably find so many examples of non-value adding activities that it will require a great deal of time and effort before you can get round to them all. However, as soon as you have completed the DPA, you should immediately go through the list of individuals' activities (Form D), looking for any significant tasks which are clearly non-value adding, and ask yourself 'Can I eliminate this task *now*?'. If so, *do it!* If it will require time and effort to find a way of eliminating the task, add it to a list of 'Future opportunities for improvement' for the quality circle or continuous improvement group to consider.

Once you've finished the DPA process described above, and every employee has his or her individual list of tasks, they should be encouraged to establish close contact with their individual customers and suppliers, to clear up any misunderstandings that might currently exist about what inputs each really needs and what problems are currently experienced. In particular, everyone should be encouraged to short-circuit 'normal' channels whenever a problem occurs in future, using the customer–supplier links they have forged through the DPA process as a means of putting things right quickly. If you can achieve this, you really will have succeeded in developing a 'quality creation system'.

12.4 TAGUCHI METHODS

You may have found some seemingly conflicting explanations offered of what are generally referred to as Taguchi Methods. The reason for this is simple. Dr Genichi Taguchi is an eminent Japanese statistician who has worked extensively in the field of quality control. Not surprisingly, over the years he has developed a number of techniques for improving quality performance, and these are often referred to both collectively and individually as Taguchi Methods.

At the heart of Taguchi's teachings is a belief that the quality and reliability of a product is to a large extent fixed at the design stage; his methodology is therefore concerned primarily with 'the routine optimization of product and process *prior* to manufacture'. In other words, he maintains that if you can make a product's design more tolerant to variations in both its manufacturing process and its operating environment, then you will have removed once and for all most of the root causes of quality and reliability problems.

This section provides a brief explanation of the three developments for which Taguchi is best known; the Bibliography includes details of where you can obtain further information on these and other aspects of his work.

12.4.1 The Quadratic Loss Function

Taguchi's definition of quality differs from the conventional view of conformance to specification; he prefers to talk about what is *lost* if the product fails to satisfy the customer completely. This includes the loss of goodwill, and hence future sales opportunities, as well as the direct costs associated with correcting faulty products. His contention is that even if the product is, from the contractual point of view, within the agreed specification, there is still a loss if the customer is in any way dissatisfied with the reliability or performance of the product.

Taguchi demonstrated that you can reduce the risk of this potential loss by reducing the extent to which you permit any variation from the 'target' value of each quality characteristic. He went on to develop a formula for calculating the degree of risk, which is generally referred to as the quadratic loss function (because the shape of the graph is usually very similar to the graph of a quadratic function). The formula can be used to determine the optimum trade off between the additional production cost that would be incurred in reducing variation in the quality characteristic, and the financial benefit that would be gained through improved quality and reliability of the product.

If you find that explanation as confusing as I did when I first heard it, don't worry! For most readers the bit that's likely to be important isn't the application of the formula, but understanding the message that comes out of it, because it's this message that makes the other two techniques important for a world-class manufacturer:

> The most effective way of improving quality and reliability performance is to concentrate on reducing variability, rather than on strict conformance to specification.

I'll explain what 'reducing variability' means in a moment.

12.4.2 The Parameter Design Concept

Taguchi defines the traditional design process, from the point of view of quality and reliability, as having two stages: *system design*, in which the design concept and proto-type product are created; and *tolerance design*, in which a compromise is reached between the 'ideal' requirements and the inherent variations that will occur in the manu-facturing process and operating environment, this compromise forming the basis for the design specification, with the product's subsequent quality and reliability performance being assessed in terms of its conformance with this specification. Taguchi's important contribution was to introduce an additional *parameter design* stage between the 'system' and 'tolerance' stages.

This introduction of a 'parameter design' stage is what has enabled Japanese manufacturers to achieve an enviable reputation for the quality of their products *without* incurring significant cost penalties – on the contrary, in fact: because the design is made more tolerant of any inherent variations in the manufacturing process, the cost of manufacture is usually reduced.

I'll use the design of a moulded rubber oil seal to explain the concept. The key quality characteristics of this rubber seal were:

- Dimensional accuracy (particularly of the bore diameter)
- Surface finish of the contact surfaces, which needed to be smooth and free from blemishes
- Resistance to compression in the thickness
- Elasticity, to ensure a tight fit on the shaft
- Resistance to deterioration from oil contact

There was no difficulty in achieving the dimensional accuracy requirements as these were well within the capability of the moulding process; the resistance to oil deterior-ation also presented no problem since this was provided by the choice of synthetic rubber used, which was completely impervious to oil in the operating conditions for which the seal was designed. However, the production process *was* sensitive to the other three quality characteristics and in initial trials as many as 50 per cent of items had to be rejected. Investigation showed that the problems were caused by variations in the moulding temperature and in the curing time (i.e. the length of time for which the mould was kept closed after the rubber had been injected, and the temperature that was maintained throughout this period at the moulding surfaces). These two elements were interdependent, since the higher the temperature, the less time was needed for cure. The optimum time and temperature combinations had been determined previously through experiment, but the problem arose because the production process wasn't reliable enough to maintain the temperature within the narrow variation range needed.

Remembering Taguchi's teaching, the design and process experts decided to review the 'design parameters' (in this case the rubber compound formula), to see if they could find a way of reducing the sensitivity of the process to temperature variation. Although the main ingredient of a rubber compound is, not surprisingly, the rubber itself, there are also a number of other ingredients which are included either to give the finished product its desired performance characteristics, or to facilitate the production process; some of the latter, which affect the curing properties of the compound, are relatively expensive and the team found that this cost factor had been taken into account when the original formulation was specified. After experimenting with alternative ingredients, the team were able to produce a new compound formulation which was much more tolerant of temperature variation during the curing process. Although the material costs were higher, this was compensated for many times over through the reduction in scrap; at the same time, the hourly production rate was increased by more than 10 per cent because the new formulation was sufficiently robust to permit a higher temperature/shorter curing time to be used. To put it in Taguchi terms, the team had used the parameter design concept to reduce the sensitivity of the process to variations in operating conditions; this in turn reduced the subsequent variations in the product's quality characteristics caused by the production process and although additional cost had been incurred, the benefits achieved were of far greater value.

With the introduction of the parameter design stage, the role of tolerance design is to deal with any further reduction in variation that is necessary, in those cases where it has proved either infeasible or uneconomic to reduce sensitivity to variation sufficiently through the design parameters.

12.4.3 Design of Experiments

In the rubber oil seal example, the team had no difficulty in deciding which parameters to change because the technical and design staff were already very familiar with the effects of using alternative additives; a few simple tests were sufficient to determine the optimum ingredient mix and process parameters. However, in many instances it's not that easy to decide which factors are likely to have a significant effect on a specific quality characteristic; tests therefore have to be carried out to determine this. Unfortunately, there can be interaction between different factors, and testing all the feasible combinations of factors would be prohibitive.

Taguchi developed a compromise approach, based on the 'design of experiments' techniques that research and development scientists have used for a number of years, in which he codified a series of easy-to-use 'orthogonal arrays'. These enable the design engineer to determine the minimum number of combinations of variables that need to be tested. The results of the tests can then be examined, using analysis of variance techniques, to establish which are the most important variables. The number of tests required is kept to a minimum by sacrificing testing of every possible interaction between factors; this means that you may need to use an iterative process, repeating the tests after removing variables that have been shown not to be significant, in order to identify any important interactions.

The Bibliography includes details of where you can obtain further information on this and the other Taguchi Methods.

12.5 STATISTICAL PROCESS CONTROL (SPC)

SPC is concerned with the monitoring and control of processes. It's particularly relevant to a world-class manufacturer because it can be used to give warning of a potential quality problem *before* it happens, so that corrective action can be taken to prevent the waste of poor quality actually occurring.

SPC was originally developed from statistical quality control; as most readers will know, this is an appraisal technique used in manufacturing companies for many years to check (by sampling) the acceptability of batches of parts *after* they've been produced. SPC simply applies the same basic approach, but the sampling is done *during* the manufacturing process.

Unfortunately, SPC's statistical basis puts a lot of people off and this has led many companies to concentrate on the key features, such as control charts, but to dispense with the mathematics; in this simplified application of the SPC concepts, control limits are determined by a combination of experience and trial and error, instead of by taking statistically controlled samples from which the standard deviation of variations can be calculated. Although purists may not like this, it has advantages which make it particularly important for a world-class manufacturer: it's easy to understand and simple to use; and, from the practical point of view, it usually works!

Consider, for example, a continuous process machine which, once set up and checked, runs for several hours churning out products. The operator's job is to keep an eye on the process, only intervening if something goes wrong; unfortunately, when it does go wrong it can take half an hour or more to correct the problem and resume normal production. However, you'll usually find that the problem didn't actually arise instantaneously: there were warning signs if only someone had noticed them, and the stoppage could well have been avoided altogether at that time by a simple running adjustment. The problem is to know *when* this running adjustment is necessary, because by the time its effects become obvious to the operator it's too late.

In most processes, however, it's possible to identify some characteristic that will start to change some time before the process fails; for example, if the direct cause of failure of a machine that's producing thin rubber sheeting is tearing of the product as it leaves the compression rollers, you will probably find that the indirect cause is that the rubber sheeting has dropped below its thickness tolerance (although not sufficiently to be noticeable to the naked eye). The operator could have adjusted the thickness setting while the machine was operating and avoided the problem altogether *if only it had been realized what was happening.* That's where the SPC control chart technique comes in.

Figure 12.13 shows a control chart for this rubber sheeting process. The specified SPC procedure for the process requires the operator to take a sample of the rubber sheeting every 30 minutes, measure the thickness and plot this on the control chart. As long as the plotted value falls in the green zone, all is well. At 11:30 the operator sees that the plotted value is in the amber zone: this doesn't necessarily mean that something is wrong; some variation in the process is inevitable because of minor variations in the rubber consistency, or in the roll temperature as a result of the thermostatic control system, or in the output speed, all of which should be automatically corrected by the process control systems. However, just to make sure, and in accordance with the SPC procedure, the operator reduces the sampling frequency to five minutes, marking the results on the control chart as x, y and z. Point x is still in the amber zone, but points y and z are back in the green: the process control system has automatically brought the process back under control, and the operator can revert to sampling at 30 minute intervals. At 15:00 the plotted point again falls in the amber zone, but this time the subsequent x, y and z values fail to show a return to green, thus triggering the next step in the SPC procedure:

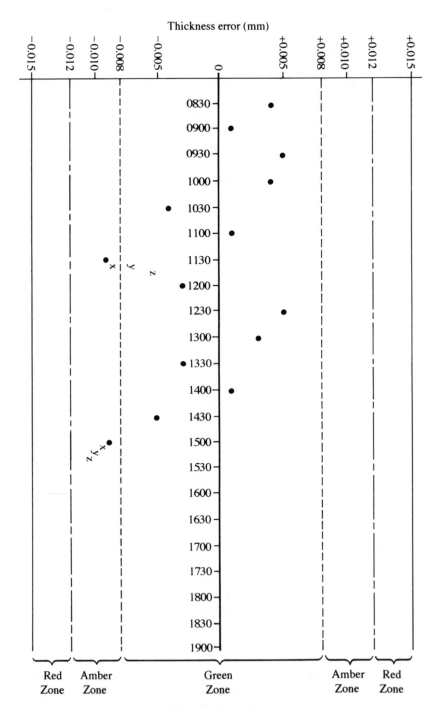

Figure 12.13 Control chart: rubber sheeting process.

- The operator switches on the overhead amber warning light and then checks the machine controls to see if the cause of the problem can be identified
- The foreman, process control engineer and maintenance engineer see the amber light and go to the machine to see if they can help
- The operator continues to take samples at five minute intervals until the problem is solved

So far, although the process is showing signs of slipping out of control, the product still meets specification and there is therefore no reject material; if the process can be returned to green, the potential quality problem will have been avoided. Supposing, however, that after sampling, the plotted value fell into the red zone, perhaps because of a new batch of rubber compound. In this case the operator switches on the red light (in most companies this also sounds a klaxon, which brings the support people running to the scene!), and at the same time stops the process: although output will be lost, scrap costs are minimized because the production of faulty product is stopped immediately.

But how do you decide what values to choose for the amber and red boundaries? If you apply SPC strictly, you will use statistically valid procedures for taking samples, measure the variation, and then calculate the standard deviation; the amber boundary can then be fixed at, say, two times the standard deviation, and the red boundary at three times. However, with the simplified approach that many people prefer, the experience of those involved is used to set initial values, these being adjusted subsequently if the amber warning is found to give too many false alarms, or if it doesn't allow enough time to get the system back under control before the red boundary is breached.

Always remember that what really matters is to prevent quality problems from occurring, and to do so with the minimum of cost and effort. What techniques you use and how you actually apply them are of much less importance, but if you do take any short cuts in your procedures, make sure that you do so in a 'fail-safe' way, so that you don't get caught out when your short cut methods occasionally let you down.

THIRTEEN

GETTING PEOPLE INVOLVED

Linked to Chapter 5, this chapter describes methods of getting people actively involved, particularly during the critical first year of a world-class programme. The first section gives advice on how to get teams working really effectively; this is followed by guidance on how to apply the teamwork approach to both strategic and local improvement projects, and on the type of training that employees at all levels might need. Details are given of the UK's 'Investor in People' National Standard, and the chapter concludes with a case study illustrating how the teamwork, cell manufacturing and 'empowering people' concepts can be combined to improve responsiveness through slimming down the traditional multi-level management structure.

13.1 EFFECTIVE TEAMWORK

You may be tempted to say: 'But I've tried the teamwork approach before and it didn't really get results; perhaps my people just aren't good enough'. Don't let such past experiences put you off. Of course it would make things a lot easier if your people were all well educated and of above average intelligence, but life generally isn't like that; in any case, the essence of becoming world-class is *to make better use than ever before of the skills and experience of your whole workforce.* You can achieve remarkable improvements with *any* group of people, provided that you go about it in the right way, remembering that what you are aiming to do is to draw on their experience of the job and their practical skills; you can compensate for any lack of intellectual or technological skills by including one or two additional people in the group who *are* strong in these respects, possibly production engineers, process technologists or computer specialists. You can also strengthen the team's problem analysis and problem solving capability by hiring a management consultant: more on that in a moment. First, let's look at why your previous efforts at teamwork might have failed to live up to your expectations. I can think of six possible reasons; I'll summarize them first, then consider each in turn in more detail, explaining how they can be overcome:

- *Choice of team leader*: the appointed leader is seen as having prime ownership rights over the project
- *Composition of team*: key 'owners' from other departments are excluded from the team (e.g. Design and Sales)
- *Equal rights*: all team members are nominally equal, but in practice some are more equal than others!
- *Implementation of solutions*: management retains all decision-making rights
- *Obstacles*: 'sacred cows' cannot be challenged
- *Conflicting priorities*: team members 'can't spare the time because of pressure of other commitments'

13.1.1 Choice of Team Leader

Figure 13.1 illustrates the traditional organizational structure for a key strategic project aimed at, say, improving delivery performance and reducing lead time. Because the project is so important, the best person available is picked for the job of Project Manager. This might be the Production Manager or a 'high flier' for whom management of the project is seen as useful experience, or it might even be the Manufacturing Director; the choice will usually depend on who is seen to be the main 'owner' of the problem (in this case probably Production), or who is seen as most likely to get results, or even who can most easily be freed of day-to-day management responsibilities. This seems very sensible, doesn't it, which is why it's the usual way of doing things. However, there are a number of problems which follow, which may well prevent you from achieving your primary objective of 'making better use of the skills and experience of your whole workforce than ever before':

- However good the Project Manager is at involving all the 'right' people, it will be seen by them as 'his' or 'her' project, simply because of the designation 'Project Manager'
- If the Production Manager or Manufacturing Director is given the Project Manager's role, those who work for other departments, such as Design, Sales or Computer Services, will see the project as primarily a Production responsibility and this may affect the amount of time and effort they are prepared to give to the project
- Whatever you say, there will be some, particularly the production foremen and supervisors, who will feel that the Project Manager and his or her team are usurping their role, and undermining their authority with those team members who normally report to them; as a result:
  - Even if they agree to whatever changes are proposed in order to achieve the improvement objectives, they may not give their whole commitment to implementation, because
  - If they think the changes will work, they will be worried that they will be criticized for not having done it before, or

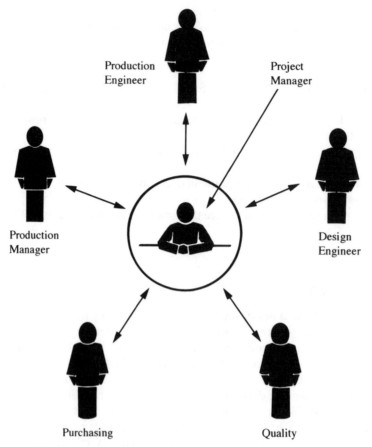

Figure 13.1 The expert project manager.

– If they are not fully convinced that the changes will work, they will be hesitant about giving the full support of their team for something which they see as a probable waste of time that they can't afford.

Many readers will be familiar with the reactions I've described above, but there will be others who have run successful projects in the past and who may, therefore, conclude that it's a rather naïve view of things. Of course, you *can* run a successful project without these problems surfacing if your Project Manager is strong and decisive, and has the full support of top management; but you'll ruffle quite a few feathers in the process and, even though you may achieve the specific objectives of the project, you will *not* have changed people's attitudes in their other day-to-day tasks. To become a world-class manufacturer you have to change the way in which people think about their work, involving them all in the process of continuous improvement: the scene for this culture change will be set by the way in which you involve people *as equals* in the initial key strategic projects.

Figure 13.2 shows an alternative team structure which will help you do this. I'll comment on who should be included in the team in a moment. At this stage the key

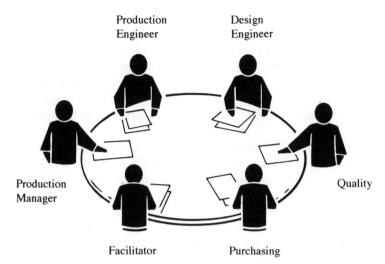

Production Engineer

Design Engineer

Production Manager

Quality

Facilitator

Purchasing

Figure 13.2 A team of experts.

point to note is that there is *no* project manager; the team members all have a particular expertise to contribute and one of them, who should *not* be one of the main owners of the problem, is the facilitator – this is usually the one who can provide expertise in problem analysis and problem solving techniques, and who looks after the administrative and organizational aspects of the team's work. The facilitator's main responsibility is to make sure that every member of the team is encouraged to contribute from his or her particular skills and experience, regardless of rank or role in the company's hierarchy. When an action plan is eventually agreed, the plan is owned by the whole team: there is no Project Manager to whom they can abrogate responsibility, since the facilitator is merely their administrator; the full responsibility for implementing their proposals stays where it should be, with those who will have to make the plan work in practice.

13.1.2 Composition of Team

The method of team working described in this chapter will nearly always produce worthwhile results, but these results will usually be better, and achieved more quickly, if you take some trouble to ensure that the team is well balanced.

The nature of the project will determine which departments are the key owners, but that still leaves you some flexibility in deciding who should represent each of these departments. Ideally the team should be made up of roughly equal proportions of managers, shop floor workers and support staff, with more than one representative in the case of the key departments involved (such as production); you don't necessarily have to select the most senior person in each department, though they should be consulted to ensure that they support the choice *and are prepared for that person to make commitments on behalf of their department.* That's important if you want the team to make progress: it's up to all team members to keep their departments informed about what the team are planning to do, and to take their views into account during team discussions, but within the team they must have the authority to speak on their departments' behalf. It's also important that team members should have credibility not just with the managers concerned, but with the shop floor too. This is particularly so in the case of the shop floor team members: their role in the team is not just to contribute their experience and an understanding of what happens 'at the sharp end'; they also have to ensure that any actions taken as a result of the team's work are seen as being to the good of the whole enterprise, workforce included, and not just something that will benefit 'management'.

Although most team members will be drawn from departments that own the problem, there should also be two or three non-owners, i.e. people who have no day-to-day responsibility for the processes and procedures that may need to be changed. Their role is to challenge the way things are done at present and, in effect, force the owners to justify traditional practices. Because they are not directly involved, they can suggest seemingly silly ideas without themselves appearing silly: experience shows that this will often stimulate the lateral thinking which will enable other, more knowledgeable, team members to come up with new ideas which *are* feasible.

You also need to consider whether each candidate will contribute practical experience or intellectual ability (or both), to ensure that you end up with a good mix of these – both will be essential to the team's success. Most teams will also need at least one member who understands computers, since the team will often need to get information from current systems and may also want to consider possible modifications to the systems. A knowledge of how to use a computer spreadsheet program for analysing data could also prove useful. Your choice of who should be the non-owner team members will usually provide the opportunity for getting the mix right; including people with a background in work study, computer services or marketing can often help get the right balance. The team's facilitator should *always* be chosen from the non-owners because he or she must be seen to be independent for the reasons explained earlier: an owner will inevitably have preconceived ideas about how to tackle the team's objectives, while the facilitator's job is to keep an open mind and encourage the development of new ideas. If you have difficulty in finding a non-owner who you believe would be suitable for the facilitator's job, it's worth thinking about hiring a professional consultant on a part-time basis. However, if you do this, make quite sure that everyone involved realizes that the consultant's role is to act as *facilitator*; it's most important that the other team members retain full ownership of their project with the consultant concentrating on helping them to use their skills and experience effectively – the consultant should *not* be allowed to become 'project leader'.

Finally, there's the question of what to do about a key person, a supervisor for example, who you know from bitter experience would be a nuisance on the team: continually taking a negative view of any new ideas brought up and using seniority to hinder any attempts to introduce change. Common sense tells you that such people must be left out if the team is to have any chance of achieving its objectives, but at the same time you know that if they're *not* involved they could well undermine the team's efforts. It's a difficult problem and, unfortunately one that often occurs. My own preference is to include the person in the team, but to ensure that the person chosen as facilitator is strong enough to keep the 'nuisance' under control and has either the same level of seniority in the organization or is seen to have the boss's ear! If that presents a difficulty, get an external consultant to sit in on team meetings for the first three or four months, nominally 'to provide support and guidance to the facilitator and team members'; if you've used a consultant to teach your people about the world-class concepts and to train team members in problem analysis and problem solving techniques, this would be a natural extension to the consultant's brief.

13.1.3 Equal Rights

When you first introduce this new approach to teamwork you'll probably find that too much attention is paid in the team's discussions to the individual members' status in the company's hierarchy; but if you want to get the best out of a team every team member must have an equal opportunity to contribute from his or her particular expertise. A machine operator, for example, will be much more aware than a supervisor of the sort of problems to be coped with when carrying out production tasks; unfortunately the supervisor won't always accept this because, as the one in charge, he's used to speaking for his department. It's the facilitator's job to make sure that everyone understands that each member of the team has something to contribute that is unique to that person and that their relative positions in the management hierarchy have to be temporarily suspended during the team sessions.

The brainstorming techniques described in Chapter 8 will provide a good opportunity for the facilitator to get this message across, but this may not be enough in the early stages. The belief that 'improving operating processes is the job of managers – operators are there to carry out managers' instructions' is ingrained in our culture; supervisors in particular may be slow to adjust to the new concept that *everyone* should be involved in the process of identifying opportunities for improvement. This often shows itself in the form of objections such as the 'not invented here' syndrome:

- 'We tried that a couple of years ago and it didn't work.'
- 'The unions would never wear it.'
- 'It would cost too much.'
- 'It can't be done.'
- 'I'm far too busy to waste time on that.'
- 'If management wants us to improve productivity they'll have to spend a lot of money on new equipment.'
- 'Of course we could do better, but we'll never manage it unless we're allowed to recruit more people.'

Statements like this should be recognized for what they are, attempts to preserve the *status quo*. They must be nipped in the bud, if possible without antagonizing the objector too much in the process: the sort of people who come up with these statements are very often the ones with the greatest experience, who could make a valuable contribution to the team's efforts if only they can be persuaded to put their objections aside and concentrate on positive ideas. My favourite way of dealing with the problem is to try to inject a little humour into the proceedings, so that neither challenger nor challenged gets too upset when someone using delaying tactics is pulled up short. Right at the beginning of a world-class campaign I remind everyone about the British television comedy programme *Yes Minister*: this has been translated into so many languages and screened in so many countries that most team members will be familiar with it, and will have been amused at the devious ways in which the top Civil Servant, Sir Humphrey

Appleby, resists his Minister's efforts to introduce change. I then tell the team members that whenever they hear one of the usual delaying tactics being used (such as those listed above) they should shout '*Humphrey*', regardless of who the perpetrator is. I've found over the years that because the whole team knows about this in advance and everyone is itching to have an excuse to shout 'Humphrey', any challenge immediately leads to laughter, enabling the objector to withdraw with good grace and without losing face. It may not seem a very dignified or business-like way of handling the situation, but it's certainly worked well in all the companies that I've seen apply it.

If you decide to use the 'Humphrey' method, make sure that the top management team know about it first, so that project team members can be told that when they shout 'Humphrey' they do so with their full authority and blessing. You'll find that the 'Humphrey' method works best if Directors make use of it occasionally themselves, so that it quickly becomes institutionalized as part of your company culture. Once resisting change becomes associated in people's minds with being thought 'silly' (however humorously), then rejecting new ideas will no longer be the easy option it may have been in the past.

13.1.4 Implementation of Solutions: Empowering People

If you think about it, it doesn't really make sense for management to appoint a team to tackle a key strategic project and then retain subsequent decision-making rights to the traditional management hierarchy. After all, if the right experts have been included in the team, and they have spent months analysing data and processes and then come up with their proposals for achieving the project objectives, why *should* anyone else second-guess them and override their conclusions? They are (or should be) the company's best experts on the subject, they've spent a lot of time considering different options, not only are they the owners of the problem, they're also the ones who will have to implement any changes. If you don't trust their judgement, why set up the team in the first place?

Most top managers, while accepting the logic of this argument, would still be very wary (and rightly so) about giving the team a free hand to decide what action is required and then let them go ahead and implement whatever ideas they came up with: a process which is generally referred to as 'empowering people'. And yet it's true that the team members are (or should be) the ones who understand the problem best. The way to overcome any reluctance to 'empower people' in this way is to get a member of the top management team to act as 'Team Champion'. This should be someone whom top management trust to look after their interests, so that when the time comes for the project team to present their proposals for change, the Team Champion can assure top management that the team have considered the various options thoroughly before reaching their conclusions. To do this, although taking no direct part in team meetings, the Team Champion will have to keep in close touch with what they are doing and have regular discussions with the team's facilitator in order to be satisfied that they are going about their task professionally. Throughout the project the Team Champion will need to offer advice and guidance to make sure that nothing is overlooked, being careful not to impose his or her ideas on them. And the Team Champion will have to ensure that any proposals for action which involve spending money are properly cost-justified in accordance with normal procedures for this. When the time comes for the team to present their proposals to management, the Team Champion should be aware of what they are proposing and prepared to support the team; if he or she feels unable to do this, the reasons must be explained to the team in advance, so that they can reconsider their proposals in the light of these objections. If the team members feel strongly enough that they shouldn't change their original plans, they should be allowed to present these to management, but they'll need to be very convincing if they don't have the Team Champion's backing!

13.1.5 Obstacles

So far I've concentrated on the sort of obstacles that arise as a result of people's attitudes. Another type of obstacle that's often met is the existence of 'sacred cows' that the team are told they are not allowed to challenge, for example:

- An incentive payment scheme that is no longer suitable and is stopping the team from introducing new operating methods, but can't be changed because 'we're not due to re-negotiate with the unions for another 18 months'
- A trade creditors policy which delays settlement of all suppliers' invoices until 60 days after delivery, which is causing the team problems in negotiating partnership sourcing agreements
- A strictly enforced debtors policy which automatically puts a customer on 'stop' if an invoice is not paid within 45 days, but which affects the team's efforts to improve delivery performance
- A computer system that is hampering progress, but can't be modified 'until well into next year because all our computer staff are busy working on the new accounting/marketing/distribution/etc. system'

Unlike the sort of objections discussed earlier, these are genuine obstacles because there's probably a very good reason why they can't easily be removed. In a way that makes them more insidious, because if you're not careful the team will get a feeling of impotence: 'What's the use of our coming up with new ideas? Management aren't really committed to change because they won't let us ... (*whatever*)'. This is where the Team Champions can help: as a first step they should use their power and influence to see if the obstacle is genuine and take steps to overcome it if it isn't; if it *is* genuine, the Team Champion must make sure that the team members understand the reasons for the obstacle, so that they can either suggest ways of overcoming it or, if they can't, *themselves* reach the decision that it's something which is in the best interests of the company to retain and which they will have to find ways of accommodating. What is essential is that the team should be involved in this decision, rather than simply having it imposed on them by management as a 'sacred cow'. If you follow this process, even if in the end management are forced to overrule the team, at least the team members will understand why they have done this and that their decision was not taken lightly: in other words, management's commitment to the world-class project will not have been undermined.

13.1.6 Conflicting Priorities

Nearly all major improvement projects go through a phase when the initial enthusiasm wears off and key members of the team start missing meetings, or fail to complete tasks by the date promised. It's such a common problem that you should always assume it will happen and watch out for it, so that the team can be put quickly back on track. If you don't act promptly you'll never free yourself of the situation where so much effort has to be put into dealing with day-to-day problems that there's never enough time left to bring about the sort of improvements that are essential if you want your company to be world-class.

The problem arises because most managers and technical support staff have more things to do than they have time for: faced with a conflict of priorities, they decide that today's problems must take precedence over tomorrow's, because that's the way they've always done it. As a result, all too often the problem is solved with a 'quick fix', so that at least for the time being the problem is overcome. The real problem, however, is that the quick fix doesn't last and before very long they're faced with having to deal with the same problem again. The world-class approach, in contrast, is to break out of this vicious circle by solving the root cause of the problem so that it doesn't keep recurring. That's what the key strategic project aims to do: many of the day-to-day problems that managers have to deal with would disappear as a result of taking whatever action is necessary to improve quality and delivery performance, and reduce lead times significantly.

Unfortunately, even if you explain this to your people and convince them that you are determined to achieve this breakthrough, it will probably take some time to achieve; meanwhile, you will be expecting them to spend time on the world-class project and, at the same time, they will have to continue to cope with all the problems of the past. No wonder that some of them start making excuses about not having enough time! In most cases it's not that they don't recognize the importance of the project, it's simply that their assessment of relative priorities reflects what has been expected of them in the past; somehow, you have to get them to change their assessment criteria. It's management's responsibility to make clear what those criteria should be, and a good way of doing this is to teach managers a simple way of recording how they spend their time each day, and then to agree targets with them for three or four main categories of task. For example, if you specify that certain supervisors should spend on average a third of their time on world-class improvement activities, they know that they will have some explaining to do at their next personal appraisal if they've spent 90 per cent of their time on day-to-day problems: when you first introduce this technique, you may well have to discuss with them ways of off-loading tasks, for example through delegation. A case study at the end of this chapter illustrates a practical example of using the time management technique to change a manager's perception of relative priorities.

To sum up: in the past managers have often spent the bulk of their time dealing with day-to-day problems. They now need to be taught that in a world-class company those who want to be considered as managers *must* devote part of their time to improving the way in which the business operates: it's management's job to agree with each manager and supervisor individually what proportion of their time should be spent on each of these two activities, and it should be made clear to them that future appraisals of their performance will reflect their achievement of their personal time management targets. If you do that, you should have no difficulty in persuading them to give their full support to the world-class initiatives.

13.2 STRATEGIC IMPROVEMENT PROJECTS

The following examples of project briefing sheets have been taken from real-life projects in a number of companies. For the purposes of this book, the names of team members shown in the originals have been replaced by their respective job descriptions.

Example A

Project title: Improving delivery time and inventory in spares division.

Background

In order to survive and prosper in the longer term in an increasingly competitive world, we must be able to achieve a step change improvement in the company's performance and significantly improve our ability to satisfy customers' requirements. Market research has shown that customers consider availability of spares to be an important factor when they are deciding whether to order new machinery from us or from one of our competitors. In the past we have managed to achieve reasonable delivery performance only by holding large stocks, but this is becoming increasingly difficult since our new range of products has considerably increased the range of spare parts stocked. In addition, many of our customers have been cutting back on their own spares stock and consequently are more dependent on our ability to satisfy their requirements quickly. We have to find ways of improving our response time, and we need to do this more efficiently than in the past so that we can reduce our inventory.

Improvement objectives

1. 98 per cent on-time delivery performance to be achieved within 12 months.
2. The lead time on spares from our suppliers to be reduced by 50 per cent within 12 months.
3. Spares inventory to be reduced by 30 per cent by year end (i.e. within 9 months).
4. Reduce response time to all enquiries to less than 24 hours within 3 months.

Reporting arrangements

1. The full team will present their provisional action plan to the Management Executive Meeting on 4 November (i.e. three weeks after completion of the training course for team members).
2. The full team will report progress to the Management Executive Meeting in February. Their report should include details of performance data prior to the project commencing, to provide a basis for measuring future improvements; key problems identified; improvements achieved to date; and proposed action plan for the next three months and beyond.

3. The full team will continue to present a report to management every three months until the project is completed.
4. The Team Champion will be the Group Manufacturing Director, John Hamner. The team's facilitator will keep him in close touch with developments, reporting to him at least once every two weeks.
5. The facilitator will produce brief minutes of each meeting of the project team, including in this what actions are agreed and who is responsible. Circulation of these minutes should be agreed with the Team Champion.

Team members

Company Quality Manager (Facilitator); Computer Manager; Export Sales Manager (Machines); Foreman, Warehouse and Despatch; Salesman (Spares); Buyer; Order Processing Clerk; Machine Shop Operative.

Others may be invited to join sub-teams as required, subject to the prior agreement of the Team Champion and the relevant managers.

Example B

Project title: Stock reduction.

Background

The pattern of demand for our products often exhibits large fluctuations from month to month and often week to week, particularly in the retail sector. While bearing in mind that we must ensure *the very best service to our customers* at the *minimum cost*, there are two basic methods of coping with these fluctuations:

- By always attempting to match output with demand (which, currently, means working overtime, adding extra shifts or, occasionally, laying people off)
- By attempting to keep output at an even level and allow stocks to fluctuate to balance the variation in demand

Neither method is satisfactory: the first is difficult to organize and causes staff upsets; the second is the preferred method at present, but is expensive because of the high stocks that are built up due to inadequate control procedures. A 10 per cent reduction in stocks could yield well over $250,000 on profits. (*The original document included a breakdown of 'ball park' costs of stockholding to justify this figure: interest charges, warehousing costs, insurance etc.*)

A separate project will be investigating ways of improving production flexibility, but this will take some time to complete and there will still be a need to improve our stock control procedures. Management have therefore decided to launch a parallel project aimed at reducing inventory.

Improvement objectives

Examine all elements of the company's stockholding (i.e. raw materials, general stores, maintenance spares, work-in-progress, packaging material and finished goods) in order to:

1. Determine accurate stockholding costs, and estimate how these would vary: (a) if stock levels continued to rise on current trends; and (b) if they reduced to the target levels, specified below.
2. Achieve a total reduction of 5 per cent on existing stock of $7,500,000 within six months.
3. Put in place adequate methods of control to maintain stock value below 75 per cent of monthly sales (this objective also to be achieved within six months).

Reporting arrangements

The Team Champion will be Jan Kemper, Vice-President (Finance). The Facilitator will keep him informed of progress weekly, and the full team will report progress to the Site Management Meeting quarterly.

Team members

Product Development Manager (Facilitator); Cost Department Manager; Marketing Manager (Automotive); Regional Marketing Manager (Export); Data Processing Manager; Stores Foreman; Purchasing Manager; Personnel Officer.

Example C

Project title: Cost reduction of widgets.

Background

Although the market leader for widgets, we have recently seen our market share reduced in the home market because of strong pressure from competitive products. Further reductions in market share would result in job losses.

Our Sales and Marketing team are looking at ways of making customers more aware of why we are market leaders: we offer better quality widgets with more strength and longer life than those of our competitors; we provide better availability from stock via our distributor network; and we provide better sales and technical support services. However, we also need to make our products more cost competitive; this means that we have to evaluate each and every one of our major cost centres for any possible cost benefit or saving that could be used to protect and increase our market share.

Project objectives

The objective is to identify and reduce areas of waste within our operation by targeting the following as potential areas for progressive and continuous improvement over 3, 6 and 12 months or longer.

1. Labour productivity improvements:
    (i) Direct process times: target a 20 per cent reduction
    (ii) Indirect process times, material travelling distance and handling: target a 70 per cent reduction
2. Manufacturing time and lead-time reductions:
    (i) Waiting times from raw to finish: target a 90 per cent reduction
3. Inventory levels:
    (i) Reduction of work-in-progress and travel: target a 50 per cent reduction
4. Inspection times: target a 90 per cent reduction
5. Utilization of space: target a 30 per cent reduction

During their initial investigations the team may identify other areas of waste in the current operations which offer further opportunity for improving manufacturing effectiveness. They should report these to their Project Adviser (*the term used in this company in preference to 'Team Champion'*), and discuss with him or her whether they should be included in the team's targeted improvement objectives.

Reporting arrangements

The team should report fortnightly to the Project Adviser, who is the Financial Director. The team will require cooperation from all staff and all departments to ensure the project is successful. If the team come up against any obstacle they should inform the Project Adviser as soon as possible.

The team will report back to the company's full executive committee at the end of the first three months and quarterly thereafter.

Team members

Internal Sales Executive (Facilitator); Machine Shop Foreman; Warehouse and Despatch Foreman; Works Manager/Production Control Manager; Personnel Officer; Customer Sales Executive; Accounts Assistant. The Buyer will be available to assist the team when required.

In addition to the above, the team should arrange for shop floor operatives to be involved through appropriate sub-teams.

13.3 LOCAL IMPROVEMENT PROJECTS

The project detailed in Example C above succeeded in achieving significant cost reductions over the ensuing 12 months. Actions taken included changing from a conventional process-oriented layout to a number of manufacturing cells, each covering a range of different widget types and sizes; this enabled flow line concepts to be applied to improve manufacturing efficiency.

However, while most of the targets set had been achieved (and some had actually been surpassed), the key cost element of direct labour had so far been reduced by only 10 per cent, compared with the target of 20 per cent. For a number of reasons management decided to replace the original strategic project team with a new local improvement team: the work that remained was primarily concerned with the actual manufacturing process and was unlikely to involve other departments; to improve the manufacturing methods further, a majority of the team members would need to understand the processes involved; and, above all, a number of the people who actually worked in the new manufacturing cells had asked to be more directly involved. A new local improvement project was therefore launched to take over the remaining work of the original project team, but with a new set of objectives.

The briefing document for the new local improvement project is shown below: guidance on methodology is included because most of the team members had no previous experience of process improvement and only a simplified one-day course was felt to be appropriate. Problems were often experienced with the castings which formed the main body of the end products; because of this, the foundry which supplied the bulk of the castings agreed that their Quality Manager should be a member of the team.

Example: Local Improvement Project

Project title: World-class machining.

Background

The step-change improvement of introducing flow line manufacture, through the installation of cells incorporating new work handling and processing equipment, has been achieved. Other smaller though vital improvements have also been made (e.g. quick-change tooling), but it is now time to focus on the elimination of wasteful activities which persist.

Within this scope (though the project is *not* limited or to be constrained in this respect), we note that between 3 per cent and 5 per cent of all castings received from our main supplier fail to reach our finished product warehouse for a variety of reasons, including foundry defects, poor galvanizing and machine shop scrap; there may be other causes. This is waste in its purest form and therefore every effort must be directed at its reduction and eventual elimination, even though much of the waste is generated by suppliers.

Methodology

The team should start by brainstorming to identify waste and wasteful activities, including, but not limited to, scrap materials.

As in previous exercises, the team should then seek quick fixes, priorities for longer term actions and analysis of data for problem solving.

With regard to scrap, analysis should lead us towards two goals:

(i) Assistance to suppliers to reduce scrap shipment to our factory
(ii) Elimination of causes of internal scrap

Even item (ii) may have external implications, e.g. poorly ground bosses which we subsequently have to machine.

Systems will be required not only to generate the information required for analysis but also to enable ongoing monitoring and improvement. Feedback to suppliers and cooperative activity is a vital part of long-term partnerships.

The team must also devise means of measuring progress, and in this regard productivity is the ultimate yardstick. Historical information will be provided.

Targets

Our historical productivity has averaged 47 widgets per manhour. The new flow lines have recently increased this to about 52 widgets per manhour.

The target is to achieve the same improvement again, to 57 widgets per manhour, through continuous improvement, within six months.

The team should also analyse historical data relating to foundry returns and will target a 50 per cent reduction within six months.

Reporting arrangements

The team will report initial findings three weeks after commencement of the project and report progress at three monthly intervals thereafter to the Executive Committee. The Project Adviser will be the Works Manager, to whom any barriers to progress should be advised.

Team members

Works Records Clerk (Facilitator); Foreman, Machine Shop; Machine Operator, Cell A; Machine Operator, Cell C; Draughtsman; Setter; Inspector/Setter; Quality Manager (Foundry); Stores Chargehand.

Other employees may be co-opted as required.

13.4 TRAINING PROGRAMMES

13.4.1 Management Skills

When it comes to sport, most people would agree that the person with the best technical skills doesn't necessarily make the best team captain. And yet, in manufacturing, all too often in the past it was the one with the best technical skills who was made Foreman. To make matters worse, he was usually expected to learn how to manage his people without being given any training in how to do this. Most companies have progressed beyond this stage now, but many are left with long-serving foremen and supervisors who have never had any formal management training: if you want them in the future to use their people more effectively than ever before you will need to do something about this.

While the new breed of managers will probably benefit from, and welcome, formal classroom training in management skills, the older hands are unlikely to do so: they will feel uncomfortable with what they see as an academic approach, they will probably have difficulty in putting what they have learnt into practice in their everyday work situation, and they may well resent the implication that they don't know how to manage when they've been doing it for years. In these circumstances I've found that a tutorial approach, tailored to suit individuals or small groups, is more effective, because it can be introduced progressively over a period of several months and can be related directly to their day-to-day tasks; but it's important that the programme involves everyone in middle management, so that individuals don't feel that they've been picked on.

Once you've got the world-class message of continuous improvement across, and shop floor workers have started to learn new job skills as part of your efforts to improve labour flexibility, it shouldn't be too difficult to introduce the concept of a 'structured self-improvement process' for middle management. However, this needs careful planning. My preferred method is as follows:

- Make a list of all your foremen, supervisors and managers; you may also find it useful to include support staff.
- Prepare a list of possible subjects to be included in the training programme; there are many books you can use for this, but I prefer *The Manager's Book of Checklists'* by Derek Rowntree (see Bibliography), for reasons that you'll see in a moment.
- For each person on your first list, choose five or six subjects which you think most appropriate for that individual.
- Ask the individuals to select (*without prompting from you*), which five or six subjects *they* each think most appropriate, then compare the lists; as far as possible, try to respect their preferences rather than your own so that they all feel ownership of the subsequent training programme.
- Finally, when you've agreed a programme with everyone on your list, combine the results on a chart showing, horizontally, which subjects apply to each individual and, vertically, which individuals are to receive tutoring in each subject.

You can then compile a programme in which each individual will receive tuition in one subject each month; reference to the chart will enable you to plan this in such a way that the initial tutoring can be done in small groups. Training then starts with a brief (20–30 minutes) briefing session in which the key points about the subject are explained to the group: the *Manager's Book of Checklists*, referred to above, can be used for this; all you need to do is to go through each item on the appropriate check-list, making sure that everyone understands it. Individuals then have an easy to use reference list of the key points that they have to put into practice in the ensuing months. All that is left is for the appointed tutor to have an informal discussion with each individual periodically to ensure that they are actually putting the new ideas into practice and to help with any difficulties they have experienced; you can use an external management consultant for this if you have difficulty finding someone suitable internally.

Two subjects that are particularly important to help managers cope with world-class improvement activities are 'managing meetings' and 'time management'. You will usually find that everyone will benefit from formal training in these subjects. The following case study illustrates how one (very experienced) manager, who had difficulty in finding time for participating in world-class activities, overcame his problem through improving the way in which he managed his time.

Case Study: Time Management

The person concerned (I'll call him Tom) had a number of responsibilities: he was Head of the Engineering Division, which included a large machine shop and press shop; he was in charge of site management, which included maintenance of machinery and equipment in a number of other divisions; and he was responsible for the development of new computer applications for manufacturing departments. Tom's problems of time management came to a head when he was also asked to coordinate a new programme of world-class manufacturing initiatives across the company.

After an initial tutoring session with a consultant, Tom decided to categorize his time under four headings:

- Engineering Division Management
- Site Management
- Computer Development
- World-class Manufacturing

His initial feeling was that he would have to devote about 75 per cent of his time to the first two of these categories because, as Engineering Manager, these were his prime responsibility. This left 25 per cent of his time for the other two, i.e. the 'strategic development' tasks. However, he recognized that he should not make this decision on his own: he should first consult his 'customer', i.e. the Managing Director, who might have his own views on the relative importance of Tom's four categories of responsibility. The Managing Director did indeed have strong views on this: he felt that Tom should delegate more of the day-to-day tasks, so that he could spend at least 60 per cent of his time on strategic development work, otherwise there would be a serious risk that achievement of the company's longer term objectives would be delayed. They agreed on the following targets:

- 60 per cent of Tom's time should be spent on strategic tasks, divided, on average, 40 per cent on world-class-related activities and 20 per cent on Computer Development; within any one week these targets might not be met, but over any four-week period the actual should be close to target.
- 30 per cent of his time should be divided equally between Engineering Division and Site Management tasks, again over any four-week period.
- Sensibly, the Managing Director suggested that Tom should assume that 10 per cent of his time would be 'lost' to miscellaneous duties that could not be classified under one of the other headings (for example, attending Executive Management Committee meetings).

In order to monitor how he actually spent his time, Tom prepared a simple daily log sheet; this was divided horizontally into half-hour time intervals, these being pre-printed in the left-hand column, with the rest of the sheet made up of a separate column for each of the four task categories plus a column headed 'miscellaneous'. He carried this form with him throughout the day and every half hour he put a tick in the appropriate column to indicate how he had spent the bulk of the last half-hour period (I would have thought this to be far too laborious, but Tom insists that after the first two or three days it became so much part of his routine that it was no more onerous than, say, lighting a cigarette!). At the end of the day all he had to do was to add up the number of ticks in each column to determine how many half-hour units had been spent under each heading. He then calculated the percentages at the end of each week and each four-week period in terms of the total number of ticks recorded: that ensured that the 'right' proportion of his time was being spent on each type of task, irrespective of how many hours a day he worked, and automatically took account of any days when he was sick or on holiday.

It sounds rather complicated when it's explained in writing, but in practice it's very simple to do. And it certainly worked. At first Tom found that he spent far too much of his time on what he referred to as 'fire-fighting', with the result that for a few weeks his work on computer developments came to a virtual standstill. However, it didn't take long for him to realize that he just had to find ways of delegating more of the daily routine management tasks: 'I found I became increasingly reluctant to spend too much time on tasks that I realized would mean a tick having to go in an over-subscribed column!', he explains. 'This forced me either to put off doing such tasks where I could, or to pass them on to one of my staff whenever this was feasible; I even wrote some periods out of my diary to make quite sure that I could devote the necessary time to such tasks as Computer Development'. Rather to his surprise he soon found that his people were perfectly capable of looking after many of the routine tasks without him having to get involved and, once they got used to it, they welcomed having more responsibility. As a result, three of Tom's foremen have now been promoted and have taken over from him much of the responsibility for day-to-day management of the Engineering Division, so that Tom is able to spend most of his time on tasks which will have a direct impact on the strategic development of the company.

13.4.2 World-Class Awareness Training

It would be pointless for me to suggest a detailed awareness training programme, because what *you* need will depend on your particular circumstances. However, I can give some guidelines that should help you decide what's needed in your own case. You can then either develop your own programme material, or (better) select an external consultant who can deliver the type of training programme you've decided meets *your* requirements (as opposed to any off-the-peg training programme which the consultant might at first suggest!).

Awareness training usually consists of a series of seminars, with every employee attending one of them. There should be an initial 'Executive Seminar', to make sure that every member of senior management knows what it's all about and, ideally, to get them involved in determining priorities for step change projects. You may need to repeat this seminar, with only minor changes, to cover the rest of your management structure; in order to encourage audience participation, try to keep the numbers attending at any one time to not much more than 20 people, which means that you may need to repeat the seminar several times, depending on the size of the company. Allow a minimum of half a day, and preferably a full day, for both the Executive and the Managers' seminars. Finally you will need a series of 'world-class briefings' for the rest of the workforce; anything from 30 minutes to two hours is likely to be appropriate.

To demonstrate that management's commitment starts at the very top, the Chief Executive should be prepared to open the proceedings at every one of the seminars and briefings, explaining why the world-class initiatives that will be discussed in the seminar are essential for the future success of the company.

For the Executive and Managers' seminars I suggest that the programme should consist of three parts:

- *Why* do we need to do something?
- *What* do we need to do?
- *How* do we do it?

In the *why* part, the objective is to convince everyone that there really *is* a need to do something, and that it involves them all – it's not just something they can leave to Manufacturing. To achieve this objective, even the sceptics need to be convinced that something is different now, and they have to understand that to 'continue as we have in the past, steadily improving' is not a real option: a step change improvement is essential. They have to be persuaded that 'steady as we go' will eventually lead to the collapse of their comfortable world – there is a *real* threat just over the horizon. Finally, you need to reassure them that there *is* something the company can do, and that it's well within their capability to do it, even if it means that their present relatively cosy existence will need to be stirred up a bit.

To do all this, start by showing the diagrams in Figs. 1.1, 1.2 and 1.3 to explain the 'step change, followed by continuous improvement' concept; you can then use a combination of videos and brief case studies to show what other people, just like them, have done in other companies (details of some suitable videos are included in the Bibliography). Before showing the videos, you should ask the audience to make notes, while each is playing, of any points that they think might be relevant to *your* company. These notes will provide the basis for them to consider later the question of *what* needs to be done and, almost as important, the need to make notes should make sure that they pay proper attention!

After showing the videos I've found that it helps everyone to get their thinking sorted out if you then hold a discussion on:

- What are the key features of the 'just-in-time' approach?
- What are the key features of the 'total quality' approach?
- What do they have in common? In what ways do they differ?
- Which is most relevant to us? Or would we be better to stick to the term 'world-class'?

If you make a list on a flip chart of the key points they noted during each of the videos, you'll usually find that they reach the conclusion themselves that the different approaches have a great deal in common; this should clear up any misconceptions anyone might have about JIT and TQ, and help to concentrate their attention on what 'world-class' is really all about. If they don't make the point themselves, you will need to stress that what matters is not so much what *they* think is important, as what your *customers* think is important, i.e. what will persuade them to want to buy more in future from your company rather than from your competitors. If you believe it to be relevant to your situation, you should also include a brief review of life-cycle diagrams (described in Chapter 2), to draw attention to any key products that are reaching the end of their life, to make sure that they include the need to get new products to the market-place quickly when they are drawing up their priority list.

They should now be ready to consider *what* needs to be done to bring the way in which your company operates up to world-class standards; for example, reducing lead time, improving delivery performance and improving quality.

For the *how* stage of the seminar you can then get them to use their notes as a starting point for brainstorming ideas for improvement that will address the key areas they've identified as being important to customers. This should be followed by the short-listing process (described in Chapter 8), in order to reach a consensus on what the key actions are that the company needs to take *in the view of the participants*.

You may be worried that they may come up with different conclusions from those reached by top management during the preceding review of strategy. In practice, I've never yet found that to be a problem; there may be some difference in the order of the three or four ideas identified as priority, but it's unusual in my experience for there to be any significant differences: if there are, you should seriously question why there are differences and be prepared, if necessary, to accept that the top management team were wrong. More usually, any differences in priority can usually be overcome by combining the two 'top priority' lists, so that both groups feel ownership of what is finally agreed.

The final step is to agree on the three or four key strategic projects that need to be tackled first; the preparation of project briefings can then be left to whoever are to be the Team Champions.

The procedure described above will need to be modified in the case of a larger company, where the number of managers is too great to accommodate in the two groups proposed. In such cases I prefer to keep as far as possible to the same programme, because it helps everyone to understand how the final action plan was developed; you can sometimes do this by holding separate sessions at divisional level, so that each group of managers can consider what action is needed for their particular division. The alternative is to stop the programme after the *what* stage, and then explain the *how* decisions that have already been taken, and the ways in which those present will be expected to contribute to the actions planned.

The world-class briefings for the rest of the workforce should be much shorter, and will generally not involve audience participation, other than in a question and answer period at the end. For these sessions the '*why* do we need to do something?' part is the most important, and should follow very much along the lines of the Executive and Managers' seminars, but with only one or, at most, two videos. You should also explain how it will affect *them*: Section 5.2 suggests the topics you might need to cover. The session can be completed with a brief summary of '*what* do we need to do?', concentrating on the action areas agreed (for example, 'improve delivery reliability and cut lead time in half'), followed by an announcement of the initial step change projects and the names of team members involved. The final summing up should emphasize, in particular, management's commitment to 'making better use than ever before of the skills and experience of the whole workforce'.

13.4.3 World-Class Project Training

As with the 'awareness' training, what training your project team members will need will depend on your particular circumstances; you will probably also have to consider the views of whoever you appoint as trainer (particularly if you use external consultants who have their own training material). However, the following programme content for a typical three-day training course should provide a useful starting point for you to consider. Ideally, all members of a team should attend the course together, so that they can start work on their project during the second and third days (this gives them an opportunity to break away from the formal classwork and starts the 'action learning' process).

Suggested programme content for three-day training course for world-class project team members. The programme should be made up of roughly equal proportions of formal instruction by the trainer, practical work on exercises (applying the techniques), videos/discussions, and work on the teams' projects.

- **Problem analysis and problem solving techniques, such as:**
    - the 'situation/vision/plan' method of organizing project work
    - process flow analysis
    - brainstorming and fishbone diagrams
    - short-listing techniques
    - analysing data, preparing histograms etc.
    - Pareto analysis
    - lead time analysis
- **Key elements of the JIT approach, such as:**
    - reducing lead time
    - reducing inventory
    - reducing set-up time
    - improving suppliers' performance
    - Kanbans
    - improving labour flexibility
- **Total quality aspects, such as:**
    - the TQ concept
    - customer–supplier relationships
    - zero defects (quality at source)
- **Involving people:**
    - effective teamwork
    - continuous improvement groups
    - overcoming resistance

During the three-day course, the teams should also spend four to five hours working on the initial planning stage of their project (provided that you can arrange for most of the team members to attend together); during the second half of the final afternoon the top management team should attend, so that the teams can present their plan of action to them for approval.

13.4.4 World-Class Training for Continuous Improvement Groups

'Continuous improvement groups' (CIGs) are most likely to become relevant some time after the initial world-class projects have been launched, for the reasons explained in Sec. 5.5. By this time the shop floor workers may well need reminding of what 'world-class' is all about: in particular, the distinction between step change projects and the continuous improvement type activities which will be their main concern. Apart from this, the only additional training they are likely to need is an introduction to brainstorming. Training in other topics should only be given when it is known to be necessary, since you should try and keep the work of CIGs as uncomplicated as possible: their prime role is to identify the everyday things that go wrong that lead to quality or productivity problems – if they identify a 'difficult' problem it's usually advisable to appoint a separate local improvement team to deal with it.

If, however, you decide to go ahead with CIGs right from the start, you may need to structure their approach to place emphasis on the customer–supplier concept – otherwise you are likely to find them concentrating on the soft options such as welfare or environmental matters (this is because they are unlikely to start thinking in real world-class terms until they see major changes happening as a result of the efforts of the key strategic project teams). The 'department purpose analysis', described in Sec. 12.3, can help provide this structure.

13.5 THE 'INVESTOR IN PEOPLE' NATIONAL STANDARD

The UK's *National Standard for Effective Investment in People* provides a benchmark of good practice for ensuring that all employees are given the appropriate training and personal development support to enable them to do their job more effectively. It should therefore be of interest to any company that wants to be a world-class manufacturer.

The requirements of the standard are reproduced here by kind permission of Investors in People (UK). Details of where further information can be obtained are given in the Bibliography.

National Standard for Effective Investment in People

An Investor in People makes a public commitment from the top to develop all employees to achieve its business objectives.

- Every employer should have a written but flexible plan which sets out business goals and targets, considers how employees will contribute to achieving the plan and specifies how development needs in particular will be assessed and met.
- Management should develop and communicate to all employees a vision of where the organisation is going and the contribution employees will make to its success, involving employee representatives as appropriate.

An Investor in People regularly reviews the training and development needs of all employees.

- The resources for training and developing employees should be clearly identified in the business plan.
- Managers should be responsible for regularly agreeing training and development needs with each employee in the context of business objectives, setting targets and standards linked, where appropriate, to the achievement of National Vocational Qualifications (or relevant units) and, in Scotland, Scottish Vocational Qualifications.

An Investor in People takes action to train and develop individuals on recruitment and throughout their employment.

- Action should focus on the training needs of all new recruits and continually developing and improving the skills of existing employees.
- All employees should be encouraged to contribute to identifying and meeting their own job-related development needs.

An Investor in People evaluates the investment in training and development to assess achievement and improve future effectiveness.

- The investment, the competence and commitment of employees, and the use made of skills learned should be reviewed at all levels against business goals and targets.
- The effectiveness of training and development should be reviewed at the top level and lead to renewed commitment and target setting.

13.6 CHANGING THE ORGANIZATIONAL STRUCTURE

Section 5.8 referred to how some companies have extended the concepts of teamwork and manufacturing cells to the way in which they manage their organization, replacing the traditional hierarchical structure and removing several layers of management. The following case study describes how this has been put into practice at Barr & Stroud.

Case Study: Barr & Stroud Limited

You'd expect a defence contractor to be innovative where its products are concerned, but it's not very often that you find such a company at the leading edge when it comes to the way in which the business is run. Glasgow-based Barr & Stroud are the exception, as this case study illustrates.

The company, which is part of the Pilkington Optronics group, has been a leading manufacturer of sighting and range-finding equipment for many years. Its current product range takes full advantage of all the latest developments in optical technology, and includes sophisticated equipment for the defence industry, such as periscopes for the Trident nuclear submarine, as well as civilian applications of thermal imaging equipment used by the police and rescue services. All the products are manufactured in small batches, often as low as just one or two per batch, with a quantity of ten being considered a large batch. Because of the technical complexity and continuous emphasis on innovation, products are, effectively, always at the prototype stage.

The company's organizational structure had developed during a time when virtually all its products were sold to the defence industry on a 'cost-plus' basis. The introduction of new defence procurement procedures in recent years, which progressively replaced cost-plus with competitive tendering and required a much tighter control of costs, had forced Barr & Stroud to look more critically than ever before at its design and manufacturing functions. The problem became even more urgent with the ending of the Cold War, which brought increasing competitive pressures and the need to find new non-military applications. Initial efforts to improve efficiency through computerization did little more than mechanize the existing operational deficiencies, and a new management concluded that a more fundamental change would be needed in the way in which the company carried on its business. This would have to include a drastic reduction in the number of employees, both to compensate for the reduced demand for its defence industry products and to enable it to compete effectively with the more commercially oriented civilian applications. Downsizing to the extent required in an already poor industrial relations climate was likely to have such an effect on morale that serious difficulties were anticipated in achieving the sort of world-class environment that would be needed to protect Barr & Stroud's long-term future.

The breakthrough came through the sale of their existing site to a supermarket chain, which enabled them to commission new purpose-built premises which would be more suitable for the size and type of operations they needed. This impending move to a 'greenfield site' provided the catalyst for a fundamental re-think of what facilities and organizational structure would be more appropriate to the company's future needs. This re-think involved extensive consultation, not just with managers, but with the workforce as a whole, both directly and through their union representatives. As Managing Director Tom O'Neill explains: 'We spelt out frankly to the workforce what was intended. We gave them the bad news about the job losses first, then we listened to their ideas; we recognized that if people don't take ownership of change, they won't change their behaviour.' Management had originally planned compulsory redundancies, but as a result of the consultation process this was replaced by a programme of voluntary redundancies and early retirements in three distinct phases; this enabled them to reduce the workforce from around 2100 to only 750 in a period of less than three years. The strife that would have accompanied such a reduction in the past was largely avoided because everyone understood that this was an essential part of the plans for reconstructing a new Barr & Stroud on its greenfield site, and they had all been involved in working out what needed to be done to make the company successful in the future. A key feature of the reconstruction process was the decision to replace Barr & Stroud's traditional hierarchical organization with a team-based structure which delegated ownership and responsibility as far as possible away from corporate management and into the hands of those 'at the sharp end'.

A separate manufacturing team, each with its own team manager, was established for each of the current products: Trident periscopes, civilian thermal imaging equipment, and so on. In effect, from the manufacturing point of view each of the main products became a separate 'family' business, with its own materials planning, capacity planning, production engineering and expediting support personnel; to keep the numbers of these support people to a minimum, some sharing of resources between smaller product teams was permitted. Optical components were already obtained from a sister company in North Wales, and with the move to the new site the opportunity was taken to re-source as many other components as possible to external suppliers, leaving only core manufacturing processes in-house. Those machine shop resources that were retained were established as a shared facility, and within the machine shop each component-manufacturing cell was designated as an independent team with its own team leader. Even external suppliers were effectively operated as a team through the development of 'partnership sourcing' with its own 'team leader', using an MRP system with vendor scheduling to consolidate material schedules covering the requirements of all the product teams. Under the old procurement procedures there were some 3000 external suppliers on Purchasing's register, about half of which were active; the new partnership sourcing team has reduced this to only 161, and of these just 23 suppliers now account for 60 per cent of all purchases.

The design and development function also adopted the team concept, adapting it to suit their particular needs. As well as 'Technology Champions', whose role is to nurture and develop technical innovation and investment, a project leader is appointed to develop each new product through all its stages, with the number and mix of people in the team varying according to the stage of the project. The process of switching people in and out of the various engineering teams needs careful planning and control to make the best use of resources, and 'engineering resource planning' has recently been introduced for this purpose. Productivity in the Electronics and Engineering functions has increased as much as two-fold in some areas through this careful planning and control of the 'skills incubator', which involves breaking all design and development jobs down to steps with a work content of never more than one week's worth, to ensure that progress can be properly monitored. These improvements in utilization would not have been achieved without the close involvement of all members of the technical teams in improving the performance of their 'family business'.

Tom O'Neill felt strongly that for the team concept to work effectively, allowing almost an entrepreneurial culture to develop, the day-to-day management of the teams must be left completely to the respective team leader. Corporate management, he reasoned, should concentrate on whether a team was achieving its output targets – the detail of what each team member was doing each minute of each day should only be of concern at the team level. This approach to the team leader concept has enabled Barr & Stroud to eliminate several tiers of management, with 22 of the previously existing 40 senior managers being included in the redundancy and early retirement programme (you could say that there are now 22 fewer people around who might have been tempted to use their position of authority to impede progress!).

All manufacturing personnel now report directly to one of 12 team leaders, who in turn report via the Manufacturing Manager for the site to the Pilkington Optronics Operations Director, Lawrie Rumens, making a total of only four levels in the hierarchy from shop floor worker to Operations Director inclusive; the number of people in each team averages about 20. Current plans are that as future products are developed one team leader will take responsibility for both the engineering and the manufacturing teams for a particular product, so that this person will need to have the potential to be a really top level manager. Once this has been established, Lawrie Rumens believes that the time may come when there will no longer be a need for his own job as Operations Director!

Such a major change in how the business is managed could not have been achieved without a considerable investment in training for the team leaders, to ensure that they were properly equipped to handle their wide-ranging responsibilities; a full-time union official was also included in this training programme. The task was seen as so important that a senior person was brought into the personnel function specifically to manage people development. Most of the training was carried out on-site in a series of evening sessions, with senior management personally conducting the training sessions. An interesting innovation is that wherever possible each element of the training programme had first to be cost-justified using a procedure similar to that used for approving capital expenditure, and a follow-up procedure was introduced to ascertain whether the planned benefits were in fact being achieved. Barr & Stroud soon hope to achieve formal recognition of their efforts to make the best use of their people resource, through the British Government's coveted 'Investor in People' award.

Perhaps the most encouraging sign that they are succeeding in involving their people better than ever before is the transformation that has occurred in the industrial relations climate. This had always been, to put it mildly, 'difficult'. Now, any problems are nipped in the bud through a combination of frequent production meetings and a formal Friday afternoon team session to review any problems that have arisen during the week. Some of these team meetings have actually been taken over by the team members, with the team leader able to take a back seat and let them get on with it; significantly, most of the problems now raised are to do with production rather than 'welfare' matters.

The changes described above have enabled Barr & Stroud to achieve some impressive improvements. In the space of little more than two years the company's fortunes have been transformed: production lead times have been cut by a typical 50 per cent; delivery performance of around 90 per cent 'on-time' is now achieved consistently, compared with little better than 10 per cent previously; and, most significantly, last year the company made a respectable operating profit for the first time for many years.

In the case described here, it was the move to a greenfield site that provided the catalyst for a fundamental re-think of what organizational structure would be most appropriate to the company's future needs; but, as Barr & Stroud have found, the same approach *can* be applied just as effectively in an existing factory. As Lawrie Rumens comments: 'We have, in parallel, introduced similar changes at our North Wales company, PPE, with equally significant gains. You do not need a new site; what you *do* need is the management vision and the will to see it through'.

MONITORING WORLD-CLASS PERFORMANCE

Linked to Chapter 6, this chapter provides guidance on those aspects of monitoring manu-facturing performance that are likely to become increasingly relevant in a company aiming to be world-class. Although aimed primarily at those who are responsible for providing the information, it should also help senior management decide what additional information they should be asking for, particularly in respect to monitoring performance improvement. The chapter ends with a suggested procedure for improving the accuracy of your computer systems.

14.1 ACTIVITY-BASED COSTING

Many manufacturing companies are still using very much the same cost accounting conventions that they've used for years, with the cost of individual products being derived by calculating the product's direct labour and material costs, to which is added a proportion of manufacturing's overhead costs based on direct labour content. When such procedures were first introduced, direct labour was a significant element of the product cost and, since the pace of change in manufacturing was comparatively slow, this method of allocating overheads was quite reasonable and was cheap to operate. Unfortunately, over the years the proportion of total cost contributed by direct labour has steadily reduced to the point where it is now often no more than 15 per cent of total manufacturing costs; overheads, in contrast, are usually very much more significant, so that labour rates have to be increased by as much as 400–500 per cent. Add to that the rapid changes in manufacturing practices that typically occur when you are introducing world-class methods, and the problem becomes even more acute because overhead recovery rates that were calculated at the start of the financial year become increasingly unrealistic as the year progresses. Just consider, for example the effect of reducing direct labour hours during the course of the year by an average of 5 per cent (a modest improvement by world-class standards): if output remains the same, you will end up with a 5 per cent under-recovery of overheads. A similar problem occurs if you manage to reduce stocks of finished products by, say, 15 per cent (again, a modest reduction when you are introducing world-class methods): if sales are not increased correspondingly, then you will under-recover overheads because some of your sales are met from stock instead of by manufacturing new products whose direct labour element would have included an allocation of overhead costs.

If we were concerned solely with the financial reporting requirements, I'm sure that your accountants could find a way of living with these problems, if only to save all the time and cost involved in developing new and more realistic costing methods. However, from the world-class point of view that won't do. Inaccurate and even misleading costing information doesn't just distort the reporting of manufacturing performance, it can also have a serious impact on decision-making, as the example in Sec. 6.3 illustrates. As I said in Sec. 6.5: 'A world-class company must have information it can depend on'; that must include information about the true cost of manufacturing and it must show accurately the effect that any changes in the manufacturing process, introduced as part of the world-class improvement process, will have on true manufacturing cost. 'Activity-based costing' (ABC) is probably the most effective way of achieving this objective.

There's actually nothing particularly new or revolutionary about the *concepts* of ABC, as the following illustration will show. If you've read Chapter 10 you will recognize the example as the one used to illustrate the strategy review process; to save you looking back I'll repeat the relevant information here.

The company concerned designed and manufactured a wide variety of paint-spraying equipment, ranging from simple spray guns at one end of the scale to sophisticated computer-controlled painting installations at the other extreme; the sale of spares was an important contributor to profits. Management had decided that teamwork was an important prerequisite of any attempts to bring the company's operations up to world-class standard, and they therefore decided to restructure the company into a number of business teams, delegating authority for day-to-day operations as far as possible to the individual team leaders; seven teams were established, based on the main product families, supported by a central support team which provided services which couldn't readily be devolved to the individual business teams. The problems arose when they started to produce separate management accounts for each of the business teams, because of the way in which they initially allocated the costs of the central support team to the individual businesses, this being based on their proportion of total sales revenue. The Spares team, for example, objected to having to pay their full share of the central design and technical services department because they didn't use them to the same extent as the product manufacturing teams, nor were they willing to contribute to the central marketing and export sales costs, since they had their own sales force and distributor network; the Special Booths team objected to their charge for rent, rates, power, heating and light, because their highly sophisticated products only required a small part of the factory floor space and in any case, they said, much of the cost of their products was due to the high bought-out content, which included a small volume of expensive computer-based electronic equipment; and the two Contract Services teams pointed out that they didn't use the central design and technical services function at all. Every team, in fact, had a sound case for objecting to the way in which the central support team's costs were allocated, and in each case they could show that this could have a serious effect when they had to make decisions which would affect the future development of their particular business.

The accountants were therefore asked to look again at the way in which the central support costs were allocated. They decided that the best solution would be to look at each part of these costs and assess how and why they were generated, which business teams made use of their output and in what proportion relative to the use made by the other businesses; in ABC terms, what they did was to identify the 'cost drivers', so that they could allocate an appropriate proportion of the central support team's costs to the specific business teams that 'drove' those costs. Not all the central costs could be allocated in this way: the costs associated with the preparation of the company's financial reports and other Head Office costs such as the Executive Vice-President and the Vice-President, Finance, for example, couldn't be apportioned to individual businesses on the cost driver basis. However, these remaining costs were sufficiently small for them to be allocated on a sales revenue basis without any further objections being raised.

This new way of allocating overheads on a cost driver basis revealed for the first time that the Special Booths product family was operating at a loss, because they were responsible for incurring most of the company's Design and Technical Service costs. Once this was realized, a special team was set up to investigate urgently ways of making greater use of standard modules which would only require minor modification or 'add-ons' to satisfy customers' requirements; this enabled the design cost of future products to be reduced or, in those cases where use of the new standard modules wasn't feasible, highlighted the need to include any additional design and development costs in the quotation. The new way of allocating costs meant that pricing decisions could in future be based on a more accurate assessment of the true costs of satisfying a customer's requirements.

As I said earlier, there's nothing particularly new or revolutionary about these concepts, which form the basis for ABC; anyone who has experience of restructuring a business into separate operating divisions will already be familiar with the problems which arise in allocating central support costs, and will probably have solved them in very much the way I've described. All that ABC does is to take this process a stage further, allocating overhead costs in a similar way by identifying the appropriate cost drivers; where it differs is that it doesn't stop at the business team or divisional level, it takes the process right through to individual product families and, if necessary (for example to differentiate between the different machines and processes used), right through to the individual component processing stages. It can even be used to put a 'cost penalty' on the use of a critical resource, by applying what is usually referred to as the 'throughput accounting ratio'. How far you should take ABC will depend on your particular circumstances; what matters is providing information that is sufficiently accurate for making the 'right' decisions, and for monitoring performance realistically.

The Bibliography includes information on where you can find a more detailed description of the ABC method.

14.2 MONITORING LEAD TIME PERFORMANCE

If you are trying to improve lead time performance you will need to break the overall lead time down into its constituent parts. For example:

- *Time taken to process the order*: i.e. translating the customer's requirements into company terminology, completing any design or technical specification work, clearing credit control and entering the order details into the computer system. In many companies improvements in this area may well offer the best opportunity for reducing overall lead time.
- *Time taken to plan and to order materials*: i.e. telling the factory what it has to make and Purchasing what it has to buy, and the dates when the materials should be available; separate reports will be required for made-in and for bought-out. This is monitoring just the administrative stage, excluding the actual manufacturing or procurement time; if you find that, by the time information on what has to be ordered reaches Purchasing, there is insufficient time left to procure some of the long lead time materials, you may be able to get round this by introducing a pre-planning stage in which materials known to have a long lead time are specified as soon as practicable after receipt of the customer's order. This too will then need to be monitored.
- *Time taken to obtain materials from external suppliers*: this will typically be reported in the form of a histogram showing the proportion of materials for each lead time category (see Sec. 11.4 for an explanation of lead time categories).
- *Time taken by Goods Inwards and Inspection*: i.e. how long a delay is there between the time when a supplier delivers and the time when the delivery details are reported on the computer system as cleared and available for Production. Typically, this report will show the percentage of deliveries cleared within 'one', 'two', 'three', and 'over three' days; the results can conveniently be presented in the form of a pie chart. Simply letting it be known that you are monitoring the time taken at this stage will usually result in an immediate improvement!
- *Time taken by feeder shops*: e.g. the time taken to manufacture components in the machine shop, or to process them through the paint shop, in terms of the percentage achieved within the target number of days. An alternative report would be the percentage of the scheduled work completed each day or week.
- *Time taken in the assembly shop*: similar to the feeder shop's report.
- *Time taken by Despatch*: i.e. how long it takes from the time when the Despatch Department receives instructions to despatch to the time when the goods are delivered to the customer.

Figure 14.1 shows another type of analysis that can be particularly useful at the start of a project aimed at reducing both lead time and inventory. This is *not* a 'snapshot' of the different categories of current inventory: what it shows is the progressive build-up of cost from the time when *raw material* is received from suppliers, through the process of converting it into finished products, to the point when it leaves the finished goods store to be sent to a customer (average values are used throughout). The longer the lead time the higher the total factory cost will be, partly because of storage and space costs, but also because of the working capital that is locked up throughout the 43 days that the process takes; reducing lead time will, therefore, reduce the factory cost, but it's not always realized that how much it reduces it by will depend on which stage of the lead

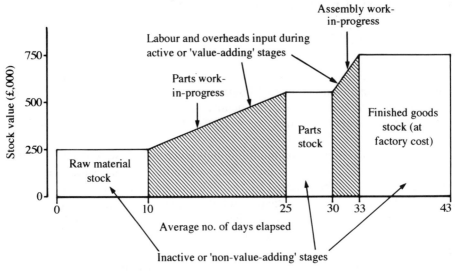

Figure 14.1 Cost build-up diagram.

time is reduced. For example, the first target would usually be the unshaded areas of the diagram, which are pure waste, since there is no value being added; however, from the stock reduction point of view, cutting stocks of finished goods by half would have three times the effect on stock value compared with cutting stocks by the same amount at the raw material stage, even though the effect on lead time would be the same. From the lead time reduction point of view, reducing finished goods stock would have no effect on lead time (other than, perhaps, increasing the risk of stock out, since once products reach the finished goods store they are available for customers). Looking at the diagram, you can see that the best compromise can be reached by starting at the end (i.e. where the cost has built up to its highest point), and then working backwards to find an area where any reduction will affect both lead time and inventory; in the example, the priority would probably be to eliminate the need for a parts stock, since this will have a noticeable effect on both lead time and stock investment.

14.3 MONITORING INVENTORY PERFORMANCE

The specific routine stock reports needed will depend on what you are trying to improve, but there are some general points worth making:

- Analyse stock reports under appropriate subheadings, such as Raw Material, Work-In-Progress and Finished Products, and/or split them by product group, or by business unit, or by location (e.g. finished products at each depot), or by category of stock (e.g. Top 200, Fast Moving, Medium, Slow Moving and Obsolete), the choice depending on what you are trying to improve or monitor. You can then produce a brief summary report for management to show progress to date, and use the full listing to identify problems which need to be attacked.

- Consider obtaining a computer listing of the top 50 stock items in descending order of stock value, to identify the stock items most worth looking at.
- As well as stock value, include in the listing the value of average usage per month and the number of average months' demand which the current stock level represents. You can then manually extract details of how many items have a current stock in excess of, say, six months' average demand, and include this in the summary report to management.
- Another useful report is a listing of all items with less than, say, two weeks' stock, shown in ascending order of number of days' stock in hand, i.e. out of stock items will be listed first. If you include details of outstanding requirements or orders, the report will also show where there is a shortage or back-order problem. Note that some of the items with a low reported stock may well be satisfactorily under control because they are included in a JIT call-off schedule.

More information on how to carry out a detailed analysis of inventory can be found in Sec. 11.4; although the procedures described there are intended for use at the start of a major stock reduction project, they include a number of different ways of categorizing stock, some of which may also prove useful for routine performance monitoring.

14.4 MONITORING SUPPLIER PERFORMANCE

Suppliers are an important resource of any world-class company, and their performance therefore needs to be closely monitored. For each of your main suppliers you should keep details of key information, such as:

- *Delivery performance*: what proportion of deliveries are made on time? If some deliveries are late, by how many days?
- *Quality performance*: has the supplier maintained a zero defects record? If not, what percentage of deliveries have been below the quality requirements? Has the quantity delivered always conformed with both your order and the supplier's advice note? What percentage of deliveries have been on a 'certificated supply' basis (i.e. the supplier guarantees that there are no defects and that the quantity is correct, so that you do not need to inspect the material on receipt)?
- *Improvement performance*: either working alone, or with your assistance, how successful has the supplier been in achieving continuous improvement (usually measured in terms of agreed price reductions)?

Most of these are so obvious that you may well be wondering why I have gone to the trouble of including them here. The reason is simple: although vendor rating procedures have been around for many years, and although most professionals in the purchasing field know all about them, I've very rarely seen them actually *used* on a regular and consistent basis. Usually someone has prepared a list of the measures he or she 'intends' to use, and sometimes they will have been used in a one-off snapshot analysis: a world-class company must go further and produce the information regularly *and then use it*, at least for the top dozen or so suppliers.

There's just one snag: because so few people have used vendor rating analyses in the past, few computer packages make provision for them. You may well, therefore, have to arrange for some programming work to be done, and this could take time. In the meantime, consider collecting as much of the key information as you can from the data already within your computer system, and then finishing the analysis manually, at least for the top dozen or so suppliers with whom you want to introduce partnership sourcing arrangements (this latter aspect, and some other elements you need to take into account when assessing suppliers' capabilities and performance, are described in more depth in Sec. 3.8). Another reason why you may find yourself having to do much of the vendor rating manually is the difficulty in defining 'good performance' with sufficient rigour to enable an adequate computer-based system to be developed. For example, suppose your machine shop scraps some of the material which had previously been supplied correct to specification and on the stated date for delivery: you ask the supplier to provide a replacement batch of the material in five days instead of allowing them the usual four weeks – if they actually take eight days they will have done you a favour, but a computer rating system would probably chalk up penalty points for a 'late' delivery!

14.5 OTHER MONITORING REPORTS

14.5.1 Productivity Improvement

I described in Secs. 11.2 and 11.3 two important aspects of productivity improvement that a world-class manufacturer will usually need to monitor routinely: an analysis of production delays and of what action has been taken to stop them recurring; and an analysis of set-up times, to show progress is being made in reducing them. To save you turning back to Chapter 11 the relevant points are summarized here.

- *Analysis of production delays*: this is similar to the type of 'down-time' analysis which is used in many companies, but instead of concentrating on either labour or machine productive time lost, the emphasis is on delays which interrupt the smooth flow of production in accordance with the production plan. For example, suppose that a planned job cannot be started because a tool is missing, but the labour and/or machine resource can be switched to another job: this would not be recorded in a traditional down-time analysis since the resources are 'usefully' deployed to another job which will contribute to the 'standard hours' produced; it *would* however be recorded on the type of Production Delay form that I prefer, because a job could not be started at the planned time. The distinction is very important if you are trying to cut production lead time, as opposed to maximizing resource utilization and accounting for bonus earnings, which are often the main purposes of down-time analysis.

   A production delay form should be prepared *by the operator* whenever a delay to planned production occurs. The purpose of the form is to *expose the problem* that has led to the delay; the form should be passed to a central control point (such as the Quality Manager), who then has the task of deciding why the problem has arisen and taking appropriate action not just to correct the immediate cause of the problem, *but also to try to prevent similar delays recurring in the future*.

   A summary table should also be prepared at weekly or monthly intervals (depending on the number arising), to show the types of problem that cause most of the delays. This table will show you where a fundamental weakness in your systems or procedures needs to be overcome.

- *Set-up times*: if one of your objectives is to reduce the productive time lost due to set-up changes (as will often be the case), you should get the operator and setter to record the time actually taken to change the set-ups (but only where it really matters, i.e. on key machines). The type of record needed can be incorporated in a traditional down-time analysis, by including headings such as 'waiting for setter', 'waiting for instructions etc.' or 'changing set-up'. A weekly summary should then be produced showing, for example, 'average set-up time' and 'number of set-ups taking more than 30 minutes' (both are important). If you start a record like this you will find that the number of set-ups taking longer than 30 minutes (or whatever other cut-off figure you have chosen) will drop dramatically, because everyone knows that there will be an inquest if this time is exceeded. Since you will thus have eliminated most of the extreme times, the overall average will also drop notice-ably – and all this before you've even started to introduce quick changeover tech-niques!

14.5.2 Quality Improvement

You may well already be producing most of the key quality performance measurements. If not, ask yourself whether you should be. Typical reports include:

- *Scrap and reject analyses*: these should be broken down to show the type of quality problem, its source, the cost of re-work and/or cost of scrapped materials, etc. An additional world-class requirement that is unlikely to be on your existing reports is 'lead time impact'.
- *Customer returns*: showing the reason for return as well as all the information included in the 'Scrap and reject analysis' (the item may have been returned because the customer's requirement has changed: if there is nothing wrong with the item you shouldn't include it in your defective quality analysis). Customer returns due to unsatisfactory quality should always provoke an inquest – since world-class com-panies normally operate a zero defects policy (at least, as far as their external customers are concerned) you need to find out what failure in your control procedures allowed the faulty product to reach your customer.
- *Concession notes*: a world-class company should always produce a report giving details of any concession notes raised, since these imply that waste in one form or another has occurred. Either the materials concerned were in fact perfectly good enough, but the specification was wrong (in which case you may have been paying for a tighter specification material than really necessary); or the material can be used, but some additional work will be required by your employees (even if you arrange to re-charge this to the supplier a delay is likely to result); or you have agreed to accept material that you know is not up to the standard you really require. More often than not concession notes are raised because you are so desperate for the material (the supplier has probably delivered late) that you would rather let it slip through than suffer further delay. Whichever is the reason, it shouldn't be acceptable to a world-class company, which is why you should examine reports of concessions made with considerable suspicion.

14.5.3 Presentation

Many of the reports suggested above will contain a great deal of information. That's fine if you are a member of an improvement team and are looking for evidence that will help you identify what action you should take in order to improve some aspect of performance. But many of the reports are far too detailed to be of much use to management, who only want an overview of your progress. Management reports should normally be clear, concise and, wherever possible, presented in the form of graphs, histograms, pie charts etc. In most cases they should show how things have changed over time (by providing comparison with previous periods) as well as progress towards the targets set by management (by including a target line on the graph).

Most companies these days have a desktop publishing system somewhere in the organization. I've found it well worthwhile to arrange for improvement teams to have access to a DTP facility in order to improve the appearance of the more important graphs and information tables they produce, particularly when these are included in the regular weekly or monthly reporting routines. Illogical as it may be, it is a fact of business life that a professionally presented document is more likely to be looked at and acted on than one which looks amateurish or relies solely on a typed table of figures.

14.5.4 How Far Should You Go?

When the subject of monitoring world-class performance is raised, you'll often find that top management instinctively want to measure 'waste'. 'After all', they say, 'attacking waste is at the heart of the world-class philosophy, so surely we ought to be measuring our current waste routinely, so that we can see where action is needed, and so that we can monitor the progress we are making towards eliminating it'. The problem is that 'waste' is such an all embracing subject that it can appear in every aspect of your operations right across the company: there's no way that you could hope to measure it in all its manifestations. So how do you whittle the possibilities down? The answer is, don't try; a much better way is to approach the problem from another direction, as I explained in Sec. 6.3: '... the whole point of reporting on manufacturing performance should be to enable management to see that progress is being made towards achieving the goals they have set, and to identify where improvements are feasible or necessary. This means that you need to introduce new methods of performance measurement which satisfy these management requirements, and at the same time you need to review existing performance measures to ensure that those that are irrelevant or counter-productive are as far as possible either modified or removed.'

You'll probably find that although most of your existing monitoring reports will need to be retained, some can usually be eliminated as no longer being relevant and some *should* be eliminated because, in a world-class setting, they could be misleading. I've summarized, above, some of the additional monitoring aspects that I've found to be most frequently needed. Details of where you can find many more ideas on what you should or could monitor are included in the Bibliography. But do remember: excessive administrative procedures are, in themselves, a waste; be very careful not to overdo the monitoring.

14.6 PROBLEMS IN COLLECTING AND ANALYSING DATA

In all the areas covered in Secs. 14.2–14.5, if you're unsure about what output you are likely to get in response to a particular request, it's a good idea to ask for a simpler or summary report first of all, so that you can get a feel for the size of the problem. For example, if you're searching for information about stocks, you could ask for a summary table to be produced as a first step, showing the value and number of items in stock sub-divided by both department or location and by category of stock (i.e. raw material, work-in-progress and finished stock): the results will show you which combinations of department and stock category are worth looking at in more detail.

Be wary of any obsolete stock reports that may already be produced: an accountant usually defines an item of stock as obsolete if there's been no transaction for that item over a given period (such as 12 months or, perhaps, two years), which is not suitable for a world-class project team that is working on the reduction of stock. For example, suppose that you have 500 obsolete white widgets in stock: as a result of the team's efforts you manage to get rid of 10 of them by painting them grey – it's not worth painting more since you only sell about five a year. You are left with 490 of the obsolete white widgets which you still have to do something about. Unfortunately they have now disappeared from the obsolete stock report because there has been a recent transaction, i.e. your issue of 10 for painting grey; it will be a year or more before the item appears on the obsolete stock report again!

I once heard of an even worse case: a team working on obsolete stock managed to get rid of the bulk of the stock of one item by selling them off at a discount; unfortunately, the stock issue was interpreted by a planner as a true demand and a replacement batch was ordered! (It wouldn't have happened if the planner had been a member of the team – as one of the owners of the problem he certainly should have been.)

The example of the 490 remaining widgets disappearing from the obsolete stock report shows how careful you need to be when specifying your requirements for a report to be generated from information held in your computer system's database. The problem could have been avoided if the request was to:

> Produce a list, in descending order of stock value, of all items for which stock currently exists and for which there have been no issues within the last twelve months, or for which current stocks exceed the last twelve months' usage.

As well as overcoming the problem referred to above, it would also make sure that you don't clutter up the list with obsolete items that are still included on the database, but which are irrelevant to your problem, since no stock exists. To help you in your search for why the items have become obsolete, it would also be useful to request:

> For each item, list each higher level item or assembly on which it is used.

In practice this information may be difficult to extract as the database may only include details of current product structures. You will need to consult your computer database manager to find out if previous product structures can still be accessed.

14.7 IMPROVING THE ACCURACY OF YOUR COMPUTER SYSTEMS

14.7.1 Identifying Problem Causes

You'll probably find that most of the problems arise because the various users of the control systems are so compartmentalized that they don't understand how the way in which they use their part of the system affects others. A good way of identifying why things are going wrong is to arrange a group meeting at which the 'owner' of each part of the system explains his or her part of the system to the others. The owners are likely to be:

- Order Entry
- Planning/Scheduling/Progress
- Purchasing
- Goods Received/Inspection
- Despatch
- Computer Department (responsible for system design and support)

and there may be others, such as Product Design and Database Management.

It helps if, prior to the meeting, each owner prepares display charts showing the system flow procedures and samples of documents for his or her part of the system. At the meeting, each owner in turn talks the group through the part of the systems for which they are responsible: the others listen to the explanation, taking notes and interrupting whenever further clarification is needed. After each of the presentations, when the owner has finished the explanation the group holds a brainstorming session, in which everyone is invited to suggest ways in which potential problems or inaccuracies might be generated as a result of the operating methods and procedures which have just been explained to them.

You can expect to end up with an average of about ten potential sources of problems from each owner. When these are consolidated for all parts of the system and duplications have been eliminated, you'll probably end up with at least 30 and often as many as 50 different sources of problems and inaccuracies. Quite a few of these will be straightforward differences of understanding as to how data in the system should be interpreted, and these can generally be cleared up immediately as a direct result of the discussions. Others will require changes to the procedures, or even to the computer programs: the latter may well take months or even a year or two to resolve, in which case you will probably have to introduce some temporary manual procedures to overcome the problems you have identified.

14.7.2 Common Causes of Problems

Most inaccuracies in inventory and planning data are caused by problems of interpretation, which should be resolved by the procedure described above. However, you should watch out for three other types of problem that often occur.

A common source of inventory errors is that wrong parts are ordered because of failure to process Engineering Change Notes (ECNs) properly. For example, a company that I was once involved with found that, following a staff change in the Accounts

Department, ECNs had stuck part way through their circulation route: for months Assembly had been attempting to manufacture products using the latest issue of drawings, while Planning had been ordering materials and components on the basis of out of date bills of materials because the ECNs had never reached them. The result, inevitably, was delays in the assembly programme while incorrect kits were sorted out. The problem arose because no one person had been made responsible for checking that ECNs were completing their circulation within an agreed time-scale. Perhaps this was rather an extreme case, but many companies do generate problems for themselves by failing to process ECNs promptly. When you are investigating inventory problems, it is well worth checking that *your* engineering change procedure is working properly.

Another irritating but common cause of hold-ups is shortages of items such as fasteners or, for electrical equipment manufacturers, cable and electrical accessories. Because these are often issued to manufacturing in bulk on an 'on demand' basis, new design specifications or unexpected demand patterns are often not picked up until the material is needed for production. The solution may be to short-circuit normal ordering procedures by introducing Kanbans (see Sec. 3.7) or to invite a selected supplier to take on responsibility for topping up ready-use stocks on the 'Supermarket' principle (see Sec. 3.8).

The third problem that often arises is caused by the holding of so-called 'good' stock which is in fact unsuitable for use. For example, a manufacturer of up-market lighting systems was very particular about the surface finish of reflectors that were built into their products: assembly operators were required to reject reflectors sent to them which in their opinion were not up to the required standard. When this happened, the parts rejected were returned to stores and replacements were issued. However, because the judgement as to what was satisfactory was based on someone's view of 'aspect', the machine shop would sometimes make a different judgement and refused to accept the write-off as a charge on them. Stores had no authority to write the parts off themselves and so the parts ended up in limbo, retained on the stock records as 'available stock', but in practice unacceptable to the Assembly Department. Once the problem had been identified the solution was simple: when disputes arose in future they were referred to the Quality Control Manager who had the necessary authority to resolve the dispute and, if necessary, allocate the costs to the appropriate department.

This reluctance to write off damaged stock is quite common, particularly when the parts have been damaged while in the care of the Stores Department, perhaps by bad handling or unsatisfactory storage conditions. When you are trying to clear up inventory problems it's always advisable to assume that this is the case in your own stores and you should, therefore, ask your stores staff to make a list of all parts which they think might fall into this category. But don't forget also to ask them *why* the damage has occurred and what can be done to help them avoid it happening in the future.

LEAD TIME ANALYSIS

The procedure for analysing lead times and illustrating the results in various ways is explained in Sec. 11.2. This appendix describes the process in more detail. The relevant figures from Chapter 11 are repeated in this appendix and the original figure numbers are included in the description for ease of reference.

A1.1 THE PROBLEM

Your company currently quotes 8 weeks delivery, but the sales force have been complaining that they are losing orders because of poor delivery performance. Management have asked you to investigate whether there really is a problem, or whether the sales force are using just a few instances of late delivery as an excuse for their failure to meet sales targets.

As a first step you decide to collect data covering all deliveries made in a typical week. You find that, in the week selected, 175 deliveries were made. For each of these deliveries you have worked out how many days elapsed from when the customer's order was received until the date when the goods were delivered. The results are shown in Fig. A.1 (= Fig. 11.3). You now need to present these results in a diagram that will enable management to see at a glance whether or not there is a problem.

A1.2 ANALYSING THE DATA

Clearly, it would be silly to try to prepare any sort of diagram in which each of the 175 values was plotted separately. We must, therefore, group the data into some convenient

56	91	59	62	64	50	53	119	55	59	63	59
69	95	68	102	66	46	65	65	36	50	64	92
68	55	45	39	66	67	53	56	62	61	88	91
47	62	33	65	85	70	55	71	65	69	81	59
100	82	63	62	74	45	86	60	61	76	50	61
101	54	77	80	58	44	71	56	82	49	108	61
64	58	76	78	97	66	77	67	60	83	60	63
89	71	107	79	51	87	50	79	90	80	58	81
67	52	59	98	57	46	58	40	69	72	72	70
70	74	84	94	83	99	52	57	57	64	57	49
75	73	74	49	84	68	78	99	63	64	102	67
50	60	79	75	98	83	61	76	58	105	52	73
51	81	37	74	59	62	66	69	67	87	65	42
69	69	48	60	94	59	68	65	90	72	63	56
64	56	69	68	61	54	88					

Figure A.1 Lead time analysis: data for exercise.

form, the ideal number of groups for this sort of diagram being somewhere between 12 and 20. Lead times in this example are quoted in weeks, so that it makes sense for us to group the results in terms of weeks. A delivery that took 6 days would therefore go in the group '1 to 7 days', i.e. '1 week', while a delivery that took 68 days would go in the group '64 to 70 days', i.e. '10 weeks'. You should prepare an analysis form, as shown in Fig. A.2 (= Fig. 11.4), with one column for the range of days and another column for

1	2	3	4	5	6	7
					Cumulative	Percentage
			Total	Cumulative	total	of total
Days	Weeks	Occurrences	occurrences	total	percentage	occurrences
29–35	5	I	1			
36–42	6	JHT	5			
43–49	7	JHT JHT	10			
50–56	8	JHT JHT JHT JHT II	22			
57–63	9	JHT JHT JHT JHT JHT JHT JHT II	37			
64–70	10	JHT JHT JHT JHT JHT JHT JHT I	36			
71–77	11	JHT JHT JHT IIII	19			
78–84	12	JHT JHT JHT II	17			
85–91	13	JHT JHT I	11			
92–98	14	JHT II	7			
99–105	15	JHT II	7			
106–112	16	II	2			
113–119	17	I	1			

Figure A.2 Lead time analysis (1).

the number of weeks. Both columns are necessary because it makes it easier for you to analyse the data if your form is, like the data table, in terms of days, while management, who are more interested in overall lead time, will want to see the results in terms of weeks.

Now complete columns 1 and 2, as shown in Fig. A.2 (= Fig. 11.4). Note that the first group of data starts at 5 weeks (29 to 35 days) because the lowest value in the table is 33 days (this is all right when you're analysing the data, but the diagram, which we'll be coming to shortly, should normally start at zero). The largest value in the table is 119, so the last group you'll need in the analysis form is 17 weeks (113 to 119 days).

We are now ready to start analysing the data. This is how you do it:

- Take each value in the table in turn and put a mark (|) in the appropriate space in column 3: for example, the first value is 56, so you put a '|' alongside the range '50 to 56'.
- As you enter each mark in the analysis, make sure you cross out the value in the table, so that if you are interrupted you know where you have got to.
- Whenever you get to the point where you have a set of four marks (i.e. ||||), your fifth mark in that class range should be drawn as a diagonal line across the first four marks (this makes it easier to add up the number of values in each class range, because you can add up in fives instead of getting eye strain trying to add up a lot of single marks!).
- If you enter your marks neatly, you will see a picture gradually appearing which will enable you to see the pattern of delivery performance (in the form of a histogram) even before you draw the final lead time diagram.
- Finally, add up the number of marks in each range and enter the result in column 4.
- As a check, add up the figures in this total column; if the result is anything other than 175, you have made a mistake somewhere! If, as is usually the case, you are only one or two out, don't worry, it's unlikely to affect your final diagram too much.

Note that I have said you should take each value in the table in turn. Some people prefer to look through the table for values in the first range, then look through again for values in the second range, and so on. I don't like that method, firstly because I think it takes longer and secondly because it's easier to make mistakes if you do it that way.

That completes the initial analysis; the remaining columns will be needed later, to prepare data for plotting the cumulative frequency distribution diagram.

A1.3 HISTOGRAM OF LEAD TIMES

You *could* stop your analysis at this point and present the results as a simple histogram: you can see what this would look like in column 3 of Fig. A.2 (= Fig. 11.4), by turning the analysis form on its side. Such a histogram would enable you to draw several conclusions:

- Lead times are typically in the range 8 to 11 weeks
- Only a small proportion of deliveries are made in less than 8 weeks
- A significant proportion of deliveries are made more than 11 weeks after the order is received (i.e. 3 or more weeks later than promised)
- Some deliveries can be as much as 9 weeks late

However, with only a little more work you can present the results in a way that will give management some useful additional information; not only will this give them a better understanding of the current situation, it will also help them decide just how serious the problem is. To do this you will need to draw a cumulative frequency diagram; the procedure for this is described below.

A1.4 CUMULATIVE FREQUENCY DIAGRAM

To produce a cumulative frequency diagram, first extend the analysis table shown in Fig. A.2 (= Fig. 11.4) by completing columns 5 and 6, following Steps 1 and 2 of the procedure below; the results are shown in Fig. A.3 (= Fig. 11.5).

Step 1 From column 4, work out the cumulative total and enter the results in column 5 (1 + 5 = 6, 6 + 10 = 16, 16 + 22 = 38 etc.).

Step 2 From column 5, calculate the cumulative total as a percentage of the grand total of 175 (1 × 100 ÷ 175 = 0.6, 6 × 100 ÷ 175 = 3.4, 16 × 100 ÷ 175 = 9.1 etc.), and enter the results in column 6.

The cumulative frequency diagram can then be plotted, following Steps 3 and 4 below; the results are shown in Fig. A.4 (= Fig. 11.6).

Step 3 Plot the S curve, as shown in Fig. A.4 (= Fig. 11.6). You should always join up the plotted points with a 'best fit' smooth curve, *not* with a series of short straight lines. The sample of 175 values you have used to plot the points isn't

1	2	3	4	5	6	7
					Cumulative	Percentage
			Total	Cumulative	total	of total
Days	Weeks	Occurrences	occurrences	total	percentage	occurrences
29–35	5	I	1	1	0.6	0.6
36–42	6	ЖТ	5	6	3.4	2.9
43–49	7	ЖТ ЖТ	10	16	9.1	5.7
50–56	8	ЖТ ЖТ ЖТ ЖТ II	22	38	21.7	12.6
57–63	9	ЖТ ЖТ ЖТ ЖТ ЖТ ЖТ ЖТII	37	75	42.9	21.1
64–70	10	ЖТ ЖТ ЖТ ЖТ ЖТ ЖТ ЖТ I	36	111	63.4	20.6
71–77	11	ЖТ ЖТ ЖТ IIII	19	130	74.3	10.9
78–84	12	ЖТ ЖТ ЖТ II	17	147	84.0	9.7
85–91	13	ЖТ ЖТ I	11	158	90.3	6.3
92–98	14	ЖТ II	7	165	94.3	4.0
99–105	15	ЖТ II	7	172	98.3	4.0
106–112	16	II	2	174	99.4	1.1
113–119	17	I	1	175	100	0.6

Figure A.3 Lead time analysis (2).

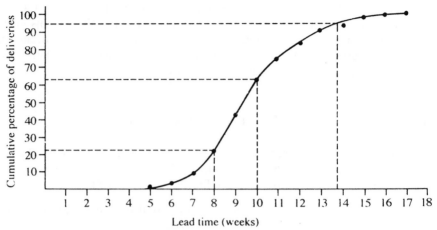

Figure A.4 Current lead time performance.

large enough to give an accurate plot at the beginning and end of the curve; drawing a smooth curve will iron out these 'sampling errors' and give a truer representation of what is likely to happen over a longer period.

Step 4 Finally, draw the dotted lines, as shown in Fig. A.4 (= Fig. 11.6), to make it easy for management to draw conclusions: make some intelligent guesses as to what sort of supplementary questions they are likely to ask. For example, since the current quoted lead time is 8 weeks, select 8 on the horizontal scale and draw a line vertically until it reaches the curve, then continue the line horizontally from this point until it reaches the other scale: you can now read off from the diagram that 'only 22 per cent of orders are delivered within the quoted 8 weeks lead time'.

You can also start at a selected point on the vertical scale line, e.g. at 95 per cent, and, by reversing the above procedure, draw the conclusion that 'on present performance, if the company wanted to be confident of meeting the delivery promise on at least 95 per cent of orders it would have to quote 14 weeks in place of the current 8 weeks'.

GLOSSARY

Benchmarking   World-class means striving to be the 'best' in your particular field; the benchmarking process quantifies what 'best' means for you. The first step in the procedure is to establish an appropriate set of product features or performance characteristics, these typically being based on factors that potential customers might take into account when assessing competing products; you then assess how your products and those of each of your main competitors rate against each of the performance criteria on your list; finally, a theoretical 'benchmark' product is established consisting of the best rating for each of the competitive criteria.

Cause and effect diagram   *see* Fishbone diagram.

CNC machine tool   A machine tool fitted with computer numerical control equipment, i.e. a machine tool in which the operations are controlled by computer software; this can be input at the machine itself or remotely through 'direct numerical control (DNC)'.

Competitive benchmarking   *see* Benchmarking.

Delivery performance   A measure of the proportion of customers' orders that are actually delivered on time. Normal practice in many companies is to define 'on time' as the delivery date promised to the customer (which may be later than requested); world-class practice, in contrast, requires 'on time' to be defined in terms of when the customer actually requires delivery.

Economic batch quantity (EBQ)   As batch size is increased, the cost of set-up and ordering per unit *decreases*, but the cost of holding items surplus to immediate requirements in stock *increases*. The EBQ is the batch size for which the cost of holding stock is equal to the batch set-up and ordering cost.

Fishbone diagram   Also known as a 'cause and effect diagram' or as an Ishikawa diagram, the 'fishbone diagram' is a graphical method of organizing a brainstorming session in which the problem being studied is analysed into a logical tree pattern; an initial set of five or six possible categories of causes is further subdivided through several iterations of sub-categories, the objective being to ensure that all categories are considered thoroughly. The term 'fishbone' originated because the completed diagram looks rather like the skeleton of a fish.

Failure modes and effects analysis (FMEA)   A procedure for analysing *at the design stage* ways in which a component or assembly might fail in service, and then assessing what the consequences of such failures might be.

Ishikawa diagram   *see* Fishbone diagram.

Just-in-time (JIT)   The aim of the just-in-time approach is to provide a fast, reliable and flexible response to customers' requirements at least cost and with minimum dependence on inventory. There is no specific set of techniques that comprises JIT: *Any* technique or procedure that helps achieve these objectives can be considered to be part of the approach, particularly if it attacks waste and involves the whole workforce.

The term 'just-in-time' is believed to have been coined originally by Western observers of the Toyota system in the 1960s, the name reflecting the part which was most visible, i.e. the continual stream of suppliers' lorries delivering materials (often direct to the assembly track) 'just in time' to meet Production's requirements. Early applications of JIT in the West often failed to live up to expectations because they concentrated on these supplier aspects, without attempting to introduce the other aspects of the true JIT philosophy within the company's own factory.

Kaizen   The Japanese term for continuous improvement activities carried out by teams in the workplace. In the West, Kaizen teams are usually referred to as 'quality circles' or 'continuous improvement groups'.

Lead time   The time required to satisfy a customer's order, starting from the point when the order is received and ending at the point when the customer receives delivery (or, where appropriate, when the equipment has been installed and accepted by the customer).

Lean production   An approach originally developed by the Massachusetts Institute of Technology. Although similar in many respects to just-in-time, 'lean production' places particular emphasis on the importance of teamwork, on improving the flexibility of both equipment and people, and on maintaining a commitment to total quality. The aim is to provide a rapid and efficient response to meeting customers needs, while at the same time continually striving to minimize the resources needed to achieve this objective.

MRP   'Materials requirements planning', the process of breaking a customer's order down into its constituent parts in order to determine all the necessary material and processing requirements; in most computer-based MRP systems the material requirements are normally netted off against available stock, and 'required by' dates are established for material delivery and for each process step by off-setting 'standard' lead times from the date when the completed order is due for delivery.

The term 'MRP2' is used as an abbreviation for 'manufacturing resources planning': this refers to the complete suite of computer programs for managing the manufacturing process, of which materials requirements planning is one part.

National Vocational Qualification (NVQ)   An examination framework in England for providing competence-based qualifications for most jobs and professions.

Pareto Principle   Also known as 'the 80/20 rule'. The Pareto Principle is named after a 19th century Italian socio-economist, Vilfredo Pareto, who originally used the technique to demonstrate how the bulk of Italy's wealth at that time was owned by a small minority of the population. The example of the Pareto Principle best known in industry is with inventories, where a typical analysis will show that 20 per cent of the items stocked will account for around 80 per cent of the total value of the inventory. The Pareto diagram is similar to the cumulative frequency diagram used to illustrate lead time performance (see Fig. 11.16), but with the horizontal as well as the vertical scale expressed in percentage form.

The Pareto Principle is most important when planning improvement activities, because it demonstrates that the bulk of the desired improvement can be achieved by concentrating the improvement activities on just those few areas that are most significant.

Problem ranking process (PRP)   A type of market research; PRP concentrates on finding out which improvements in your products and services would be most likely to influence potential customers in their future purchasing decisions. The procedure is to prepare a long list of 'problem statements' (i.e. 'What's wrong with our products and services?') from the customer's point of view, and then to get a sample of customers to rank the importance of each.

Product life cycle   A graph of sales against time, showing how demand for a product changes through its life cycle, i.e. the period from initial launch to the point where it is classified as obsolete. The life cycle is usually considered as having four stages: market entry, rapid growth, maturity and decay.

Reliability-centred maintenance (RCM)   RCM is a maintenance planning procedure that enables you to target your maintenance resources precisely. Its effects are to concentrate attention where it really matters, because the process is based on a detailed consideration of what would be both the safety and the economic implications of failure: if these are not significant, RCM concludes that *no* preventive maintenance is required and this usually means that maintenance costs can be significantly reduced. Because the process is centred on the *consequences* of failure, RCM also recognizes that maintenance needs to be considered in terms of the operating environment of each item of equipment, in contrast to traditional preventive maintenance practice in which the item is considered independently from its operating context.

Scottish Vocational Qualification (SVQ)   The equivalent in Scotland of the English National Vocational Qualifications.

'SMED'   Single minute exchange of dies: a procedure to dramatically reduce machine set-up times, developed by Shigeo Shingo, the Japanese consultant and production engineer who played a major part in the early developments of world-class practice at Toyota. The SMED procedure involves analysing the elements of a set-up task into 'internal' activities that can only be carried out when the process is stopped, and 'external' activities that do not need the process to be stopped (such as collecting tools from the stores); the time the machine is out of action for set-up change can usually be cut by over 40 per cent, and at little cost, simply by arranging for all external activities to be carried out in advance.

Further reductions to under ten minutes (the 'single minutes' referred to in the technique's name) will usually require the conversion of internal activities to external, for example by introducing pre-set tooling; whether or not such further reductions are worthwhile may depend on the costs involved, but account should also be taken of the value in world-class terms of the increased flexibility achieved when batch sizes can be cut as a result of shorter set-up times.

Statistical process control (SPC)   The application of statistical quality control principles to provide advance warning of potential processing problems, so that corrective action can be taken *before* the problem actually occurs.

'SWOT'   An analysis of strengths, weaknesses, opportunities and threats; usually conducted as part of the strategy review process.

Taguchi Methods   A term used to describe a number of techniques developed by Japanese statistician Dr Genichi Taguchi, in particular: the 'quadratic loss function'; the 'parameter design concept'; and, the most widely used, his 'design of experiments' techniques. Although the last of these is used extensively for troubleshooting quality problems, at the heart of Taguchi's Methods is his belief that the quality and reliability of a product is largely determined at the design stage; his methodology is therefore concerned primarily with the routine optimization of product and process *prior* to manufacture.

Total employee involvement (TEI)   The process of involving the whole workforce in the continuous improvement process, for example through 'continuous improvement groups' or 'quality circles'. The process also involves empowering people, by delegating authority to take decisions and implement improvements as far as possible to improvement team members.

Total productive maintenance (TPM)   The involvement of operators in the process of reducing the waste caused by equipment either breaking down *or* operating below par. At the heart of TPM philosophy is the belief that equipment failures can be dramatically reduced if the people who use the equipment can be taught to recognize signs that something isn't quite right.

Total quality (TQ)   'Total quality' (also referred to by many people as 'total quality management') can be thought of as a 'quality creation' approach, in which every member of the workforce, from Chief Executive to shop floor worker, is encouraged to accept personal responsibility for 'getting it right, first time, every time'. The TQ philosophy is based on *defect prevention* in place of the traditional *defect detection and correction*, the concept being that customers will only get full value for money if this hidden cost of quality is eliminated.

The TQ concepts played a key part in bringing about the 'Japanese Miracle', thanks largely to American gurus such as Dr Deming: his ideas were eagerly adopted in Japan even though they had previously been ignored in the USA.

Waste   In a world-class context 'waste' is usually defined as 'any activity that does not add value'.

BIBLIOGRAPHY

GENERAL

Garrahan, P. and P. Stewart: 'Nissan Enigma: Flexibility at Work in a Local Economy', Mansell, London, 1992.

Goldratt, E. and J. Cox: 'The Goal', North River Press, New York, 1984.

Schonberger, R. J.: 'World Class Manufacturing: The Lessons of Simplicity Applied', Free Press, New York, 1986.

CHAPTERS 2 AND 10: STRATEGY AND MARKETING

Dealtry, T. R.: 'Dynamic SWOT Analysis: Guide for Developers'. Obtainable from Prof. T. R. Dealtry, Dynamic SWOT Associates, Prince's Corner, Harborne Park Road, Birmingham B17 0DE, England (021 427 8491).

Department of Trade and Industry: 'Competitive Manufacturing: A practical approach to the development of a manufacturing strategy', IFS International, Bedford, UK, 1991.

Green, T.: 'Marketing – Making it Work for You'. A do-it-yourself business development pack developed in conjunction with the UK's Department of Trade and Industry, 1993. For more information, telephone Active Marketing Works Limited (UK): (0789 450160).

McNair, C. J. and K. H. J. Leibfried: 'Benchmarking: A Tool For Continuous Improvement', Harper Business, New York, 1993.

Porter, M. E.: 'Competitive Strategy: Techniques for Analysing Industries and Competitors', Free Press, New York, 1980.

Watson, G. H.: 'Strategic Benchmarking: How to Rate Your Company's Performance Against the World's Best', Wiley, Chichester, UK, 1993.

CHAPTERS 3 AND 11: JUST-IN-TIME

Burbidge, J.L.: 'The Introduction of Group Technology'. Heinemann, London, 1975.

Just In Time!, video, BBC Enterprises Ltd, London.

Lagadec, P.: 'Preventing Chaos in a Crisis: Strategies for Prevention, Control and Damage Limitation', McGraw-Hill, London, 1993.

Maskell, B. H.: 'Just-in-Time', Hitchcock, 1989.

Mather, H.: 'Competitive Manufacturing', Prentice-Hall, Englewood Cliffs, NJ, 1988.

Moubray, J.: 'Reliability-centered Maintenance', Butterworth-Heinemann, Oxford, 1991.

Nowlan, F. S. and H. F. Heap: 'Reliability-Centered Maintenance, Report Ref. AD-A066-579, 1978'. This report, prepared by United Airlines staff, was sponsored by the US Defense Department; copies may be obtained from The National Technical Information Service, U.S. Department of Commerce, Springfield, VA 22161.

The Partnership Principle, video, Business in the Community, London, 1992.

Partnership Sourcing Ltd: 'Making Partnership Sourcing Happen', The Confederation of British Industry, London, 1992.

Schonberger, R. J.: 'Japanese Manufacturing Techniques – Nine Hidden Lessons in Simplicity', Appendix: The Kanban System, pp. 219–238, Free Press, New York, 1982.

Shingo, S.: 'A Revolution in Manufacturing: The SMED System', Productivity Press, Cambridge, MA, 1985.

Suzaki, K.: 'The New Manufacturing Challenge: Techniques for Continuous Improvement', Free Press, New York, 1987.

Szymankiewicz, J., J. McDonald and K. Turner: 'Solving Business Problems by Simulation', McGraw-Hill, London, 1988.

U.S. Department of Defense Military Standard MIL-ST-1629A, 1980: 'Procedures for Performing A Failure Mode, Effects and Criticality Analysis'. Obtainable in the UK from London Information, Index House, Ascot, Berkshire SL5 7EU (0344 23377).

CHAPTERS 4 AND 12: TOTAL QUALITY

Bendell, A. (ed.): 'Taguchi Methods', Elsevier Science Publishers Ltd, Oxford, 1989.

British Standard BS 5750 (ISO 9000): 'Guide to Quality Management and Quality System Elements', British Standards Institution, London, 1987.

British Standard BS 6143: 'Guide to the Determination and Use of Quality Related Costs', British Standards Institution, London.

British Standard BS 7850: 'Total Quality Management', British Standards Institution, London, 1992.

Company-Wide Quality Improvement, video, Department of Trade and Industry. UK companies can obtain the video on free loan from DTI's agents, Mediascene Ltd, Wales (address below).

Crosby, P. B.: 'Quality is Free', McGraw-Hill, New York, 1979.

Cullen, J. and J. Hollinghum: 'Implementing Total Quality', IFS International, Bedford, UK, 1987.

Dale, B. and J. Plunkett: 'The Case for Costing Quality', Department of Trade and Industry, 1989. UK companies can obtain copies free of charge from DTI's agents Mediascene Ltd, Wales (address below).

E.F.Q.M.: 'Total Quality Management: The European Model for Self-Appraisal', European Foundation for Quality Management (E.F.Q.M.), Eindhoven, The Netherlands, 1992 (address below).

Fox, M. J.: 'BS 5750 Ensuring Your Business Achieves and Profits from Registration: A Practical Guide', IFS International, Bedford, UK, 1991.

Fox, M. J. and M. Roberts: 'Quality Costs: Their Impact on Company Strategy and Profitability,' IFS International, Bedford, UK, 1991.

Juran, J. M. *et al.*: 'Quality Planning and Analysis: from Product Development Through Use', McGraw-Hill, New York, 1980.

Mann, N. R.: 'The Keys to Excellence: The Story of the Deming Philosophy', Prestwick Books, Los Angeles, 1985.

'*Quality Assurance Poster Programme.*' Further details obtainable from: Waterlow Communications, Milton Keynes MK1 1UJ, UK (0800 373013).

Shingo, S.: 'Zero Quality Control: Source Inspection and the Poka-Yoke System', Productivity Press, Cambridge, MA, 1986.

Taguchi, G.: 'Systems of Experimental Design', Unipub/Krause International Publications and American Supplier Institute, New York, 1978.

CHAPTERS 5 AND 13: TOTAL EMPLOYEE INVOLVEMENT

Lynn, J. and A. Jay: 'The Complete *Yes Minister*', BBC Publications, London, 1984.

Rowntree, D.: 'The Manager's Book of Checklists', Corgi, London, 1988.

CHAPTERS 6 AND 14: INFORMATION SYSTEMS

Bicheno, J.: 'Measuring Integrated Manufacturing', Proceedings of the Twenty-Third European Technical Conference on Production and Inventory Control, The British Production and Inventory Control Society, London, 1988.

Cooper, R.: 'Implementing Activity Based Cost Management', Institute of Management Accountants, Montvale, NJ, 1992.

Kaplan, R. S.: 'Measures For Manufacturing Excellence', Harvard Business School Press, Boston, 1990.

Kaplan, R. S. and R. Cooper: 'The Design of Cost Management Systems: Text Cases and Readings', Prentice-Hall, Englewood Cliffs, NJ, 1991.

Maskell, B. H.: 'Performance Measurement for World Class Manufacturing', Productivity Press, Olney, Bucks, UK, 1991.

CHAPTER 7: MANAGING THE CHANGE

Kanter, R. M.: 'The Change Masters: Corporate Entrepreneurs at Work', Unwin Hyman, London, 1983.

Kanter, R. M.: *Managing Change*, video, BBC Enterprises Ltd, London.

USEFUL ADDRESSES

British Standards Institution   copies of British Standards are obtainable from: BSI Sales Department, Linford Wood, Milton Keynes MK14 6LE, UK (0908 220022).

Business in the Community   227a City Road, London EC1V 1LX, UK (071 253 3716).

Department of Trade and Industry   a wide range of publications and videos on world-class subjects such as just-in-time and total quality are available to UK readers from Mediascene Ltd, Bowen Industrial Estate, Bargoed CF8 9EP, Wales (0443 821877), or from any DTI Regional Office.

European Foundation for Quality Management   Building 'Reaal' Fellenoord 47A, 5612 AA Eindhoven, The Netherlands (31 40 461075).

HOCUS (Hand or Computer Universal Simulator) computer modelling system: details obtainable from P-E International plc, Park House, Egham, Surrey TW20 0HW, UK (0784 434411).

Institution of Electrical Engineers   a distance learning package of 6 course modules and 19 videos on Engineering Management, including a module on Management of Change, can be obtained from: Marketing Officer Publishing, IEE, Michael Faraday House, Six Hills Way, Stevenage, Herts SG1 2AY, UK (0438 313311).

Investors in People (UK)   UK companies can obtain details of Investors in People publications from their local Training and Enterprise Council; companies outside the UK should contact: Investors in People (UK), Room N805, Moorfoot, Sheffield S1 4PQ, UK (0742 739190).

Management Charter Initiative   pamphlets and other information on National Standards for Management Training can be obtained from: MCI Centre, Russell Square House, 10–12 Russell Square, London WC1B 5BZ, UK (071 872 9099).